Contents

W9-DIS-861

Key to Pronunciation Guide

Some words in this book that may be unfamiliar to you or hard to pronounce are followed by a pronunciation guide in parentheses. The guide syllable printed in capital letters should be given the greatest emphasis when you say the word. In the key below, the first column is a list of the letters or marks used in many dictionary pronunciation guides, with an example of the sound that each one stands for. The next column shows how the same sound appears in the guides in this book. The third and fourth columns list examples of words that contain that sound, and their pronunciation guides.

Letter or mark	Appears in this book as:	Example	Guide
a (hat, map)	a	alphabet	AL fuh beht
ā (age, face)	ay	Asia	AY zhuh
ã (care, air)	ai	share	shair
ä (father, far)	ah	farming	FAHR mihng
ch (child, much)	ch	China	CHY nuh
e (let, best)	eh	test	tehst
ē (equal, see machine, city)	ee	leaf	leef
		tangerine	tan juh REEN
ėr (term, learn, sir, work)	ur	earth	urth
i (it, pin, hymn)	ih	system	SIHS tuhm
ī (five, ice)	y	alive	uh LYV
	eye	island	EYE luhnd
k (coat, look)	k	corn	kawrn
o (hot, rock)	ah	otter	AHT uhr
ō (open, go, grow)	oh	rainbow	RAYN boh
ô (order, all)	aw	normal	NAWR muhl
		always	AWL wayz
oi (oil, voice)	oy	boiling	BOYL ihng
		poison	POY zuhn
ou (house, out)	ow	fountain	FOWN tuhn
s (say, nice)	s	mice	mys
sh (she, revolution)	sh	ration	RASH uhn
u (cup, butter, flood)	uh	study	STUHD ee
		blood	bluhd
u̇ (full, put, wood)	u	pull	pul
		wool	wul
ü (rule, move, food)	oo	tune	toon
zh (pleasure)	zh	measure	MEHZH uhr
ə (about)	uh	America	uh MEHR uh kuh
(taken, purple)	uh	middle	MIHD uhl
(pencil)	uh	citizen	SIHT uh zuhn
(lemon)	uh	lion	LY uhn
(circus)	uh	focus	FOH kuhs
(curtain)	uh	mountain	MOWN tuhn
(section)	uh	digestion	dy JEHS chuhn
(fabulous)	uh	famous	FAY muhs

Adapted from *The World Book Encyclopedia.* © 1977 Field Enterprises Educational Corporation.

Preface

This book is about you—what your body is made up of, how the parts work together, how you can become fit and stay that way, how you can help yourself to look the way you want, and how to deal with your personal problems.

You will learn about preventing or coping with disease. You will find out how to avoid most accidents and how to help yourself and other people when injuries occur. And you will discover what health services are available in your community and how to choose the ones that are best for you.

A lot of the information in this book is new. It is based on recent discoveries by physicians and scientists. Among other topics, you will probably enjoy discussing such subjects as nonverbal communication ("body language"), the double brain, meditation techniques, and the likely cause of Spring fever.

In addition to reading and discussion, many activities and investigations will help you learn things you need to know to look good and feel good. Some of these activities will help you analyze your personal feelings and beliefs—factors that should be taken into account when you make decisions that affect your health.

1

Here Comes Everybody!

After completing the work in this chapter, you will be able to:

identify many characteristics that you have in common with other people.

describe how cells, tissues, organs, and systems are combined within the body.

list some kinds of information about the environment that your skin communicates to you.

explain the structure and function of the three layers of the skin.

explain the importance of tactile experiences in people's lives.

1

The Personal Experience

There was once a foolish race of people called Loners. Each Loner was unique, or thought so anyway. Nobody had exactly the same body as anybody else, so they all had their clothes custom-made. Each person lived alone in a different kind of house but complained about the neighbors' peculiar dwellings. Their conversations always broke off in the middle because each individual felt entitled to his or her own opinion, regardless of the facts. Besides all that, the men and women had a double share of differences and couldn't bear each other's company for more than a minute.

Most experts agree that this race of people perished from the earth long ago. The experts are at a loss to explain why so many people today claim that they are Loners.

People like to repeat that everyone is an individual—that everyone is unique. In some ways, of course, that's true. But it's only partly true. The more you think about it, the more ways you find that you and other people are alike—more alike than different.

As human beings, we all have the same kinds of cells, tissues, and organs. We all have elbows, toes, hair, eyes, and muscles. We all have blood flowing through our bodies. We all digest food and breathe air. We each have a mind and a body that work together and influence each other. We all are born, grow, age, and die. And we all share an environment, the earth, that keeps us alive but sometimes threatens us too.

Our survival needs are the same: we all need food, water, oxygen, and tolerable temperatures. Beyond that, to be healthy—not just to survive—we need to feel safe and protected. We need to feel that we belong to a family, a culture, and perhaps another group, such as a neighborhood or school friends. We need to feel that people like us. We also need some respect from the people around us. It may seem strange, but we even have real needs for truth, beauty, justice, and some other abstractions, qualities that we can't touch but that are very real. If you doubt that, consider whether you could feel and act healthy if you spent all your time in ugly surroundings. And how would your mental health be affected if everyone were unfair to you or lied to you all the time?

Do you think that you have only these basic characteristics and needs in common with other people? Perhaps you feel alone in the world because there is so much else about you that is special and unique. Maybe you think that no one else has the same joys and worries that you do or that no one really understands you. Do you feel that way?

Oddly enough, most people are also alike in feeling separate and alone at least part of the time. And if you and your classmates compared some of your very private concerns with each other, you might be surprised to discover just how personal (that is, just how true of people in general) your own personal concerns really are.

2

Getting in touch with people takes reaching out.

Being Human

● 1-1 Individual or Common?

Think of some of the things that you hope for, things that bother you, and things that make you happy. Then make a table similar to the one below, on a piece of paper. You don't have to put your name on the paper. No one's table will be identified.

Try to list in each column at least three things that are important to you. If you cannot think of three things, or if you want to list more than three, it's all right. There doesn't have to be the same number of items in each column.

If you list any people, use categories (people who . . .), occupations (one of my teachers), or people's relationships to you (my girl friend), rather than actual names.

These questions may help you get started:

Column 1   What do you most hope for or dream about doing? What goals have you set for yourself? If you could have anything you wanted, what would it be?

HOPES	WORRIES	JOYS
	Copy This Table on a Piece of Paper	

Column 2 What is bothering you? What are some things that you are afraid of doing or feeling?

Column 3 What makes you happy? What gives you great satisfaction?

DISCUSSION

1. What common hopes do many members of your class have?

2. What things bother many of your classmates? Do you worry about your weight, your looks, or your health? Getting accurate information about the structures and functions of your body will probably relieve some of your concerns. That's one of the aims of this book.

3. Name some things that make many of your classmates happy.

4. Which things that many class members have in common surprise you?

5. You've probably heard the expression, "We're all in the same boat." In what sense are we all in the "same boat"? Is it a good "boat" to be aboard?

1-2 What Living Things Are Made Of

There is something you have in common with all the plants and other animals on Earth, not just with all the other people. All living things are made up of **cells.** Cells vary in size, shape, complexity, and function. Each cell has many parts that work together. Most animal cells have a **cell membrane** that contains all the cell parts and allows materials to flow between the cell and its surroundings. The cell **nucleus** (NOO klee uhs) controls cell activity. Some living things, such as bacteria, are made up

of only one cell. Each person has about 30 trillion (30,000,000,000,000) cells.

Each cell carries out basic life functions. It takes in food, converts it to energy and necessary materials, and gets rid of wastes. Except for nerve cells and red blood cells, which cannot reproduce themselves, most cells also divide from time to time. In other words, each microscopic cell is alive in its own right.

Some of our cells, red blood cells for example, live only a few months. They get pretty battered by tumbling around the circulatory system and don't last long. But many nerve cells, unless they are damaged, last a lifetime—a person's lifetime and theirs being the same. Some nerve cells repair themselves if they are damaged. For example, after an injury, certain nerves of the hands or feet may slowly become healthy again. But it appears that the nerve cells of the brain and spinal cord do not repair themselves once they are damaged.

Besides carrying out its own business, each cell in the body also carries out some part of the body's business, such as transmitting messages, or growing hair, or contracting to help make a limb move. So your sense of yourself as a simple being, an "I," is somewhat misleading. We are complex arrangements of vast numbers of microscopic living things that live and die at different rates and carry out different functions. We are what happens when 30 trillion specialists work together.

It took precise directions to make all the cells in the body develop specifically into what they are and where they are. These directions were all carried in the one special cell that everyone began life as, called a **zygote** (ZY goht). The zygote forms when a sperm cell from the father combines with an egg cell in the mother. Each of your parents' cells contributed half the directions to make you who you are.

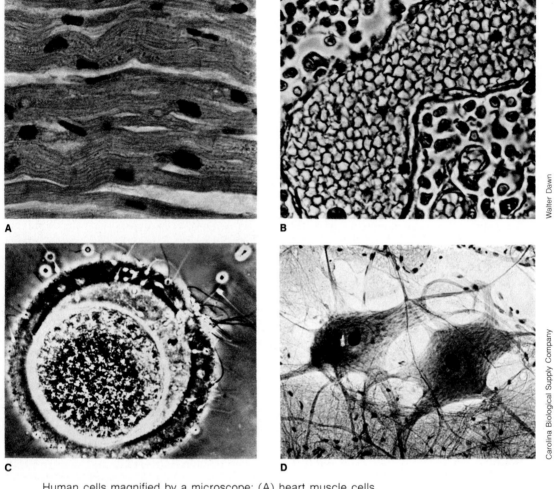

Dr. Landrum B. Shettles

Walter Dawn

Carolina Biological Supply Company

Human cells magnified by a microscope: (A) heart muscle cells,
(B) fat cells, (C) an egg cell and sperm cells, (D) nerve cells.

The directions for building and operating cells are carried by **chromosomes** (KROH muh sohmz) in the nucleus of each cell. The zygote receives 23 chromosomes from the father's sperm cell and the same number from the mother's egg cell, adding up to 46. All human cells, except for sperms and eggs, have 46 chromosomes. The chromosomes are made up of smaller bits of material called **genes.** The genes actually carry the directions for all the traits you

inherited from your parents. Except for identical twins, no two people have exactly the same set of genes. But we all have many of the same genes, those that make us members of the human race.

Almost as soon as the zygote forms, it divides into two cells. The new cells divide, and these four become eight, the eight become sixteen, and so on. The genes in each new cell are the same as the ones in the original cell. These genes—which are made of a chemical you've probably heard of, **DNA** (deoxyribonucleic acid)—direct and control development. They govern the growth of the cells and their specialization into nerve cells, muscle cells, bone cells, and so on. The genes in your cells continue to direct the cells' complicated activities right now and will do so for as long as you live. If you become a parent, you will pass your genes on to your children. Your children will pass them on to their children. So each generation of people will consist of individuals with a number of common, inherited traits.

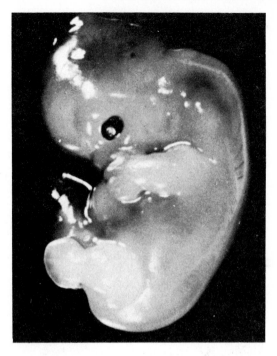

The developing baby, five weeks old. Many specialized cells have yet to form.

1-3 Tissues and Organs

Tissues are groups of cells that have a similar form and do the same kind of work. Liver cells group together to form liver tissue; bone cells group together to form bone tissue. The cells in a tissue are held together tightly or loosely. When a tissue has completely developed, the reproductive rate of its cells slows down and it stops growing. But this isn't always the case in other animals. Fish, for example, seem to keep growing until they die.

Several kinds of cells make up the tissues of the body. These cells vary in size and structure, depending on the jobs they do. For example, the long, flexible bundles of fibers in muscle cells contract and expand to move parts of the body. Branched nerve cells receive and send messages. Flexible epithelial (ehp uh THEE lee uhl) cells cover the outside of the body and the organs inside. Blood is a liquid tissue containing several kinds of cells. Elastic, fibrous, or fatty connective cells help support body structures and keep them in place. Bone and cartilage (KAHR tuh lihj) cells, along with

calcium and phosphorus minerals, make up the skeleton.

In most tissues, the cells stay in one place. However, some cells do move about the body. The cells in blood circulate through the body with the bloodstream. White blood cells can squeeze through small spaces to reach an infection, where they consume dirt and germs. Some skin cells can move about in the area of a healing wound.

As cells combine to form tissues, so different types of tissues often combine to form **organs.** For example, nerve, epithelial, and muscle tissues combine to form the heart. The stomach, eyes, and mouth are other organs formed of different tissues. The so-called vital organs are necessary for life to continue. The brain, heart, liver, lungs, skin, and kidneys are all vital organs.

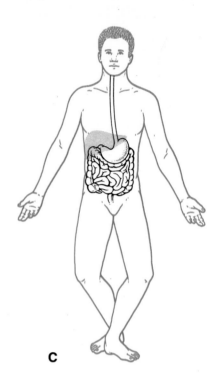

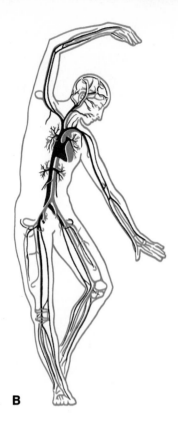

B

C

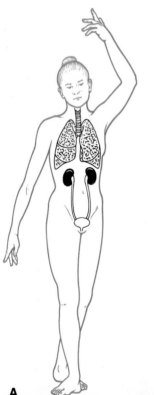

A

A. Respiratory and Urinary Systems
B. Circulatory System
C. Digestive System

Some vital organs, such as the heart and kidney, can sometimes be transplanted from one person to another. Parts of other organs, such as heart valves, can sometimes be replaced with artificial versions. However, so far, there is no human-made replacement for any entire organ. There are machines, such as kidney machines, that can do the work of certain organs, but they cannot be placed inside the body.

1-4 Body Systems

At the next level of organization in the body are **systems.** Cells combine into tissues. Tissues combine into organs, and organs are

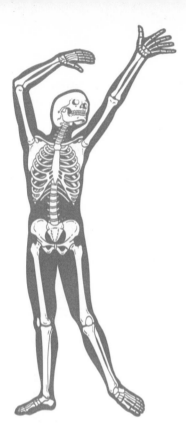

D

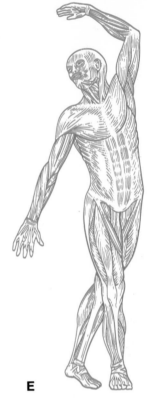

E

D. Skeletal System
E. Muscular System
F. Nervous System

organized into body systems. (What are body systems organized to form?) The mouth, throat, esophagus, stomach, intestines, and anus are organs in the digestive system. (Some organs are part of two or more systems. The mouth, for example, is part of both the digestive and the respiratory systems.) Together, the organs of the digestive system can perform more functions than any one of the organs can separately. As a system, these organs digest the various foods that we eat, absorb the usable parts, and expel the unused parts from the body.

There are many other systems in the body

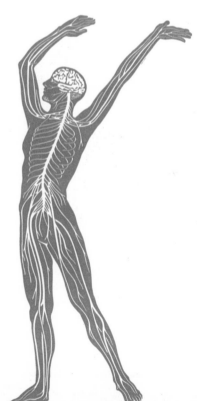

F

along with the digestive system. These are the circulatory, respiratory, reproductive, endocrine, urinary, nervous, skeletal, and muscular systems. In the remaining chapters of this unit, you will learn in greater detail about the structure and function of body systems and the organs that make them up.

When one organ within a system is diseased or doesn't function correctly, the entire system can be affected. And because the activities of all body systems are coordinated, every system can affect every other system. You are probably aware of some ways your systems are interrelated. Do you ever have difficulty digesting your food when you have a headache? How well can you play basketball or take part in an interesting conversation when you have an upset stomach?

The functioning of body systems is also affected by emotions, personal relationships, and the environment. When you are worried and upset you may be unable to think clearly. When the air around you is heavily polluted, you may have difficulty breathing, and your eyes may itch and water. On a very hot or cold day you may find yourself moving slower or faster in response to the temperature.

SELF CHECK

1. What physical traits do all people have in common?

2. What kinds of feelings do all people have at different times in their lives?

3. Describe the functions of cells. How can you compare one cell with an entire human body?

4. How do chromosomes and genes make people both alike and different?

5. Choose one organ and describe some of the different functions of its tissues.

6. What are some organs that are part of more than one body system?

Skin and Touch

1-5 Skin—Our Connection With the World

The **skin** is the largest human organ and accounts for about six percent of body weight. It completely covers the exterior of the body and extends into all the body openings. Inside the nose and mouth, for example, a special form of skin called **mucous** (MYOO kuhs) **membrane** produces protective, cleansing, and lubricating fluids.

It may look like a simple covering, but the skin is a complex organ. The hair, pores, nails, ridges, and wrinkles you can see on the outside suggest its underlying complexity. The inside layers of the skin are a kind of fabric. It is woven of nerves, blood vessels, sweat and oil glands, hair- and nail-producing cells, fat, and tiny muscles. These cells and tissues do a lot of different jobs. They enable the skin to ward off physical injuries, help regulate body temperature, get rid of waste products, and keep out disease-causing organisms.

Skin is also one of the chief information gatherers. It keeps us in touch with the world. A rich supply of nerve endings in the skin gives information about things we

Blind and deaf from birth, Helen Keller learned by touch and became a famous author and lecturer. With her hands she "saw" President Eisenhower's face and "heard" by hand signals from her friend what he said.

touch and things that touch us. Some parts of the skin are incredibly sensitive, while other parts seem dull. Often the skin sends us a lot of messages that we just don't pay attention to, being distracted by our other senses or thoughts. We are likely to substitute looking for touching as a way of learning about things. You can probably think of lots of things you've seen today. Do you remember anything you've touched?

Blind people often develop their senses of touch and hearing to their full potential. They can show people who can see just how much they could also be feeling. Trained blind people can read by moving their sensitive fingers over the closely packed patterns of small bumps in a book printed in the Braille system. Different patterns of bumps stand for letters and words. In some communities there are gardens for the blind. People with little or no vision learn about and enjoy flowers by touching and smelling them.

Besides collecting information about the environment, the skin reveals a lot of information about you. Hundreds of ailments, serious and trivial, show up in the skin and affect its color, thickness, and texture. Doctors can often tell a lot about a person's health from skin, hair, and fingernails.

The way you touch people tells them about your feelings. So does the appearance of tension or relaxation in your face. Dark circles under your eyes show when you are very tired. Anger, fear, or other strong feelings may lead to visible sweating. Fear or cold may give you "goose bumps." You can probably think of other ways of "reading skin." Sherlock Holmes was a keen observer of the skin. Are you?

Pictures can suggest the feel of things, but looking doesn't substitute for touching.

1-6 Investigating Skin Messages

In this investigation you will find out what kinds of information you can get through your sense of touch. More precisely, you will find out what kinds of messages the nerve endings in your skin send to your brain.

MATERIALS

baby oil	paper towels
basins or sinks	sand
ice cubes	soap (liquid or solid)
newspaper	water

PROCEDURE

You are going to wash your hands or rub them together with a number of substances. Be sure to get your hands clean and dry before testing each substance. After each step, write down what you felt.

1. Rub your hands together with a handful of dry sand as though you were washing them.

2. Repeat the action with wet sand.

3. Wash your hands with a few drops of baby oil (over newspaper or a sink).

4. Wash your hands with soap and warm water.

5. Wash your hands with soap and cold water.

6. Rub your hands together with a few ice cubes. Don't leave the ice in your hands for a long time.

DISCUSSION

1. Which substance was the most pleasing to your sense of touch? Which was the most unpleasant? Does everyone in the class agree with you?

2. How did your sense of touch vary from one part of your hand to another with each substance?

3. What can your skin tell you about the environment?

4. Do you feel your hands are sensitive? Is there anything you can do to become more aware of the feel of things?

1-7 The Protective Epidermis

Keeping you in touch with the environment is only one of the skin's important jobs. To understand its other functions you have to look at each of the three layers that make up the skin: the epidermis (ehp uh DUR mihs), dermis, and subcutaneous (suhb kyoo TAY nee uhs) layer.

The **epidermis** is the thin, outside layer of skin. One of its major jobs is to keep you and the environment separated all the while you are in touch. For example, the epidermis keeps disease-causing organisms from getting into the body. So long as the epidermis remains intact, it keeps the moist internal tissues from drying out and, when you get wet, it keeps water from getting inside. If it were not for the toughness of the epidermis, the environment would be constantly rubbing and scraping its way into us.

The parts of the skin getting the roughest treatment from the environment have the thickest epidermis. The soles of the feet have an especially thick epidermis. In addition, any parts of the feet or the rest of the body that get an extra amount of rubbing will develop **calluses,** which are extra thick, hard layers of epidermis. In contrast, the backs of the hands require less protection

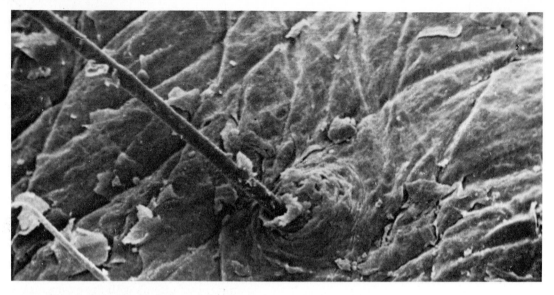

Skin protects the body from the wear and tear of the environment. Old skin cells peel off and are replaced from below.

and have a thinner epidermis. The tips of the fingers and toes get extra protection from fingernails and toenails.

Fingernails and toenails are another form of skin. The nails grow outward from roots below the epidermis. The nail under the skin is made up of living cells as far as the pale lunule, which is visible where the nail emerges from the skin. The rest of the visible portion of the nail is made up of dead cells, which are formed into a hard, colorless substance. The natural "color" of the nails is really the color of the underlying tissues and blood vessels.

Nail cells take three to four weeks to grow from their roots, or bed, to where you can see them. Do you sometimes think your nails grow long almost overnight? The average growth rate is only about one twenty-fifth of an inch (one millimeter) a week. If you do a lot of hard work with your hands, the fingernails will probably be constantly worn down and broken at the ends. Most

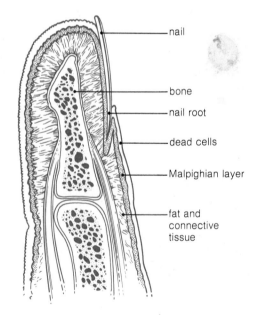

nail

bone

nail root

dead cells

Malpighian layer

fat and connective tissue

What use are fingernails? Are long ones more useful than short ones?

people don't wear off new nail growth each week, however, and so nail trimming becomes necessary.

The outside layer of the epidermis consists of dead cells that are constantly being lost by bathing and rubbing against things. The dead cells are replaced from underneath by the reproducing cells in the inner or **Malpighian** (mal PIHG ee uhn) **layer** of the epidermis. Unlike the cells of the outer epidermis, the cells in the Malpighian layer are alive. As the new cells are pushed outward, they die and become the flat, lifeless cells of the outer layer of the epidermis.

Skin color is another protective aspect of the epidermis. The darker the skin, the greater the protection it gives against sunburn and skin cancer caused by too much exposure to ultraviolet rays from the sun.

The color of the skin is determined by two pigments, **melanin** (MEHL uh nihn) and **carotene** (KAR uh teen), and by the blood in the small blood vessels near the surface. Melanin is dark colored, while carotene is yellowish. These pigments are found in the Malpighian layer of the epidermis. Their colors and those of the red blood cells show through the outer layer of the epidermis.

Dark-skinned people have more melanin in their skin than light-skinned people. Only a few people, called **albinos** (al BY nohz), have no melanin at all. Albinos have pale skin and white hair, and their irises (the colored parts of the eyes) look pink. Albinos should stay out of the sun as much as possible because they have no protective melanin in their skin. They should also protect their eyes against strong sunlight by wearing sunglasses.

In countries near the equator, a rich supply of melanin provides some protection from the direct, intense rays of the sun. Most of the people in these countries are dark skinned. In areas farther from the equator, where the sunlight is not as strong, people need less protection with melanin. Most of the people in these areas are light skinned. But almost anyone anywhere can get a sunburn.

Your chances of getting a sunburn are less if you do not suddenly spend a lot more time in the sun than your skin is used to. If you gradually build up your sunning time, more melanin will be produced in your epidermis. That will give you a suntan, if you are light skinned. A suntan allows longer exposure to the sun without getting a sun-

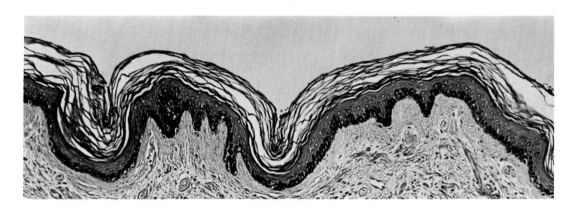

The Malpighian layer in a dark-skinned person has lots of melanin.

burn. If you spend much less time outdoors in the weeks after getting a suntan, the melanin will begin to disappear, and your suntan will fade.

The color of your skin is only one of the physical traits you inherited from your parents. As with other physical characteristics, skin color has nothing to do with intelligence or personality.

● 1-8 Investigating Your Epidermis

In this investigation, you will use a magnifying lens to observe and test your epidermis.

MATERIALS

eyedropper	soap
magnifying lens	stamp pad
paper towels	water
scissors	ruler

PROCEDURE

1. Work in pairs.

2. Look at the following parts of your epidermis with the magnifying lens. Move the lens up and down to focus it. Sit so that the maximum amount of light falls directly on what you are viewing. If possible, use your lens against a white background. Make a sketch of each part and label it.

a. *Comparative hair size.* Cut one hair from three different parts of your body. On white paper, line up the hairs and look at them with the lens. Note the thickness, curl, transparency, and color of each hair.

b. *Skin surface.* Observe the inside (less hairy side) of your forearm. Choose an area with few hairs. In your drawing, try to show details of the skin's texture and of the depressions where the hairs come out of the skin.

c. *Hair count.* In three separate areas on the outside of your forearm, make a rough count of the number of hairs you see in a square measuring one-quarter inch (about 6 millimeters) on a side. Add up the numbers and divide by three to get the average number of hairs per square. What function do you think hair has?

d. *Fingers.* Look under your fingernails by holding the lens to your fingertips. Observe the coarse, dry skin under the fingernails. How does the skin under your fingernails differ in appearance from the skin on the back of your hands?

e. *Fingernails.* Look at several fingernails and compare their color and markings. What size and shape are the hardened margins of skin, the cuticles, around the fingernails? Notice the crescent-shaped lunule at the base of the fingernails. Sketch your own and your partner's fingernails and describe their differences and similarities.

f. *Pigmented areas.* Moles and freckles are concentrated areas of melanin. Try to draw an exact outline of a few pigmented areas.

g. *Palm.* The palm of your hand has a large number of sweat glands. What function do you think they have? Observe and feel the lines in your palm. What causes them?

h. *Wrist.* Place a few drops of water on your wrist. How does your skin feel as the water evaporates? Observe the water drops through the lens. Describe the appearance of the water on your skin.

i. *Fingerprints*. Your fingers, palms, and the bottoms of your feet have ridges that improve their gripping ability. Use a stamp pad to print the fingers of your left hand on a sheet of white paper. Roll each finger from left to right lightly over the pad. Then roll your fingers from left to right over the white paper. When you are finished, wash your fingers with soap. Look at your fingerprints through the lens, and then look at the fingerprints of some of your classmates. What are the differences between the fingerprints you looked at?

j. *Pores*. **Pores** are tiny openings in the epidermis that lead to sweat glands and oil glands in the dermis. Sweat and oil are released through these pores onto the surface of the skin. Most pores are too tiny to see without a very strong magnifying glass. Where can you see pores with the unaided eye?

DISCUSSION

1. What acts as a cooling mechanism for the skin? How does the process work?

2. What parts of your skin might work as well as fingerprints for identification?

3. If you could redesign skin, what features would you add or remove?

1-9 The Versatile Dermis

The **dermis** is the most complex of the three skin layers. An area in the dermis the size of a fingernail may contain hundreds of nerve endings, sweat glands, blood vessels, oil glands, hair follicles, and muscles.

The bundles of nerves in the skin branch out in an enormously complex network. Different kinds of **nerve endings** are located in different layers of the skin, many of them in the dermis. The nerve endings that are sensitive to pain and extreme temperatures extend into the epidermis. Each nerve ending specializes in one sensation: touch, pressure, pain, heat, or cold. All the different touching experiences we have are made up of combinations of the five basic sensations.

The dermis contains two to three million **sweat glands** over the entire body. They are most abundant in the armpits, hands, feet, forehead, and groin. Most sweat glands are stimulated to work by physical activity and help regulate body temperature. Slightly different sweat glands in the armpits and groin, however, are stimulated primarily by fear, anger, anxiety, or other strong emotions. Bacteria grow rapidly in sweat and break it down. This action of bacteria on sweat causes strong body odors.

Sweat glands never stop working. Even though the skin often does not feel moist (when the weather is cold, or when you are sitting still) some sweat is always being released. About one quart (one liter) of perspiration leaves the skin daily. As sweat evaporates from the skin, the body cools. You have probably noticed this cooling during dry, hot weather. If the weather is humid, perspiration accumulates on the skin faster than it evaporates. As a result, you feel hotter in high humidity.

Microscopic blood vessels called **capillaries** (KAP uh lehr eez) carry the skin's blood supply through the dermis. The blood flowing through these capillaries takes oxygen and food materials to the skin cells and takes away their wastes. The capillaries also

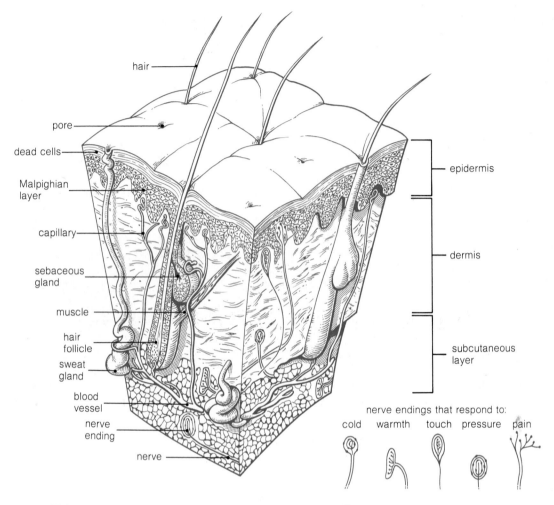

hair

pore

dead cells

Malpighian layer

capillary

sebaceous gland

muscle

hair follicle

sweat gland

blood vessel

nerve ending

nerve

epidermis

dermis

subcutaneous layer

nerve endings that respond to:

cold   warmth   touch   pressure   pain

This cross section of skin shows the three main layers. The thicknesses of these layers are different at different locations.

help protect the body from becoming too hot or too cold. When the body is warm, the capillaries grow larger, allowing the blood supply in the skin to increase. Since larger, or dilated, capillaries have more surface area than smaller ones, more heat can be transferred to the outer skin where it increases evaporation. The more evaporation that takes place, the cooler you become. Capillaries become smaller when people are cold, and heat is saved as the blood flow decreases.

Hair is another one of the body's temperature-control devices. It shields the head from overheating and overcooling. Hair has other functions as well. Eyebrows and eyelashes help protect the eyes, and the thick hair on the head is some cushion against injuries. The roots of the hairs are very near nerve endings in the dermis. When hairs

Differences can be fun.

move they stimulate the nerve endings near the roots. So hairs also act as an alarm system that warns you, for example, when a biting insect has come aboard. Some people seem especially sensitive to feather-light touches on their hairs while others can sit on an ants' nest for a long time and not realize their mistake.

Each hair grows from a separate pocket or **follicle** (FAHL ih kuhl) in the dermis. The inside layer of the follicle consists of epidermis cells, the outside layer of dermis cells. Capillaries provide nourishment for the base of each follicle. Whether the hair will be fine or coarse, and straight or curly, depends on the shape of the follicle and the angle the follicle forms with the skin. Hair texture and thickness vary on different parts of the body. They also vary among individuals, sexes, and races.

Hereditary factors determine the color, texture, and distribution of hair over the head and body. As long as follicles are alive, hairs will grow. Sometimes follicles die or are destroyed by illness. Baldness, the loss of hair from the head, means that the follicles no longer function. If baldness is caused by disease, the hair may grow back. Most often, however, baldness is hereditary and is called "male pattern baldness." Medicine cannot make the hair follicles grow back.

Natural hair color depends on the amount of melanin and the amount of air in the central core of each hair. Dark hair has more melanin than light hair. Gray hair has air instead of pigment in the hair shaft. Like balding, the tendency for hair to turn gray is inherited. There is no evidence that grayness in humans is caused by a vitamin deficiency or by a sudden emotional crisis.

The average scalp has about 100,000 hairs. Blond-haired people have about 20,000 more hairs and red-haired people about 20,000 fewer.

As the picture on page 18 shows, each hair follicle is attached to a muscle. When these muscles contract, the hairs stand on end. When the muscles relax, the hairs fall back into place. Excitement, fear, or cold can set these muscles into action. The slight change in position of hairs produces the "goose-bump" effect. This muscular activity in the skin takes place without your conscious control.

What function this "hair-raising" action has is unclear. Many animals, when threatened, make their hair stand up and they look bigger than they actually are. If we had hairier, prehuman ancestors that had the same reaction, the mechanism may be a now useless holdover.

When the hair muscles contract they also exert pressure on the capillaries and reduce the blood flow to the skin. This action is a highly useful response by the body to threatening situations. It means that surface wounds will bleed less, and muscles and vital organs will have a greater blood supply when they need it.

Hair and skin are kept soft and flexible by the action of the **sebaceous** (sih BAY shuhs) or **oil glands** located throughout the dermis. The sebaceous glands are especially numerous in the skin of the face and scalp, but are lacking in the palms and soles where there is no hair. Sebaceous glands are also concentrated around the openings of the anus, nose, mouth, and ear. These flask-shaped glands produce **sebum** (SEE buhm) and send it onto the surface of the skin. Sebum is an oily material that leaves the glands most often through the hair follicles. Sebum forms a thin film on the surface of the skin. This film acts as an additional barrier that helps to keep disease-causing organisms from getting into the body.

Usually sebum is liquid and can easily pass through the follicles. However, when this pathway is obstructed or if the sebum becomes thick, an inflammation (swelling and redness) such as acne may result.

1-10 The Padding Layer— The Subcutaneous

Beneath the dermis lies the **subcutaneous layer,** which is elastic and attached to the inner structures of the body, such as the large muscles. Blood vessels and nerves pass through the subcutaneous layer into the dermis, although some nerves end at the boundary of the two layers.

The subcutaneous layer forms a thick, fibrous, and fatty pad that covers the back and buttocks. In other regions of the body it tends to be thinner and softer. Like the outer layers of the skin, the subcutaneous layer varies in thickness from one place on the body to another. Fatty and fibrous tissues in this layer insulate the body from heat and cold and cushion the inner organs against shocks and jolts.

As people grow older, the fatty tissue in the subcutaneous layer is absorbed by the body. The outer layers of the skin then form uneven folds, or wrinkles. Perhaps you have heard older people complain about ex-

Years of smiles, frowns, and other expressions draw the lines on our faces.

tremes of heat or cold when you have felt comfortable. The gradual loss of fatty tissue partially accounts for their discomfort.

1-11 Tactile Needs

If we only discussed the layers of the skin and the various jobs they do, we would be leaving out an important subject: the skin needs to touch and be touched.

In the nineteenth century many of the infants in the United States died in their first year of life from a disease called marasmus (muh RAZ muhs). The actual cause of the deaths was unknown; all the word means is "wasting away." In some orphanages as late as the 1920's, most of the babies—lying in their cribs with feeding bottles held between the slats—wasted away mysteriously. During this time mothers were supposed to care for their infants "scientifically," in order not to "spoil" them. Mothers were advised not to handle their babies very much, not to pick them up when they cried, and to feed them at fixed intervals, regardless of when the baby was hungry. Doctors eventually discovered that this lack of loving care was the cause of marasmus.

Babies have tactile needs: they need to be held, touched, and caressed. They can't survive without it. It is impossible to spoil an infant with frequent touching or holding. If a baby is held only occasionally, the child may grow physically but suffer emotional difficulties later in life. Of equal importance is the kind of touching. It must be pleasurable, last long enough, and occur often enough to be satisfying. When mothers, nurses, and caretakers in orphanages supplied tender, loving care, marasmus disappeared.

Older children and adults need touching,

Every family has to find the level of touching that it is comfortable with. There are many ways of sharing feelings with other people.

too, not for survival but for mental and emotional health and growth. Have you ever felt better after a frightening experience if someone held you closely? Can you remember someone kissing an injury of yours to "make it better"? Doesn't it feel really good to have a back rub, hug a friend, or hold hands with a person you like?

The importance of touching is shown in many of the expressions we use. You "get in touch" with a "warm" friend. Some people "rub you the wrong way" or give you a "hard time." You may be "touched" or deeply moved by someone's showing concern or affection for you. Can you think of any other words and phrases that show how important touching is to our language and thought?

If being touched makes you "touchy," you may have a hard time seeing that it's a basic human need. In some families a lot of physical contact takes place. In other families affection, anger, and other feelings are usually expressed in words or not at all. Each family has its own way of dealing with tactile needs. The way you were brought up probably influenced the way you now feel about touching.

Cultures vary in the amount of physical contact between people. One group of Eskimos, who live north of the Arctic Circle, touch a great deal. Eskimo infants, wearing only a small diaper, are strapped to their mothers' bare backs. Until they can walk, the babies remain snuggled between their mother's skin and her furry parka. They are

only unstrapped for feeding and cleaning. A great deal of communication between mother and child takes place through their skins. It becomes easy for the mother to anticipate her baby's needs, and so an Eskimo baby rarely cries. Adult Eskimos show unusual generosity and concern for others. This may be partly the result of their early relationships with their mothers. The comfortable, reassuring life of the infant may also be one reason the adults show great calmness and courage in the face of danger and hardship.

In countries like the United States and Canada, there is no single way of doing anything, let alone child-rearing. But babies in these North American countries are often brought up without much touching.

They are left by themselves a great deal. Most of their handling comes during feeding, bathing, and diaper changing. Otherwise they play alone a lot and sleep alone. Their communications with their parents tend to be verbal and visual. The older the children get, the less touching they get, boys especially.

These early experiences may partly explain why many English-speaking people avoid physical contact with each other. Men especially avoid showing affection toward each other. Continental Europeans often regard the English and Americans as "cold fish." But there is a growing movement toward greater contact between babies and parents, and we may be becoming a more tactile society.

1. Why is the skin considered an organ rather than a tissue?

2. What different kinds of information about the environment can you get through your skin?

3. What can you tell about someone's feelings just by looking at that person?

4. How would you rank these parts of your skin in sensitivity: forehead, palm, elbow, heel, and armpit?

5. What are the functions of each layer of skin?

6. How does environment affect skin color?

Chapter Summary

All human beings have many of the same physical and mental characteristics. But within the human race, every member is an individual who interacts with other individuals and with the environment.

All organisms are made up of basic units called cells. Cells with similar specialized forms and functions group together into tissues, which are often organized into organs. Organs usually work together in body systems.

The largest organ is the skin. The epidermis, or outer layer of skin, keeps you in touch with the environment, and at the same time keeps you and the environment separated. The dermis is a complex fabric of nerves, blood vessels, hair follicles, sweat glands, oil glands, and connective tissue. The subcutaneous layer of skin consists of a mat of fatty and fibrous tissues.

The skin has many functions. These include protection against disease-causing organisms, regulation of body temperature, and informing you about heat, cold, and other touch experiences. Your state of health is reflected in the skin, as are many of your emotions.

Being touched and held during infancy is vital. The amount of loving contact during infancy is directly related to a person's later health. But different societies have different ideas about touching, during infancy and throughout life.

Chapter Self Check

1. What are some of the ways you show your humanity? Your individuality?

2. What functions do all human cells have in common?

3. Why does every child look like both parents in some ways?

4. What chemical in cells directs and controls the way they develop?

5. Name and describe at least four kinds of human cells.

6. Which of the following traits do you think you inherited through your genes: (a) the color of your eyes; (b) your tendency to be heavy or slender; (c) the sound of your voice; (d) your style of speaking; (e) your muscular strength? Do any of these traits result from both heredity *and* environment?

7. Identify several ways you have noticed your emotions influence the way you feel physically.

8. Name ten organs of the human body.

9. The dermis is sometimes called the "true skin." Describe the dermis and decide whether you think this name fits.

10. What are the major functions of skin?

11. What part of the skin lets you feel pain?

12. Describe skin changes under the following circumstances: (a) when you are frightened; (b) when you are worried; (c) when you have a bad cold; (d) when you have been exercising.

13. How is the skin protected against rubbing?

14. Why don't you feel pain when your nails and hair are cut?

15. What pigment is the most significant in determining overall skin color?

16. What parts of the body produce the most odor?

17. Describe the role of the skin in regulating body temperature.

18. Why are people your age more likely than older men and women to adapt easily to changes in air temperature?

19. "A baby who is not held regularly will probably grow up with some emotional difficulties." Do you agree with that statement? Why, or why not?

20. What are some ways people communicate by touching?

Read More About It

Hyde, Margaret O. *Your Skin.* New York: McGraw-Hill Book Company, Inc., 1970. The structure of the skin. Also includes information about hair and nails.

McGough, Elizabeth. *Your Silent Language.* New York: William Morrow & Company, Inc., 1974. The way you communicate through the unconscious movements of your body. Various effects of posture, facial expressions, and eye movement. The human need for touching and how society regulates touching. Some references to research.

Montagu, Ashley. *Touching: The Human Significance of the Skin.* New York: Harper and Row, 1972. The importance of touching for growth and development.

Nilsson, Lennart, with Jan Lindberg. *Behold Man: A Photographic Journey of Discovery Inside the Body.* Boston: Little, Brown and Company, 1974. A collection of photographs of parts of the human body, including many microscopic views of the structure of cells, tissues, organs, and the skin.

Pfeiffer, John, and the Editors of Time-Life Books. *The Cell.* New York: Time Inc., Time-Life Books (Life Science Library), 1970 edition. The structure and function of cells, genetics, kinds of cells, and how cells relate to health and illness. Well-illustrated.

Silverstein, Alvin, and Silverstein, Virginia. *The Code of Life.* New York: Atheneum Publishers, 1972. The structure and function of DNA, its role in genetics, and research relating to DNA.

Sternberg, Thomas H. *More Than Skin Deep.* New York: Doubleday & Company, Inc., 1970. The skin, how to care for it, and skin diseases.

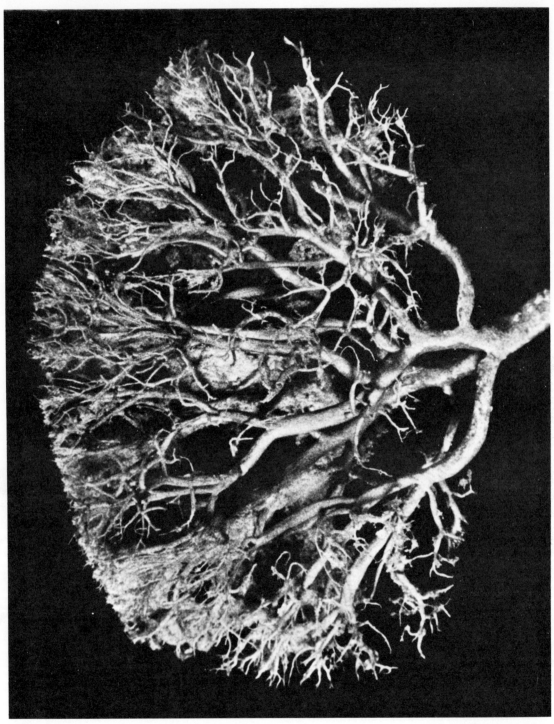

The arteries in a kidney.

2
Energy Systems

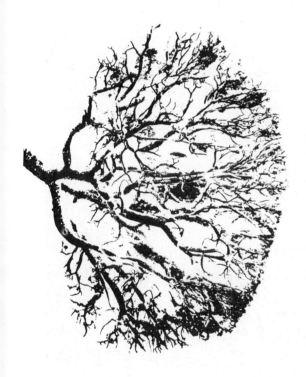

After completing the work in this chapter, you will be able to:

tell what body systems supply the cells with the materials they need and remove the wastes.

name the major parts of the digestive system and describe their functions.

name the major parts of the respiratory system and describe how they work.

describe the flow of blood through the circulatory system and the flow of lymph through the lymphatic system.

list the components of blood and describe their functions.

name the major parts of the urinary system and describe their functions.

Liveliness

Energy Is Eternal Delight
William Blake

Joy and delight come from doing, from achieving, from using energy. Laughing, singing, dancing, solving problems, scoring runs—whenever we use our energies freely or skillfully, we can stop what we are doing and realize how happy we are.

Energy produced in cells makes all the action, all the liveliness possible. Cells are the basis of thinking, moving, and feeling, and it takes energy from food and oxygen to do all three. It also takes materials in food to build cells and to keep them working.

People have body systems that solve four important problems in providing cells with materials for producing energy:

Problem one Breaking down meats, vegetables, and other foods into materials that cells can use, and removing the unusable parts of food.

Problem two Getting oxygen from the air into the body and getting carbon dioxide out of it.

Problem three Delivering usable food materials and oxygen to the cells and carrying away waste materials.

Problem four Removing the waste products of cell activities, which would otherwise poison the cells.

This chapter discusses the body systems that solve these problems: the digestive, respiratory, circulatory, and urinary systems.

Getting Materials for Energy

2-1 The Digestive System

More than half of the energy we need every day is used just to carry out the business of staying alive. We also need energy for all kinds of physical activities and for growth. Where does all this energy come from?

The supply of energy that we need comes from reactions between oxygen and other materials within our cells. These other materials come from the food we eat. In addi-tion to materials for producing energy, food also provides the body with materials for building cells, tissues, and organs, and materials for regulating the activities of cells. These aspects of food are discussed in Chapter 6.

Stop and think about all the different materials people eat—nuts, celery, dried meat, and eggs, for example. How we challenge our **digestive system** to convert food into materials for energy and growth!

The process of taking food and changing it into the forms that cells can use is called **digestion.** Digestion is aided by chemicals, called **enzymes** (EHN zymz), which are produced by the tissues of the digestive system. These enzymes help speed up the breakdown of food, without being changed themselves. The digestive tissues produce many different enzymes. Each digestive enzyme can help in breaking down only one type of material in food.

Digestion takes place in the **digestive tract,** a long, often twisted and coiled tube that begins with the mouth and extends about 11 yards (ten meters) in length to the anus. The openings at both ends of the tube are opened and closed by circular muscles.

After studying the parts of the digestive system on pages 42–45, do the following activity.

● **2-2 Food Breakdown**

Digestion is both mechanical and chemical. Food is broken up into small pieces in the mouth and stomach. And these bits of food are chemically broken down into tiny particles in the mouth, stomach, and beginning of the small intestine.

This activity will provide a simple model of factors at work in digestion.

MATERIALS

4 paper cups	teaspoon
2 pieces of rock salt	water
table salt	watch (or wall
2 straws (or stirrers)	clock)

PROCEDURE

1. Half fill each cup with water.

2. Put a piece of rock salt in each of two

It is surprising to see how long the digestive system is when it is stretched out.

cups and a teaspoonful of table salt in each of the other two cups.

3. Using straws, constantly stir the water in one of the cups with rock salt and in one of the cups with table salt.

4. Time how long it takes the salt to dissolve in all four cups.

DISCUSSION

1. What effect does stirring the salt and water have on the time it takes the salt to dissolve?

2. In what way does the size of the salt particles affect the time it takes the salt to dissolve?

3. How does the way you chew your food affect digestion?

4. What is one way your stomach helps digestion?

2-3 The Respiratory System

All body processes require energy. This energy usually comes from reactions between oxygen taken from the air and other materials within the cells. One of the materials produced by these reactions is carbon dioxide, which is returned to the air from the cells. Most body cells are not in contact with the air, and most cells that are, such as skin cells, cannot take oxygen directly from the air, or release carbon dioxide directly to the air.

The **respiratory system** provides a means by which oxygen and carbon dioxide can move between the cells and the air. The respiratory system warms and moistens air as it passes through to the lungs. In an unusually hot environment, it may even cool the air. Once inside the lungs, the conditioned air passes into microscopic air sacs that have thin walls lined with capillaries. Here oxygen passes from the air into the blood, and carbon dioxide passes from the blood into the air. The blood carries the oxygen to cells throughout the body, and the carbon dioxide leaves the air sacs and lungs when you exhale.

In addition to a means for breathing, parts of the respiratory system provide the mechanical means for talking. The voice box, or **larynx** (LAR ihngks), forms the upper part of the windpipe, where it joins the throat. The larynx has two strong folds of tissue surrounded by mucous membrane, called the **vocal cords.** Muscles regulate the

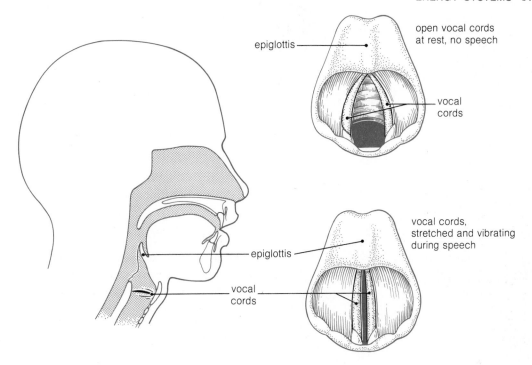

open vocal cords
at rest, no speech

epiglottis

vocal
cords

epiglottis

vocal
cords

vocal cords,
stretched and vibrating
during speech

The size and thickness of the vocal cords determine whether a person is a soprano, alto, tenor, or baritone. The pitch of the adult voice has nothing to do with body size.

distance between the vocal cords and the amount of tension put on them. When you shout loudly, muscles pull the vocal cords apart, allowing a rush of air from the lungs to pass over them. This burst of air causes the vocal cords to vibrate vigorously. A loud sound results. When you whisper, the vocal cords are closer together, and only a small amount of air passes over them from the lungs, causing a softer sound.

The harder the muscles pull on the vocal cords, the greater the tension on them. Increasing the tension on the vocal cords shortens them, causing a higher-pitched sound. Relaxing the vocal cords creates lower sounds. Men usually have lower-pitched voices than women, because the

vocal cords in males grow longer and thicker. However, the size of the adult vocal cords has nothing to do with body size.

After you have studied the parts of the respiratory system on pages 46–49, do the following investigation.

● **2-4 Investigating Your Lung Capacity**

In this investigation you will do three tests of your lung capacity and then compare the results with those of your classmates. Your teacher will give you a breathing tester to do the tests or you will make one for yourself.

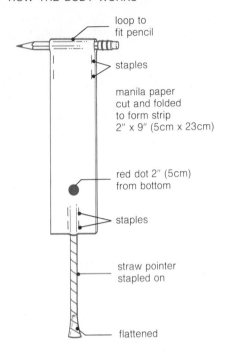

loop to
fit pencil

staples

manila paper
cut and folded
to form strip
2" x 9" (5cm x 23cm)

red dot 2" (5cm)
from bottom

staples

straw pointer
stapled on

flattened

MATERIALS

colored pencil	scissors
manila paper	stapler
one-hole rubber stopper	stop watch
pencil	straws
ringstand	utility clamp
ruler	weight scale

PROCEDURE FOR MAKING A TESTER

1. Use these pictures to help you make and set up the breathing tester.

2. Cut a strip of manila paper, 2 inches by 18 inches (5 centimeters by 45 centimeters).

3. Fold the strip in half and insert a pencil at the fold. Then staple the manila strip around the pencil to hold it loosely in the fold. (The strip must be able to move freely around the pencil.)

4. Make a pointer by inserting a short piece of straw between the ends of the folded manila strip. Make sure the straw extends about 4 inches (about 10 centimeters) outside the ends of the strip, and staple it in place.

5. Draw a small, colored circle about 2 inches (5 centimeters) from the end of the strip where you attached the straw. (This circle is the target that you will aim at when you are doing your breathing tests.)

6. If you use a ringstand to hold the breathing tester, insert the sharpened end of the pencil into the hole of a stopper. Clamp the stopper and attach it to the ringstand, high enough from the table so that the breathing tester can swing freely. If you don't use a ringstand setup, you and your partner can take turns holding the breathing tester while the other does the tests.

7. Put the zero end of a ruler under the pointer of your breathing tester and the other end on a book.

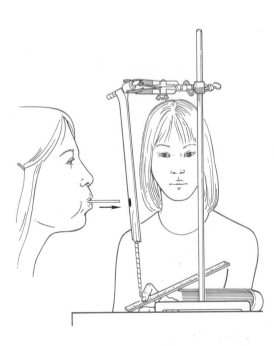

PROCEDURE FOR BREATH TESTS

1. Copy the table below.

2. Weigh yourself without your shoes and write your weight in the table.

3. Place a straw in your mouth and stand with the end of the straw half an inch (about one and one-half centimeters) from the colored spot. Blow as hard and as steadily as you can through the straw at the colored spot. Practice this a few times. When you do the actual test, your partner should watch how far along the ruler you can keep the pointer by blowing through the straw. Make three trials and write the results in the table under "Maximum Air Pressure." Find the average of your results and write it in the table.

4. Have your partner put his or her finger at the two-inch (five-centimeter) mark. Blow through your straw at the colored spot with enough force to keep the pointer at the two-inch (five-centimeter) mark. Practice this a few times, and then have your partner time the number of seconds you can maintain this force. Make three trials and write the results in the table under "Time at 2 inches (5 centimeters)." Find the average of your results and write it in the table.

5. Hold your straw on the colored spot and inhale so that the strip clings to the end of the straw. Move your head back and continue inhaling so that you are holding the strip against gravity. Practice this a few times, and then have your partner time the number of seconds you can hold the strip against gravity by inhaling through the

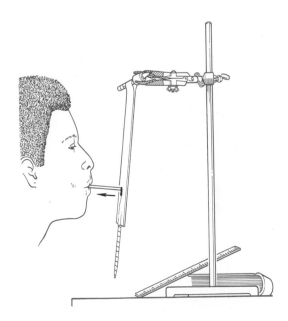

NAME	WEIGHT	MAXIMUM AIR PRESSURE (DISTANCE ALONG RULER)				TIME AT 2 INCHES (5 CENTIMETERS)				INHALING TIME			
		Trial 1	Trial 2	Trial 3	Average	Trial 1	Trial 2	Trial 3	Average	Trial 1	Trial 2	Trial 3	Average

Copy This Table on a Piece of Paper

straw in one breath. Make three trials and write the results in the table under "Inhaling Time." Find the average of your results and write it in the table.

DISCUSSION

1. Is there a relationship between weight and lung capacity among your classmates? If so, what relationship did you find?

2. Among your classmates, what relationship exists between lung capacity and regular exercise? What do you think might cause this relationship?

3. What relationship exists between lung capacity and cigarette smoking?

4. Did most people's lung capacity increase or decrease from Trial 1 to Trial 3?

5. What could you do to increase your breathing capacity?

SELF CHECK

1. Describe the most important function of the digestive system.

2. List the organs of the digestive system and tell how they work.

3. A person may have most of the stomach removed during surgery and still lead a normal life. How do you think this is possible?

4. Name the parts of the body that do the following: (a) keep dust and pollen out of the lungs; (b) provides a passage through which air reaches the lungs; (c) prevents food from entering the air passageway; (d) allows talking and singing; (e) allow oxygen and carbon dioxide to pass between the blood and the air.

5. What are the health disadvantages of breathing through the mouth?

6. Is breathing rate voluntary, involuntary, or both? Tell the reason for your answer.

Transportation and Purification

2-5 The Circulatory System

The blood moving through the **circulatory system** is a vital link between the body cells and the outside environment. The circulating blood delivers digested food materials, water, and oxygen to each cell, and carries carbon dioxide and other waste materials away from each cell.

The network of blood vessels throughout the body amounts to a complete circulatory route of about 100,000 miles (160,000 kilometers) in length. In a single day, the blood completes more than one thousand trips throughout the body.

The complicated system of blood-carrying tubes consists of three different types of blood vessels. **Arteries** carry blood away from the heart, and **veins** (VAYNZ) carry blood toward the heart. The arteries and veins both divide and subdivide as they get farther from the heart, forming smaller and smaller tubes. The third type of blood vessel, called a **capillary,** has walls that are one cell layer thick. These microscopic blood vessels form extensive networks connecting microscopic arteries to microscopic veins.

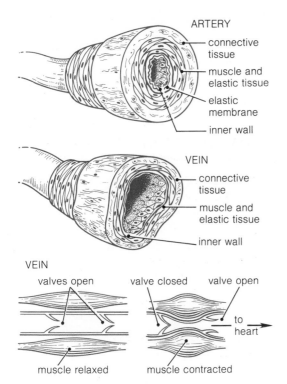

ARTERY
connective tissue
muscle and elastic tissue
elastic membrane
inner wall

VEIN
connective tissue
muscle and elastic tissue
inner wall

VEIN
valves open   valve closed   valve open
to heart
muscle relaxed   muscle contracted

Top: the layers of arteries and veins; *bottom:* muscles next to veins help circulation.

In the networks of thin-walled capillaries, the flow of blood slows down. Useful materials pass from the blood through the thin capillary walls into the body cells, and waste materials pass in the opposite direction into the blood, to be carried away.

Arteries aren't just tubes that simply carry blood from the heart to the capillaries. Arteries actually control the direction and the amount of blood flowing into different parts of the body. They are able to do this because the walls of the arteries are thick and largely composed of elastic and muscular tissue. The elastic tissue expands with a pump of the heart and contracts in between, and helps to maintain a steady flow of blood. When you feel your pulse, on the inside of your wrist, for example, you are really feeling the expansion and contraction of the walls of a large artery. Through contraction and expansion of smaller arteries, the force of blood flow, or **blood pressure,** is held relatively steady throughout the body.

The walls of veins are thinner and less elastic than those of arteries. However, the important difference between arteries and veins is that most veins contain small **valves** that open in one direction only: toward the heart. These valves prevent the blood from flowing the wrong way in the veins, particularly when going "uphill" toward the heart, as when blood flows from the legs to the heart. When muscles around veins contract, they squeeze the veins, which helps push blood through the valves toward the heart. This is one reason that exercise helps the circulation.

The **heart** is a strong muscular pump that keeps the body's five quarts (five liters) of blood constantly moving through the blood vessels. At rest, it circulates the body's entire blood supply about once a minute, or about 5000–6000 quarts (5000–6000 liters) per day.

The pumping action of the heart is shown on pages 52–53.

Valves control the flow of blood through the heart chambers. As the valves in the heart close, they make a "thumping" noise. When you listen to a heartbeat through a stethoscope, for example, the beating you hear is mostly the noise of valves closing after each contraction of the heart.

A special nerve and muscle tissue in the wall of the heart, called the **pacemaker,** triggers each heartbeat and controls the rhythm of the contractions. The pacemaker fires electric impulses that spread across the heart and cause the heart to pump. Other parts of the body regulate the heartbeat rate according to the body's need for oxygen in different circumstances, such as during a

Four people with heart problems are connected to this machine. The wavy lines on the screen show the patterns of their heartbeats. If someone's heart begins to fail, the nurse will know immediately.

hard workout. The faster the heart beats, the harder it works, as during strenuous exercise.

The vessels of the circulatory system aren't completely sealed tubes. The pressure of blood in the capillary networks squeezes a watery material, called **lymph** (LIHMF), out of the tiny, thin-walled capillaries. This clear liquid circulates around the body cells. Some of the lymph re-enters capillaries, and the rest enters a separate system of circulatory vessels called the **lymphatic** (lihm FAT ihk) **system.** The smallest lymphatic vessels, **lymphatic capillaries,** resemble blood capillaries except they are closed at one end, near the blood capillaries. The lymphatic capillaries carry lymph to larger and larger lymphatic vessels until the largest one drains into a vein near the base of the neck.

An important function of the lymphatic system is to return to the bloodstream food particles in the lymph that are not absorbed by the cells. Food particles are returned to the bloodstream from every part of the body. Another important job of the lymphatic system is to absorb tiny fat particles from the villi of the small intestine into **lacteals** (LAK tee uhlz), a type of lymphatic capillary. The fat particles are later delivered to the bloodstream. Fat particles pass more easily from the villi into lacteals than into blood capillaries.

After you study the parts of the circulatory system on pages 50–53, do the following investigation.

● **2-6 Investigating How Exercise Affects Your Heartbeat Rate**

The heartbeat, or pulse, can be felt and counted where an artery near the skin is also close to a bone or firm tissue, such as at the inner side of the wrist on the thumb side. In this investigation, you will find out how exercise affects your heartbeat rate and how quickly the heartbeat rate returns to normal. You will also compare the heartbeat rates of males and females in different age groups.

MATERIAL

wrist watch or wall clock with a second hand

PROCEDURE IN CLASS

1. Place your fingers on your wrist, using this picture as a guide. Press lightly until you feel your pulse. Practice counting your pulse a few times.

2. Copy the table below.

3. While sitting, count your pulse for 30 seconds and multiply by 2. Record your pulse as the number of beats per minute in the table under "Trial 1."

4. While sitting, have two partners separately count your pulse. Record their results in the table under "Trial 2" and "Trial 3." Find the average of the three trials and record it in the table under "Average."

5. Run in place, do push-ups, hop on one foot, or do some other form of moderate exercise for $1\frac{1}{2}$ minutes.

6. Immediately sit down and count your pulse for 30 seconds. Multiply by 2 and record the results in the table under "After Exercise."

7. After two minutes of sitting, count your pulse again for 30 seconds and multiply by

NUMBER OF BEATS PER MINUTE

NAME	TRIAL 1	TRIAL 2	TRIAL 3	AVERAGE	AFTER EXERCISE	TWO MINUTES AFTER EXERCISE
		Copy This Table on a Piece of Paper				

2. Record the results in the table under "Two Minutes After Exercise."

PROCEDURE AT HOME

1. Copy the table below.

2. Count the pulses of as many people in the different age groups listed in the table as you can. These pulses should be taken only while people are sitting. You should include pulses of both males and females.

3. Find the averages of the pulses of all the males and females in each age group, and record the results in the table. You can use the class results to calculate the averages for the 13–18 age group.

DISCUSSION

1. Why is it not a good idea to take your pulse with your thumb?

2. Generally, among your classmates, what is the difference between pulses counted while sitting and pulses counted right after exercising?

3. Among your classmates, what relationship exists between regular exercise and increase in heartbeat rate caused by exercising?

4. Recovery rate is how rapidly the heartbeat rate returns to normal after exercising. Among your classmates, is there a relationship between regular exercise and recovery rate? If so, what do you think might cause this relationship?

5. Find the averages of the results from seven or eight students' tables for the different age groups. Graph the average male and the average female pulse rates separately for the different age groups. What factors might account for sex differences in pulse rates? For age differences in pulse rates?

2-7 The Components of Blood

The fluid seeping among the cells is mostly **plasma,** the watery part of blood, which delivers some food materials to the cells. Blood cells (making up about 45 percent of blood) and other materials in the plasma cannot pass through capillary walls. A **red blood cell** carries oxygen to cells and some carbon dioxide from cells. It is a circular cell without a nucleus, that gets its color from an iron compound called **hemoglobin** (HEE muh gloh buhn). Hemoglobin combines with oxygen in the lungs, and becomes bright red. But after losing most of its oxygen to body cells and combining with carbon dioxide, hemoglobin becomes a darker red that is somewhat blue or purple. Being curved inward on both sides, a red blood cell has more surface area to carry oxygen and carbon dioxide. On the average, people have about 25 trillion red blood cells.

White blood cells are also carried in the plasma. A white blood cell is two to three times larger than a red blood cell, and has a nucleus. There is only one white blood cell

AVERAGE PULSE RATES

0–6 YEARS		7–12 YEARS		13–18 YEARS		19–29 YEARS		30–50 YEARS		OVER 50 YEARS	
Male	Female	Male	Female	Male	Female	Male	Female	Male	Female	Male	Female
				Copy This Table on a Piece of Paper							

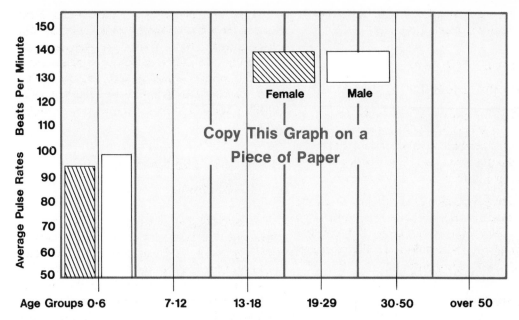

This is a sample graph of pulse rates for different age groups. Fill in your own results on your own graph.

to about every 600 red blood cells. White blood cells destroy certain kinds of disease-causing organisms that enter the body, by surrounding them completely and consuming them. When the body is fighting an infection, the number of white blood cells increases.

Platelets (PLAYT lihtz) have an important part in the clotting of blood. They are fragments of cells in plasma that prevent fatal bleeding when the skin or another organ is cut. They do this by forming a "plug" in the cut blood vessels. A platelet has no nucleus, is flat and colorless, and can have one of a number of possible shapes. The blood has more platelets than white blood cells, but fewer platelets than red blood cells. Blood cells are shown on the next page.

Red blood cells live only for about four months before the spleen filters them out of the bloodstream. The liver breaks down the

hemoglobin from dying red blood cells; what then remains of the iron compound gives bile its color. White blood cells are thought to live for only a few days, depending on whether they fight infection. The dead ones are destroyed in the spleen, liver, and lungs. Platelets last only eight to ten days or less in the blood before they are filtered from the bloodstream by the spleen, liver, and lymphatic system.

In addition to blood cells, digested food particles, and waste materials, plasma transports many important chemicals to and from all parts of your body. You will find out about one type of chemical in Chapter 4 and others in later chapters. Blood tests can show the amounts of each blood component, which provide many clues to a person's health.

When a person has lost so much blood that he or she needs a blood transfusion, or

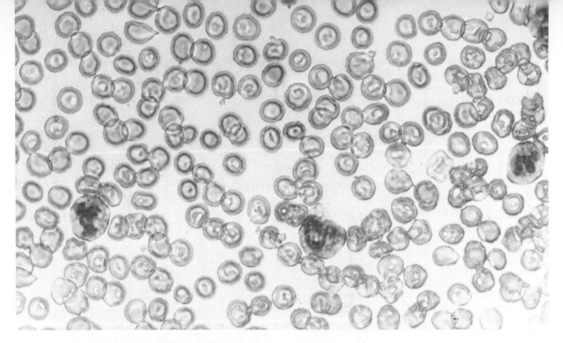

The red blood cells shown above are shaped almost like doughnuts, but without holes. The larger cells are white blood cells.

replacement, the **blood type** must first be determined by a blood test. There are four different blood types: **A, B, AB,** and **O.** The letters stand for two substances found in red blood cells, called "A" and "B."

Blood type A has only substance "A"; blood type B contains only substance "B." If blood types A and B come into contact with each other, they react against each other, forming clumps that block blood circulation. People with these types of blood should not receive transfusions from each other. Blood type AB people have both substances "A" and "B" in their blood. They can receive transfusions of any one of the four types of blood, but can donate blood only to another type AB person. Blood type O people have neither substance "A" nor "B" in their blood. They can donate blood to people with any one of the four blood types, but can receive transfusions of only type O blood.

People all over the world have one of these four types of blood, although types O and A are the most common. People of different races, sexes, or nationalities can safely receive transfusions from each other if they have compatible blood types. Do you know what your blood type is?

Another important substance in blood is called the **Rh factor,** which is found on the surface of red blood cells. It is named after the Rhesus monkey, in which it was first discovered. People have either **Rh-positive** or **Rh-negative** blood. If you are Rh negative, you do not have the Rh factor in your blood. Your blood would react against a transfusion of Rh-positive blood, which does contain the Rh factor. If you are Rh positive, however, you can receive a transfusion of Rh-negative blood. The Rh factor, in addition to blood type, has to be determined for both donor and receiver before a transfusion is given.

The Rh factor sometimes causes a problem when an Rh-negative mother is pregnant with an Rh-positive baby, because the mother's blood reacts against the baby's blood. This sometimes endangers the baby's life. As soon as these babies are born, they may have to have an almost complete transfusion of fresh blood.

In case of emergency, your personal identification should show your blood type and whether you are Rh negative or Rh positive. How many of your classmates know their blood types, and whether they are Rh positive or Rh negative?

2-8 The Urinary System

The blood takes oxygen and digested food particles to individual cells within the body. Some food particles and oxygen react in the cells, producing energy for body processes. Other food particles are used for growth. The waste materials—carbon dioxide, water, and nitrogen compounds—pass into the bloodstream. The alveoli of the lungs get rid of the carbon dioxide. A small amount of water and waste is removed by the skin in perspiration. The **urinary system** removes most of the nitrogen compounds and excess water from the blood, and carries these wastes out of the body.

Study the parts of the urinary system on pages 54–55.

The function of the **kidneys** is to remove materials from the blood that are not needed by the body or that are harmful if they remain in circulation. The kidneys also prevent the loss from the blood of materials that are useful to the body, and keep the quantity of water in the body at the right level. Only a part of the blood enters the kidneys at any one time, but all of the body's blood is filtered at least once every half hour.

The kidneys are able to regulate the quality of the blood efficiently because each kidney has over one million blood-filtering units that filter and clean the blood.

The fluid produced by the kidneys and released from the body is called **urine** (YOOR ihn). Urine is about 95 percent water and 5 percent urea (yoo REE uh), which is a food waste material formed in the liver from nitrogen compounds. Urine also contains salts of minerals such as sodium, potassium, and calcium. The color of urine is due to a small amount of bile pigment that is removed from the bloodstream by the kidneys.

Sometimes certain materials that would normally be returned to the blood by the kidneys are found in urine, which may indicate an illness such as diabetes (dy uh BEE tihs). Laboratory tests of urine, called urinalysis (yoor uh NAL uh sihs), are part of a regular medical checkup. The contents of urine provide valuable information about a person's health, either concerning the urinary system itself or other parts of the body.

SELF CHECK

1. What is the function of each heart chamber?

2. Describe the structure and function of arteries, veins, and capillaries.

3. What are some functions of the lymphatic system?

4. Name the cells found in blood. What does each one do?

5. What are two functions of the kidneys?

6. What is the blood-filtering unit of the kidney called?

7. What parts besides the kidneys make up the urinary system?

The Digestive System

The inside of the **mouth** is lined with mucous membrane that ends at the lips. The **lips** lack mucus-producing glands, which is why they sometimes become dry and uncomfortable.

The **saliva** (suh LY vuh) flowing from three pairs of **salivary** (SAL uh vehr ee) **glands** moistens food, and contains an enzyme that begins the breakdown of starch to sugar.

Teeth tear and grind food into smaller pieces that are mixed with saliva, turning the food into a soft mixture that is more easily digested.

The **tongue** helps mix food and saliva and moves the mixture into positions for chewing and swallowing. Groups of cells along the tongue's surface, called **taste buds,** react to certain chemicals that touch them, telling you something tastes sweet, sour, salty, or bitter.

In swallowing, muscle action of the tongue and throat pushes food into the opening of the food tube, or **esophagus** (ih SAHF uh guhs). It is about ten inches (25 centimeters) long and about three quarters of an inch (2 centimeters) in diameter. The esophagus is lined with mucous membrane and two layers of muscles: circular muscles that squeeze inward, and lengthwise muscles that push downward. By pushing and squeezing, the muscles of the esophagus move food into the stomach. This muscle action is **peristalsis** (pehr uh STAWL sihs).

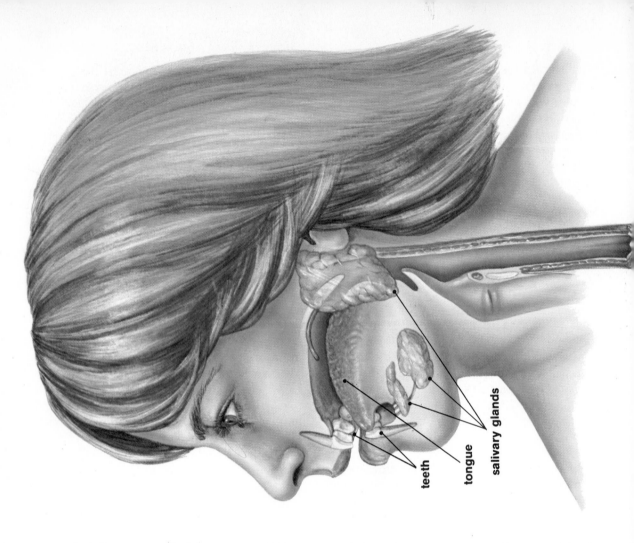

teeth

tongue

salivary glands

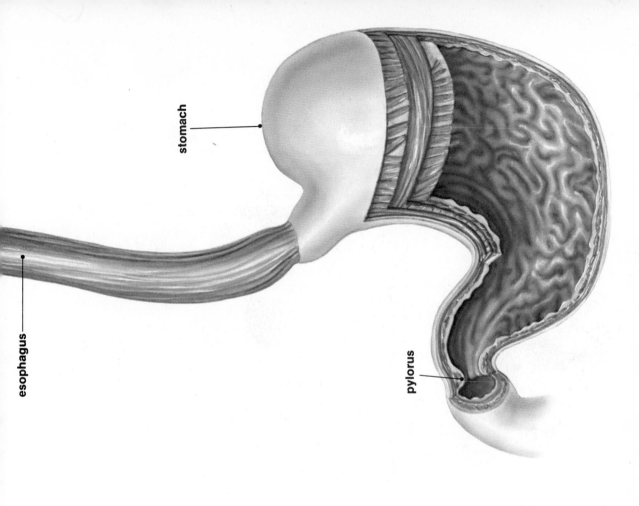

esophagus

stomach

pylorus

The **stomach** is the widest and most muscular part of the digestive tract. When it is full, it holds up to one and one-half quarts (one and one-half liters) of food. Peristalsis of the stomach muscles thoroughly mixes the food with enzymes produced by the inner surface of the stomach. These enzymes require acid to be present in order to help break down protein. One of the chemicals produced by the stomach is hydrochloric (hy druh KLAWR ihk) acid. This acid is so strong it would damage the lining of the stomach if the lining were not protected by stomach mucus. This is what happens when a person develops an ulcer (UHL suhr)—too much acid accumulates and eats away at the wall of the stomach, causing a **stomach ulcer.** Stomach acidity is also useful because it kills some bacteria in food.

Food may remain in the stomach for as long as four hours. A strong circular muscle called the **pylorus** (py LAWR uhs) pinches off the opening between the stomach and intestines. As the stomach juices and peristaltic movements gradually break down the food into a mushy material called **chyme** (KYM), this muscle relaxes. The chyme is then forced in spurts into the small intestine by peristalsis.

(continued on next page)

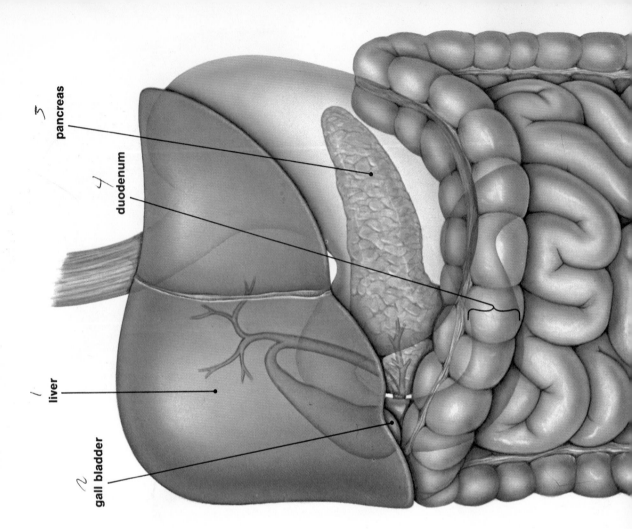

pancreas 3

duodenum 4

liver 1

gall bladder 2

The **liver** is one of the largest organs of the body, weighing three pounds (one and one-third kilograms) or more. It carries out many chemical reactions, including the production of a fluid called **bile.** This fluid passes through a duct leading to the beginning of the small intestine and to the **gall bladder,** where it is stored between periods of digestion. Bile helps to break up large fat particles in the chyme into smaller particles, which then thoroughly mix with water. The smaller fat particles are then absorbed into the walls of the small intestine. Another important function of the liver is to maintain a constant level of blood sugar.

The **pancreas** (PANG kree uhs) produces pancreatic juice containing many enzymes that help break down different food materials. The pancreatic juice passes through a duct from the pancreas into the beginning of the small intestine. The pancreas also produces an important product called **insulin** (IHN suh luhn), which is necessary to help the body use sugar.

The first part of the small intestine is called the **duodenum** (doo uh DEE nuhm). The duodenum receives the highly acidic chyme from the stomach, as well as digestive chemicals from the liver and pancreas. Enzymes from the pancreas and liver and from cells lining the duodenum complete the process of digestion. Since the material that comes into the duodenum is highly acidic, the duodenum can also develop an ulcer, called a **duodenal ulcer.**

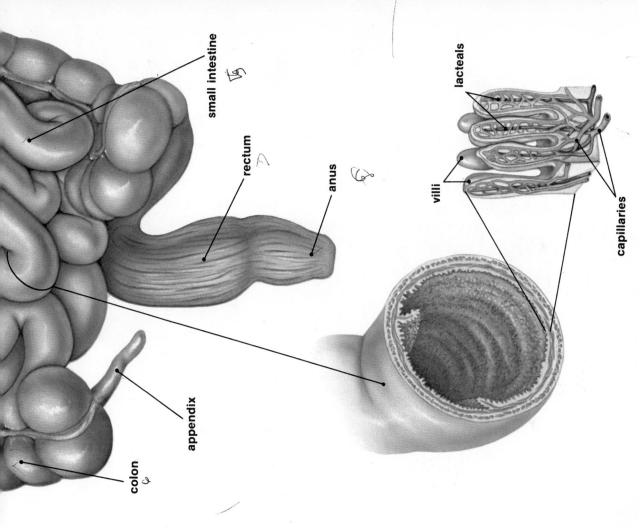

Labels on diagram: small intestine, rectum, anus, appendix, colon, villi, lacteals, capillaries

Food takes about three hours to pass through the **small intestine** before the left-over waste materials are pushed into the large intestine, or **colon** (KOH luhn). While peristalsis pushes the waste materials through the colon, water is removed and absorbed by the cells of the colon.

The food waste materials gradually become more solid, and in the last section, the **rectum,** the waste materials are a soft solid called **feces** (FEE seez). The more time the waste remains in the rectum the more water is removed and the more firm the feces become. Muscle contractions and the accumulating feces exert pressure on circular muscles that pinch off the opening of the rectum, called the **anus** (AY nuhs). You interpret this pressure as the need to empty your bowels. Your brain sends nerve impulses that relax these muscles, allowing the feces to leave the rectum.

The **appendix** has no known function but can become inflamed and cause pain and illness. Inflammation of this organ is called **appendicitis** (uh pehn duh SY tihs).

The small intestine below the duodenum has many large folds as well as many tiny projections. Within the thin walls of each of these fingerlike projections, called **villi** (VIHL eye), is a complex network of tiny blood vessels, called **capillaries.** The digested food materials pass through the thin walls of the villi and capillaries into the blood.

Particles of fat pass through the walls of the villi, too, but into different tiny circulatory vessels, called **lacteals,** which are part of the lymphatic system, described in Section 2-5.

The Respiratory System

Breathing in through the nose is much healthier than breathing in through the mouth. The **nose** moistens and warms or cools the air before it reaches the throat.

Hairs at the entrances to the nostrils help clean the inhaled air by preventing large particles in the air from getting inside.

The sticky mucous membrane lining the **nasal passages** catches small particles and pollen in the air that is inhaled. Tiny hairs on the surface of the mucous membrane, called **cilia** (SIHL ee uh), sweep the trapped particles out toward the openings of the nostrils.

Four pairs of hollow bones called **sinuses** are lined with mucous membrane that helps moisten incoming air. The air in these sinuses also mixes with incoming air and helps warm it.

The nasal passages and mouth join in the **throat.** From the throat, air enters the windpipe, or **trachea** (TRAY kee uh), which extends down the front of the neck and chest. Air also leaves the lungs through the trachea and throat.

Food and water are prevented from entering the trachea during swallowing by a flap of tissue called the **epiglottis** (ehp ih GLAHT ihs), which is attached to the base of the tongue. If the epiglottis doesn't cover the trachea in time and food or liquid goes down the "wrong pipe," you automatically cough it up.

The voice box, or **larynx,** is in the upper part of the trachea.

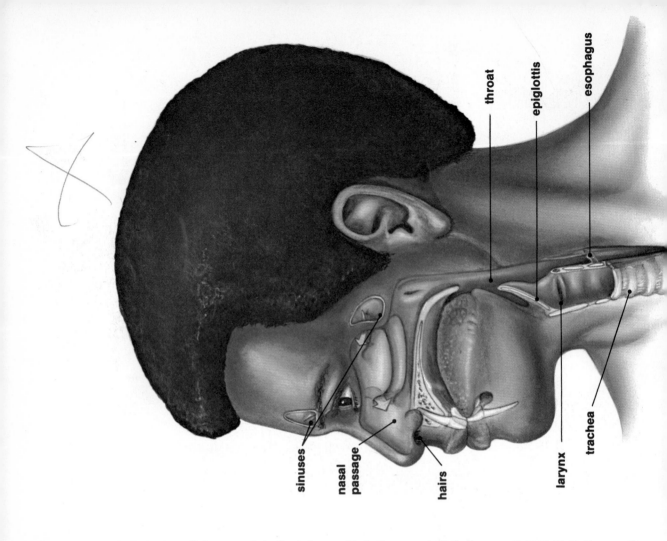

throat

epiglottis

esophagus

sinuses

nasal passage

hairs

larynx

trachea

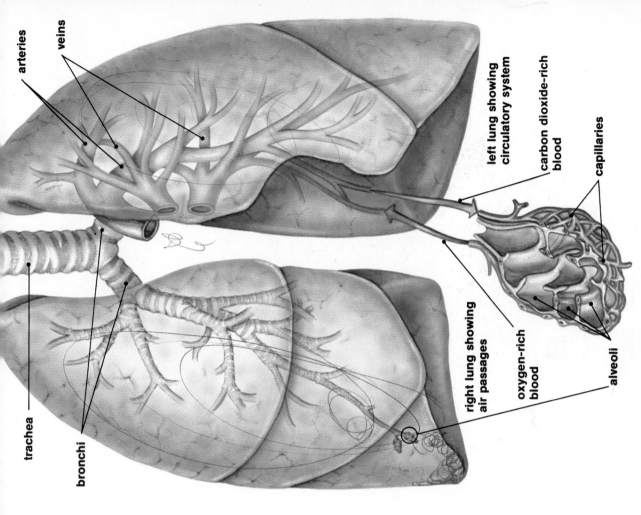

arteries

veins

trachea

bronchi

left lung showing circulatory system

carbon dioxide-rich blood

capillaries

right lung showing air passages

oxygen-rich blood

alveoli

Mucous membrane also lines the **trachea.** Dust and disease-causing organisms are trapped in the sticky mucus and forced up and out of the trachea toward the mouth by the sweeping motions of cilia. The foreign particles are swallowed or coughed out.

The lower part of the trachea divides into two tubes, or **bronchi** (BRAHNG ky). Each tube or bronchus divides and subdivides in each lung, like a tree.

Arteries and **veins** are intertwined within each lung. They branch out into smaller and smaller vessels, just as the air tubes do.

The **lungs** consist of spongy tissue. Each lung weighs about one to one and one-half pounds (about 450–650 grams).

The smallest air tubes lead to thin-walled air sacs, called **alveoli** (al VEE uh ly), resembling tiny bunches of grapes. The inside membrane of each alveolus is in contact with the air inhaled. The outside of each air sac contains a fine network of thin-walled capillaries. In the alveoli, oxygen and carbon dioxide pass between the blood and air.

The inside walls of the alveoli are extremely thin and moist. The wetness protects the delicate lung tissue. The moisture dissolves oxygen from the air breathed in, and the dissolved oxygen passes through the thin walls of the alveoli and capillaries into the blood. At the same time carbon dioxide produced by the body moves in the opposite direction, passing from the blood through the thin walls into the air in the alveoli.

47

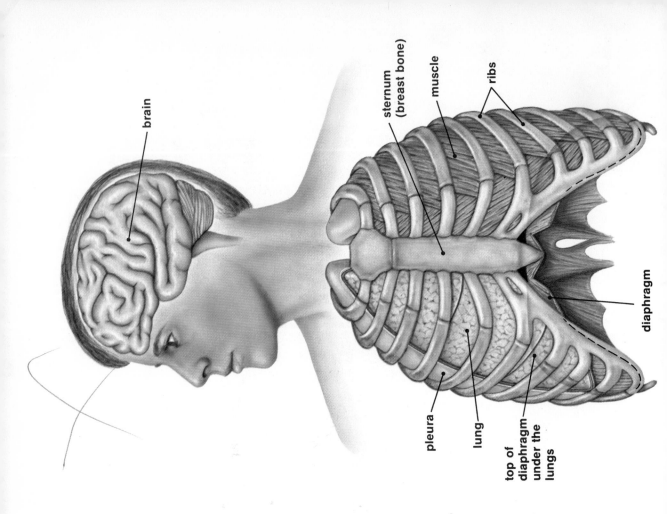

The labels in the figure: brain; sternum (breast bone); muscle; ribs; diaphragm; pleura; lung; top of diaphragm under the lungs.

Inhalation

The rate of breathing is mostly controlled by several locations in the **brain.** These locations in the brain seem to respond primarily to the amount of carbon dioxide in the blood. When the concentration of carbon dioxide in the blood increases, the brain signals the muscles that control breathing, and you automatically inhale and exhale more rapidly. As soon as the concentration of carbon dioxide in the blood decreases, the special locations in the brain are no longer stimulated. Your breathing rate returns to normal—about 12 to 18 times a minute.

Up to a certain point, you can consciously control your breathing rate. For instance, you can hold your breath for a while. But before you could pass out, or die from holding your breath, your brain would start your breathing again.

The **lungs** are protected by a double membrane, the **pleura** (PLOOR uh), and a fluid between the two layers. The membrane and fluid prevent the ribs and lungs from rubbing against each other while you breathe.

When you **inhale,** a large, tough muscle at the bottom of the chest cavity, the **diaphragm** (DY uh fram), contracts and flattens out. At the same time, **muscles** between the **ribs** lift them up and push them out. In this way the space inside the chest cavity increases, and the air pressure inside the chest cavity decreases. At the same time, air rushes into the lungs because the air pressure outside the body is now greater than the air pressure inside the chest cavity. The elastic tissue of the lungs stretches as the air rushes in.

Exhalation

When you **exhale**, the diaphragm and the muscles between the ribs relax. The space inside the chest cavity decreases, and the air pressure inside the chest cavity increases. As a result, the increased pressure forces the air out of the lungs and the lung tissue shrinks.

During the short time between inhaling and exhaling, the composition of the air in the alveoli quickly changes. The air inhaled is about 21 percent oxygen and 0.03 percent carbon dioxide; the air exhaled is about 14 percent oxygen and 5.6 percent carbon dioxide.

The **stomach** and part of the **liver** are right below the diaphragm. When you inhale, the diaphragm contracts and pushes down on these organs. If you have overeaten, you may have felt so full that it was hard to breathe. The diaphragm has to work harder to push down against an overstretched stomach.

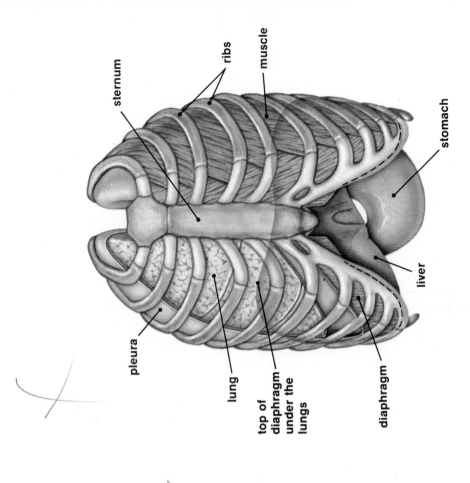

sternum

ribs

muscle

stomach

liver

pleura

lung

top of diaphragm under the lungs

diaphragm

The Circulatory System

Blood Circulation

Arteries are blood vessels that carry blood from the heart to the rest of the body. Large arteries leaving the heart branch into smaller and smaller arteries that finally become microscopic in size. Except for those leading from the heart to the lungs, arteries carry oxygen-rich blood.

Veins are blood vessels that carry blood from all parts of the body back to the heart. They usually parallel the arteries. Veins start out microscopic in size and become larger and larger as they get closer to the heart. Except for those leading from the lungs to the heart, veins carry oxygen-poor (carbon dioxide-rich) blood.

The **heart** is the strongest and most efficient muscle in the body. It is about the size of a fist. When it relaxes, blood enters the heart from large veins. During a contraction, the heart squeezes blood out through large arteries. A single cycle of contraction and relaxation of the heart is called the **heartbeat.**

The **spleen** is an organ that stores up to a quart (a liter) of blood. It produces some new red blood cells and destroys some old red blood cells. It also destroys disease-causing organisms in the blood.

Capillaries are microscopic blood vessels that connect arteries and veins. Blood passes from microscopic arteries to microscopic veins through the capillaries, throughout the body. The thin capillary walls permit tiny food particles and oxygen to pass out of the blood to the body cells, and waste materials and carbon dioxide to pass from the body cells into the blood.

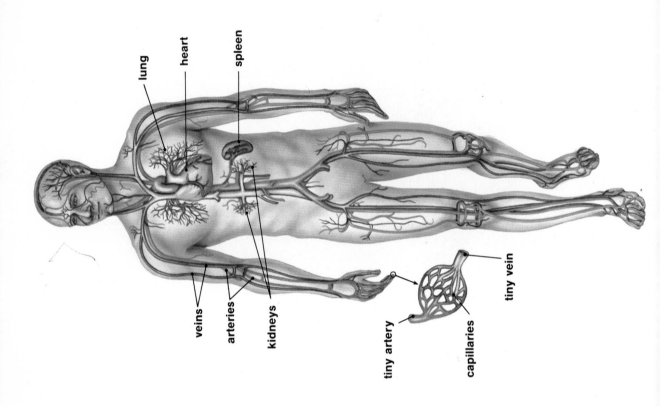

lung

heart

spleen

veins

arteries

kidneys

tiny artery

capillaries

tiny vein

Lymph Circulation

The **lymphatic system** consists of circulatory vessels that usually parallel the blood vessels. **Lymph** leaves the blood through the capillary walls, bathes the body cells, and then enters the lymphatic system. **Lymphatic vessels** carry lymph away from the cells. As in veins, the large lymphatic vessels contain one-way **valves.** When muscles around the lymphatic vessels contract, lymph is pushed by the pressure through the vessels, toward the neck. Lymphatic vessels start out microscopic in size near blood capillaries, and become larger and larger as they get closer to the neck.

The lymphatic vessels all lead to the largest one, the **thoracic** (thuh RAS ihk) **duct** in the neck. It empties into a large vein at the base of the neck. Here the lymph re-enters the bloodstream and returns to the heart.

Along the lymphatic system are places where lymphatic vessels pass through **lymph nodes.** Lymph nodes filter lymph, removing disease-causing organisms and old cells, and produce **lymphocytes** (LIHM fuh sytz), which are a kind of white blood cell that destroys harmful organisms in the lymph nodes and throughout the body. Enlarged lymph nodes indicate the body may be fighting an infection near the nodes.

The **thymus** produces lymphocytes also.

The **spleen** also filters lymph.

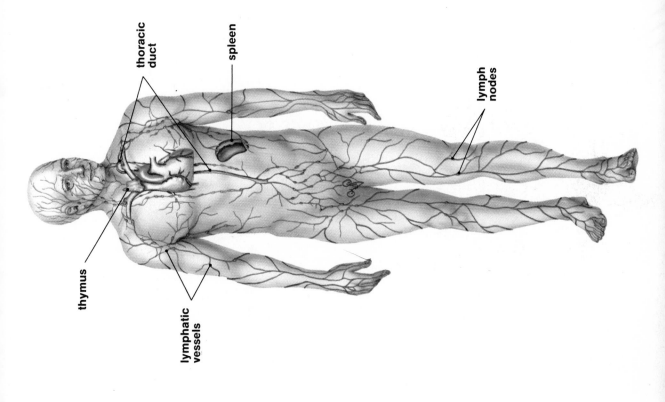

thoracic duct

spleen

lymph nodes

thymus

lymphatic vessels

51

The Flow of Blood to and from the Heart and Lungs

After the blood takes oxygen to the cells throughout the body, it comes back to the heart through the veins, loaded with carbon dioxide. This blood is shown in blue. The **superior** (upper) **vena cava** (VEE nuh KAY vuh) and **inferior** (lower) **vena cava** bring the blood to the **right atrium** (AY tree uhm). When it has filled, the atrium contracts, and the **valve** between the right atrium and **right ventricle** (VEHN trih kuhl) is forced open. Blood flows into the right ventricle.

The **right ventricle** contracts and the one-way valve between the right atrium and ventricle closes. The **valve** to the **pulmonary** (POOL muh nehr ee) **arteries** is forced open and blood is pumped to the lungs. The carbon dioxide in the blood then passes into the lungs and is exhaled. (To make this diagram clearer, the circulatory system of the lungs has been shown smaller than it actually is in relation to the heart.)

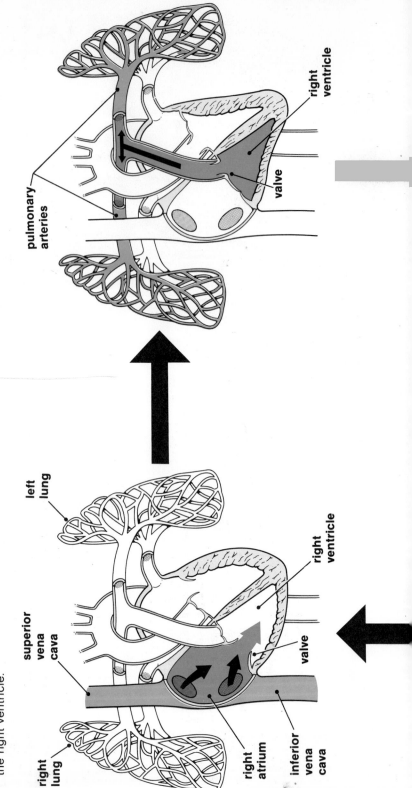

pulmonary arteries

right ventricle

valve

left lung

right lung

superior vena cava

right atrium

inferior vena cava

valve

right ventricle

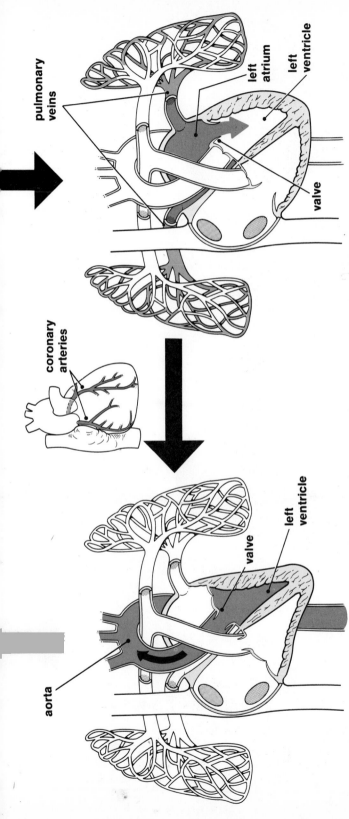

pulmonary veins

left atrium

left ventricle

valve

coronary arteries

aorta

valve

left ventricle

The **left ventricle** contracts, forcing blood through another one-way **valve** into the **aorta** (ay AWR tuh), the body's largest artery. Oxygen-rich blood is then on its way throughout the body. The **coronary** (KAWR uh nehr ee) **arteries** carry to the heart cells the blood they depend on also.

Inhaled oxygen passes from the lungs into the blood. This oxygen-rich blood (shown in dark red) returns to the **left atrium** through the **pulmonary veins.** The heart is resting between beats as the atrium fills with blood. The atrium then contracts, forcing blood through the one-way **valve** into the **left ventricle.**

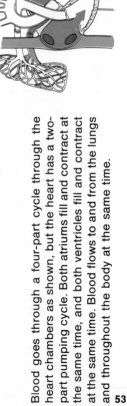

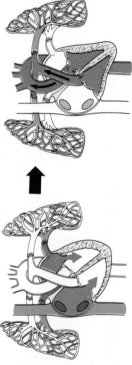

Blood goes through a four-part cycle through the heart chambers as shown, but the heart has a two-part pumping cycle. Both atriums fill and contract at the same time, and both ventricles fill and contract at the same time. Blood flows to and from the lungs and throughout the body at the same time.

53

The Urinary System

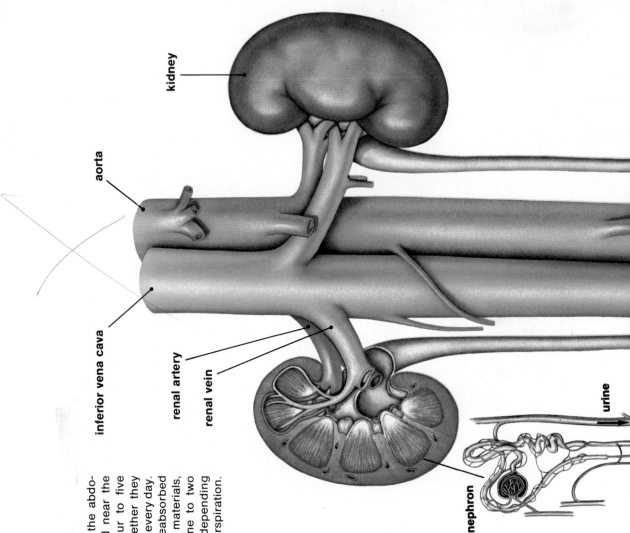

kidney

aorta

inferior vena cava

renal artery

renal vein

nephron

urine

The **kidneys** are located in the back of the abdomen, behind the liver and stomach and near the spinal column. Each kidney is only four to five inches (10 to 12 centimeters) long. Together they filter about 35 gallons (140 liters) of blood every day. Most of the water and chemicals are reabsorbed into the body; the rest, containing waste materials, form urine. Healthy kidneys produce one to two quarts (one to two liters) of urine daily, depending on fluid intake and water loss through perspiration.

Blood flows directly from the heart to the kidneys through the **aorta.**

The **renal** (REE nuhl) **arteries** carry blood from the aorta to the kidneys.

The **renal veins** carry cleaned blood from the kidneys back to the inferior vena cava.

Cleaned blood flows directly from the kidneys back to the heart again through the **inferior vena cava.**

As in the lungs and small intestine, the principal work of the kidneys is done in many tiny structures, consisting of large working areas crowded into a small space. These tiny structures are blood-filtering units called **nephrons** (NEH frahnz). Each kidney has over a million nephrons. Nephrons filter and clean the blood, and form urine from the water and waste materials removed from the blood.

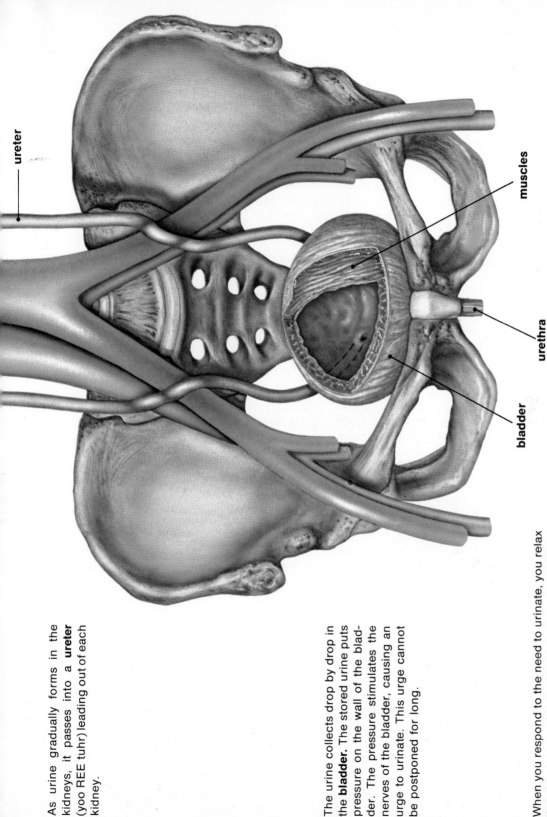

ureter

muscles

urethra

bladder

As urine gradually forms in the kidneys, it passes into a **ureter** (yoo REE tuhr) leading out of each kidney.

The urine collects drop by drop in the **bladder.** The stored urine puts pressure on the wall of the bladder. The pressure stimulates the nerves of the bladder, causing an urge to urinate. This urge cannot be postponed for long.

When you respond to the need to urinate, you relax the circular muscles that hold the lower opening of the bladder closed, and urine flows through the **urethra** (yoo REE thruh) and out of the body.

55

Health Frontier

Successful Organ Transplants

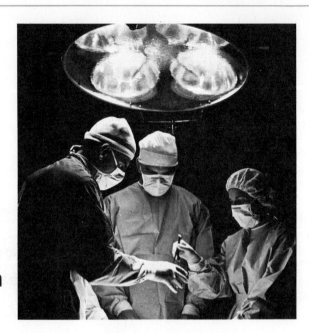

Surgeons can transplant organs such as the kidney or heart from one person to another. But the recipient's body often fights the transplanted organ. The body has a protective mechanism, the **immune reaction,** that helps it resist tiny disease-causing organisms or tissues from other bodies. The immune reaction can work against a person by treating a transplanted organ like an invader, an enemy.

When doctors transplant an organ to save someone's life, they try to hold back the immune reaction with drugs. But this also is dangerous. The patient's body is then less able to fight infection. Bacteria always present in small numbers in the body can become dangerous if the immune reaction is reduced. Disease-causing organisms that everyone breathes in, usually without getting sick, can also take hold if the immune reaction is reduced.

Scientists have recently identified protective substances in the body that can be used to match organ donors with recipients. The process resembles matching blood types, but is much more complex. If the protective substances involved in the immune reaction in the bodies of an organ donor and a recipient match, there is a much better chance of success for the transplant. Success means that the body will not reject the transplanted organ.

Each person carries four protective substances, two inherited from each parent. Each of the four can occur in at least 25 forms. Because of the many possible combinations, any two people rarely have all four protective substances exactly matched.

National and international medical data centers now store information about people who need transplants and the availability of needed organs. Information about matching protective substances is also becoming available. The combination of accurate medical information, computer storage of vast amounts of data, quick air transportation, and new surgical techniques will make organ transplants more successful in the near future than they are today.

Chapter Summary

Using the body and the mind requires energy and materials for building and regulating cells. Food and oxygen are the sources of these materials and energy. Taking these substances into the body, transporting them to the cells, and getting rid of the wastes require the action of four body systems. The digestive, respiratory, circulatory, and urinary systems work together to provide the cells with what they need and to remove the wastes.

Cells need a constant supply of usable food materials. Digestion, aided by enzymes, begins in the mouth and is completed as food passes through the esophagus, stomach, and duodenum. Usable food particles then pass through the villi and capillary walls into the bloodstream or lymph. The remaining food parts continue into the colon, where water is removed and retained. Food parts that the body cannot use leave the rectum through the anus. The liver, gall bladder, and pancreas also take part in digestion, as well as in other body processes.

Cells need a constant supply of oxygen from the air and need to release carbon dioxide to the air. The upper parts of the respiratory system clean, moisten, and warm or cool the air breathed in. The structures that help condition the air in this way are hairs at the entrances to the nostrils, mucous membranes within the respiratory system, and hairlike cilia lining the

Do you ever feel out of shape from what you eat?

nasal passages and trachea. Inside the lungs, the conditioned air enters the alveoli lined with capillaries, where oxygen passes into the blood, and carbon dioxide leaves the blood and passes into the air in the lungs to be exhaled.

The blood carries digested food materials, water, and oxygen to cells throughout the body, and carries carbon dioxide and other waste materials away from the cells. The heart acts as a double pump, sending oxygen-poor blood to the lungs from the right side and oxygen-rich blood to all other parts of the body from the left side. The atriums receive blood from veins and the ventricles send blood out through arteries. Valves control the flow of blood through the heart. The pacemaker controls the rhythm of the heartbeat.

Arteries with elastic, muscular walls carry blood away from the heart. They branch off, becoming increasingly smaller until the blood passes into thin-walled, microscopic capillaries. From the capillaries tiny food particles and oxygen pass into the cells, and waste materials pass from the cells into the blood in the capillaries. Blood then enters tiny veins, which join larger veins with valves and thin walls, that bring blood back to the heart.

Each person has one of four blood types: A, B, AB, or O, and is either Rh positive or Rh negative. Blood plasma contains red blood cells, white blood cells, platelets, and other chemicals and materials either needed by the body or disposed of as waste. Some blood plasma enters the lymphatic system as lymph. The lymph returns food particles to the bloodstream through the lymphatic vessels.

The quality of the blood is regulated by the kidneys, which remove the nitrogen-compound wastes and the excess water from the blood. The two kidneys each have over one million nephrons. All of the blood flows through the nephrons in the kidneys, which filter out fluid and unneeded and harmful materials, and return the rest to the blood. The urine produced by the kidneys passes through the ureters to the bladder. There, urine is stored until it is released through the urethra. Urinalysis and blood tests provide information about health.

Chapter Self Check

1. What body systems take in the materials the cells need for energy, for growth, and for maintenance? Describe the parts of each system briefly.

2. How do the body systems that take in needed materials work together with the circulatory system to get these materials to the cells?

3. The body can rid itself of wastes in the forms of gas, liquid, and solid. Describe the body's different methods of waste disposal.

4. How does each of the organs that make up the digestive system work?

5. What organs that help in digestion are also part of another body system?

6. What chemicals produced by the tissues of the digestive tract help break down food? How many types of food does each of these chemicals help break down?

7. Hydrochloric acid could dissolve the stomach lining. What usually prevents this from happening?

8. How does digested food pass into the bloodstream? Where in the digestive tract does this occur?

9. In addition to bringing oxygen into the body, the respiratory system makes it possible for you to talk and sing. What is the structure involved in speech and where is it located?

10. How is air cleaned, moistened, and warmed or cooled before it enters the lungs?

11. What is the function of the epiglottis?

12. How do the lungs, ribs, and diaphragm work together every time you breathe?

13. In what part of the respiratory system do oxygen and carbon dioxide pass between the air and the blood?

14. "The heart is a double pump." Explain this statement by describing the pumping action of the heart and the flow of blood through the heart. What is the function of heart valves?

15. How do arteries and veins differ in structure and function? What controls the flow of blood in the arteries and in the veins?

16. Describe how blood flows from arteries to veins.

17. How do cells get the materials they need from the blood and send waste materials into the blood?

18. Explain some differences between red and white blood cells.

19. What are the different blood types called?

20. Describe the structures and functions of the lymphatic system.

21. In what two ways do the kidneys regulate the quality of the blood?

22. What are some substances normally found in urine? Why is urinalysis important in a medical examination?

Read More About It

Asimov, Isaac. *Fantastic Voyage.* Boston: Houghton Mifflin Company, 1966. Body organs and systems presented in an exciting science-fiction journey through the bloodstream.

Eckstein, Gustav. *The Body Has a Head.* New York: Harper & Row, 1970. The parts of the body from individual cells to creativity, and how they are related in human activities.

MacKenzie, Rachel. *Risk.* New York: The Viking Press, 1971. A brief, moving account of a woman's triumph over open-heart surgery.

Nourse, Alan E., and the Editors of Time-Life Books. *The Body.* New York: Time Inc., Time-Life Books (Life Science Library), 1971 edition. Explanations of the body systems. Well-illustrated.

Smith, Homer W. *From Fish to Philosopher.* Summit, New Jersey: CIBA Pharmaceutical Products Inc., 1959. How the kidneys evolved as regulators of the body's fluid content.

Thompson, Thomas. *Hearts.* New York: McCall Publishing Company, 1971. The story of two prominent heart surgeons and their pioneering work.

3
The Joy of Moving

After completing the work in this chapter, you will be able to:

describe the structure and functions of the bones in the body.

compare the different kinds of joints within the skeleton.

describe the functions of three types of muscle tissue.

identify the differences between training skeletal muscles for endurance and for strength.

describe how to treat overworked and injured muscles.

Running the Marathon

Bernard Plain from Cardiff, Wales:

"I think the Boston race is the most famous aside from the Olympics. . . . The hills, as I studied them, aren't that difficult. It's the fact that they appear at about 17 miles, when you are beginning to pay an oxygen debt, that makes them serious."

Elaine Pederson, 35-year-old from California, the second woman to finish the 1975 Boston Marathon:

"I jog 50 miles each week for pure enjoyment."

John Graham, Monroeville, Pennsylvania:

"The sense of well-being that comes from running one of these is fantastic. It's not 2000 people competing against each other. It's 2000 people competing against themselves."

Leigh Montville, of the *Boston Globe*, describing the winner of the 1974 Boston Marathon:

"Neil Cusack, 22, from Johnson City, Tennessee . . . that was the winner . . . the one in the corner. The one shivering under the blankets. The one who had just had the oxygen mask removed from his face . . ."

Nina Kuscik, 34-year-old mother of three children, from Huntington, New York, the first woman to finish the Boston Marathon (1972):

"I'm tired, but I feel great. I've got one blister."

William Rodgers from Jamaica Plain, Massachusetts, the winner in 1975 and 1979:

"About two miles from the finish line I began to think I might win if my legs didn't cramp on me. I knew I'd get across that line. I would have crawled across if I got up there 100, 200 yards from the end and my legs went on me."

Why do people compete in a 25-mile (40-kilometer) race? Why do they run for hours over hills and through crowded streets, sometimes in a cold rain, sometimes in the hot sun?

Some are runners who want to prove to themselves or to others that they are in good physical condition. Other racers want the fame of winning the Boston Marathon. Some people probably enter the race because they want to participate in a tradition that goes back to ancient Greece. The first marathon runner was a Greek who raced across the plains of Marathon to tell the citizens that their army had defeated the invading Persians.

Why people run is not as hard to understand as *how* they manage to do it. A marathon is a terrible challenge to the body. The racers talk a lot about their bones, muscles, and connective tissues. They have learned how to work out stiffness and soreness in their muscles. They know what oxygen debt is and all about cramps. And they know how to train to bring out their best capabilities.

Maybe only a few people reading this would want to get into good enough condition to run a marathon. Would you like to? Whether you can run 25 miles (40 kilometers) or not, you still want to be able to stay on the go for the probable 70 to 80 years of your life span. That's your longest "marathon."

The Body's Framework

3-1 Skeletal Support and Protection

You began life with many more separate bones in your **skeletal system** than you have now. Babies have about 300 bones that are largely composed of **cartilage,** a tough, flexible tissue. Many of these bones fuse, or grow together, during the first few months of life. Some bones do not completely fuse until adulthood. Adults usually have 206 bones in their skeletons, which support and protect them all of their lives.

People sometimes have more or fewer bones than the average number. For example, some have an extra rib or an extra bone in the arch of a foot. Some people may have one fewer rib. An extra bone, or one fewer, doesn't usually cause trouble. A person may not even know about it until it is discovered during a medical examination or in an X ray.

There are four kinds of bones: long bones, such as leg and arm bones; short bones, such as those in the fingers and toes; flat bones, such as ribs and those that make up the skull; and irregular bones, such as vertebrae (VUR tuh bree), the bones that make up the "backbone."

Calcium, phosphorus, and other minerals make up about half of a bone's structure. Water makes up about one-fourth. The rest of a bone's structure consists of a material called **collagen** (KAHL uh juhn). Collagen forms a dense network of threads that bind calcium, phosphorus and other minerals

If you had wire and glue, would you know where to put all of these pieces to make a whole skeleton?

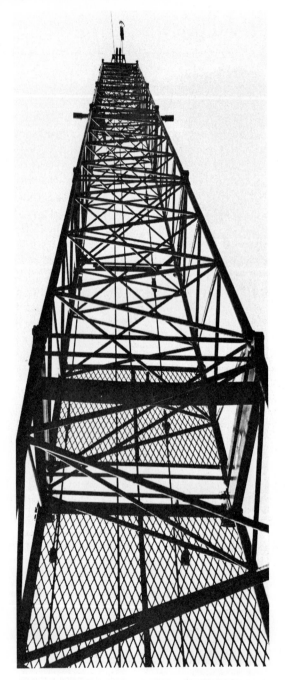

Bones and cranes have spaces in the right places, making them lightweight as well as surprisingly strong.

together into a rigid meshwork. This structure gives bone its characteristic strength and hardness, as well as its porous nature.

Two different kinds of cells form, shape, and repair bone tissue. **Bone-forming cells** build up the collagen-mineral structure, and **bone-destroying cells** break it down. During growth, bone-forming cells deposit minerals in the cartilage next to the existing bone at the ends of long bones. In this way the cartilage becomes **ossified** (AH suh fyd), or changed to bone. The bone formed by this process is porous. As more bone-forming cells convert the cartilage to bone, new cartilage is formed at the ends of the bones, and then ossified. Through this continuing process, the long bones grow in length until the skeleton reaches its full growth. Bone-forming cells also add layers along the surfaces of bones and repair broken bones.

Bone-destroying cells shape and polish bones on their surfaces. Bone-tissue materials that are dissolved by these cells enter the bloodstream and circulate throughout the body. These materials are either used in different parts of the body or disposed of. Bone-destroying cells within bones hollow out central canals that blood and lymphatic vessels branch through. As bone tissue is destroyed, each central canal branches out into a network of smaller canals. As bones grow larger, the canal networks also grow larger.

At the core of bones there is a spongy **marrow** (MAR oh). It makes most of the body's red and white blood cells. These blood cells are primarily formed in the red marrow of the vertebrae, ribs, breast and collar bones, pelvis (hip bone), and in the long bones of arms and legs.

Most of the body's calcium and phosphorus is in the bones. The body maintains a balance between the build-up and breakdown of calcium in bone tissue. Even in mature bones, bone-forming and bone-

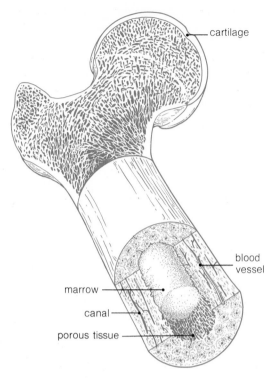

cartilage

blood vessel

marrow

canal

porous tissue

The internal structure of bones.

destroying cells are constantly building up new bone tissue and breaking down old bone tissue. Not only are calcium, phosphorus, and other minerals responsible for the hardness of bone, but calcium and phosphorus are also necessary for nerves and muscles to work properly. The way the body maintains a proper calcium balance is complex and not completely understood. However, scientists do know that vitamin D and chemicals produced by certain tissues affect calcium balance. If people do not get enough calcium and vitamin D in their diet, the body's need for calcium can cause breakdown of the mineral structure of the bones.

In older people the calcium balance becomes upset. One reason for this is that many older people do not get enough vita-

min D. Their bones lose calcium and become brittle. A fall that could cause a bone fracture in an older person would probably just bruise you. Lack of strain on bones also causes them to lose calcium and soften. That is one reason older people need exercise, too. While astronauts are in space for a long time, they exercise to put strain on their bones. If they didn't, without the resistance of gravity their bones would soften. Someone who starts jogging or dancing regularly will soon develop stronger bones.

Besides supporting the body, skeletal structures protect internal organs. The thick, flat bones of the skull provide a helmet for the brain. The curved rib cage protects the heart and lungs. The pelvis protects the soft, delicate organs of the lower abdomen. The characteristic strength and hardness of these bones enable the skeleton to withstand some pressures that might otherwise cause severe injury to internal organs.

Bones are light in weight in comparison to their strength. The lightness is partly due to their construction. Even dense, hard layers of bone are porous rather than solid. The ends of large bones are especially porous. Such lightweight strength enables the skeleton to support the weight of the entire body without adding much weight itself. The bones of a 154-pound (70-kilogram) person would probably weigh only about 29 pounds (13 kilograms).

3-2 Bone Linkage

Parts of the skeleton are always in motion. Even in sleep, the rib cage expands and contracts and the body twists and turns. If connecting bones rubbed against each other every time you moved, bones would quickly become damaged. However, the structure of the **joints,** places where two or

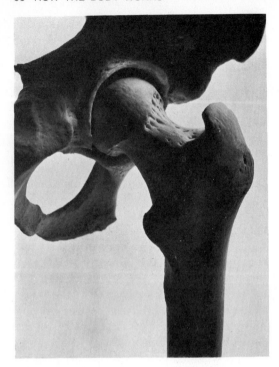

The biggest joint in the body—where the thigh bone joins the pelvis.

more bones come together, prevents such damage.

There are three kinds of joints in the body: fixed, partially movable, and freely movable. Each kind has a different structure and function.

The bones meeting at a **fixed joint** appear to connect directly to each other. However, there is a thin layer of transparent connective cartilage between them. Skull bones are interlocked at special fixed joints called **sutures** (SOO churz). These joints are immovable. However, at birth, they are loose enough to permit the skull bones to move and overlap as the baby's head passes through the narrow birth canal. This prevents the skull from being crushed during birth. During the first few months of life, the skull bones fuse at the joints, except for two

small places. These "soft spots" can be felt at the top of an infant's head. These spaces soon close, and by the time the brain reaches full growth, the skull is a solid covering of bone.

Other types of fixed joints are found where the nose bone connects to other skull bones and where the teeth join the jawbone. Because slight movement is possible at teeth joints, badly positioned teeth can be moved into the correct position. In special dental work, called orthodontia (awr thuh DAHN shuh), braces or other devices are used to gradually move crooked teeth.

Individual vertebrae are connected at **partially movable joints.** Each vertebra is separated from the next one by a **disk,** or broad, flat pad of cartilage. Other partially movable joints are found where the rib bones connect to the breast bone.

Lifting a heavy object the wrong way, having bad posture, or sleeping on a bed that is too soft can cause a disk between two vertebrae to slip out of position. A "slipped disk" pushes against spinal nerves, causing pain or numbness. If the condition

A damaged disk presses on a nerve.

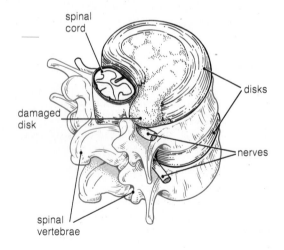

spinal cord

damaged disk

spinal vertebrae

disks

nerves

cannot be corrected by rest, special exercises, or improved posture, the dislodged or crushed disk is surgically removed.

Most joints are **freely movable.** In comparison to the limited movement of partially movable joints, freely movable joints allow much freedom of movement in many directions. Of the several types of freely movable joints in the body, the hinge, pivot, and ball-and-socket types are the most obvious.

Hinge joints permit only two-way movement, like the hinges on a door. The elbow and finger joints are examples of a hinge joint. Though the knee joint can move slightly from side to side and rotate, it is considered a hinge joint because the knee primarily bends backward and forward in one direction. The wrists are double hinge joints, permitting easy sideways and backward and forward motion.

Pivot joints allow rotating motion. Connections at the ankles and at the base of the thumb are pivot joints. The head and the first neck vertebra are also connected at a pivot joint.

At **ball-and-socket joints,** the rounded end of one bone securely fits into the cup of another, allowing great freedom of movement in all directions. This type of joint is found where the long bone of the upper leg and the hip bone meet, and where the long bone of the upper arm and the shoulder bone meet.

Freely movable joints have a more complex structure than the other kinds. The ends of the bones that meet at a freely movable joint are covered by cartilage. They may fit together loosely or closely. The type of connection determines the kind and amount of movement that takes place.

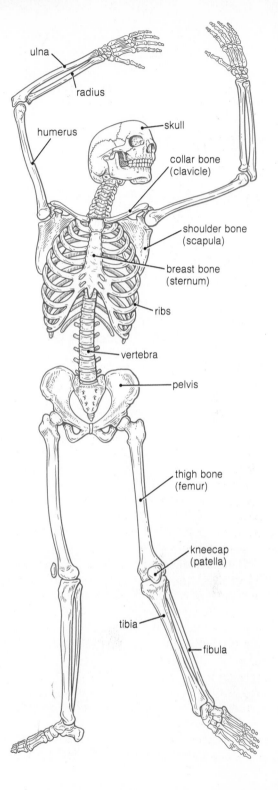

ulna
radius
humerus
skull
collar bone (clavicle)
shoulder bone (scapula)
breast bone (sternum)
ribs
vertebra
pelvis
thigh bone (femur)
kneecap (patella)
tibia
fibula

How many of the different kinds of bones and joints described in the last two sections can you identify in this picture?

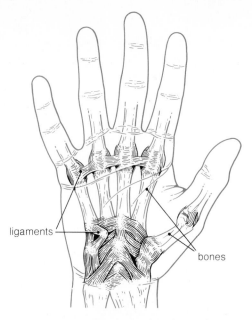

Ligaments hold bones in the hand together.

Whatever the connection, the ends of the bones are surrounded by tough, fibrous tissue that holds the bones together at the joint. The inside lining of this tissue produces a fluid similar to egg white called **synovial** (suhn OH vee uhl) **fluid.** This fluid moistens the joint and reduces friction between the ends of the bones.

Bones are also held together at joints by strands of tough tissue called **ligaments** (LIHG uh muhntz). Ligaments are mainly composed of either parallel or intertwined collagen fibers. Twisting a joint too far can **sprain** it. In a sprain, the ligaments holding the joint together are torn. Muscles and nerves may also be damaged. A bad enough jolt to a joint can even knock a bone out of place. **A dislocated bone,** as it is called, may have to be put back into place by a doctor.

Nobody is "double-jointed," but some people have unusually flexible joints. Can you do this?

1. Give an example of each type of bone and describe its function.

2. Briefly describe how bone tissue is formed and name the main materials in bone.

3. Name the three basic kinds of joints in the body. Give an example of each and describe the type of motion it allows.

4. What are the functions of cartilage, ligaments, and synovial fluid? Where are all three found together?

The Body in Motion

3-3 Muscles
for Moving

One thing bones can't do is move by themselves. Muscles and connective tissue of the **muscular system** make that possible. The longest muscles in the body move the thighs. Shorter ones make the toes wiggle and the eyes blink.

Muscles also help hold the skeleton together, support the joints, and protect internal organs from injury. But muscles are mainly involved with moving—if not bones, then other tissues, organs, and materials. Muscles move food along the digestive tract and release urine from the body. For about five months before birth and throughout life the heart muscles continuously pump blood. What are some other examples of muscular movement that you can think of?

Like bones, muscles vary in size and shape. The stomach is mostly a muscular sac. The esophagus contains circular muscles and muscles that run lengthwise. And sheets of muscles in the back hold the body upright.

Muscles consist of bundles of microscopic **fibers.** The fibers, in turn, consist of hundreds of even smaller threads called **fibrils** (FY bruhlz). Long molecules in the fibrils, resembling an accordion, fold up or open up when a muscle contracts or relaxes.

All muscles have this in common: they can contract (shorten) and relax (lengthen). Of all the body tissues only muscles can do this.

While some muscle fibers contract slowly and others quickly, there is no such thing as a partial contraction. A fiber is either contracted or relaxed. The reason you can use a muscle gently or with great force involves the nerves. Directions from a nerve, called **nerve impulses,** make a muscle contract. After a contraction, muscles relax by themselves. Each group of muscle fibers is connected to a separate nerve. When more nerves send impulses to different fibers in a muscle, more fibers contract. If you do something gentle, such as pet a cat, fewer nerve impulses and muscles are involved than when you are forceful. To do something continuously, such as hold up a book, requires the nerves to keep sending impulses to the muscles in your arms and hands. Otherwise, after the first contraction, the muscles would relax and drop the book.

Even a person at rest has some nerve and muscle activity. A few fibers are contracted. This state of constant muscle contraction is called **muscle tone.** It would tire the muscles if the same fibers stayed contracted all the time, but they don't. The fibers alternate contracting and relaxing: one group contracts while another group relaxes. Without

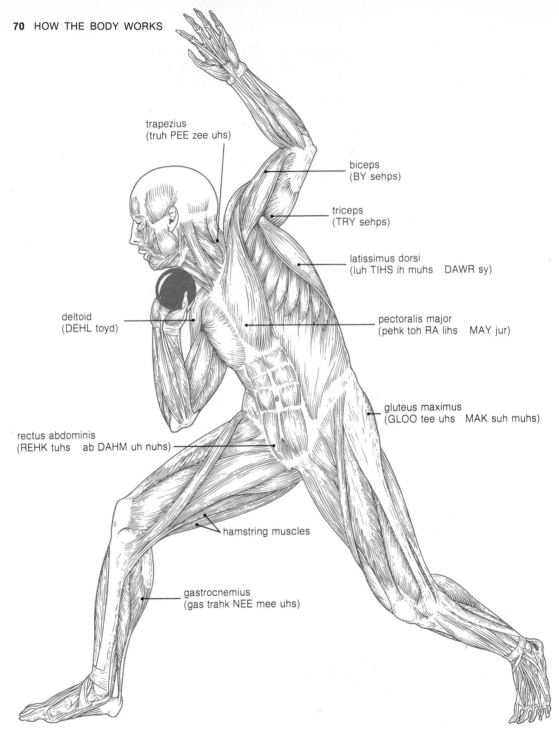

trapezius
(truh PEE zee uhs)

biceps
(BY sehps)

triceps
(TRY sehps)

latissimus dorsi
(luh TIHS ih muhs   DAWR sy)

deltoid
(DEHL toyd)

pectoralis major
(pehk toh RA lihs   MAY jur)

gluteus maximus
(GLOO tee uhs   MAK suh muhs)

rectus abdominis
(REHK tuhs   ab DAHM uh nuhs)

hamstring muscles

gastrocnemius
(gas trahk NEE mee uhs)

What movement takes place when each muscle contracts? Can
you tell which bones each group of muscles connects to?

Experiments showed that astronauts had to exercise to keep their bones and muscles strong in a weightless environment.

some muscle tone, you would slump to the ground like a puppet on loose strings.

The amount of tone and elasticity that a muscle has makes the difference between a healthy muscle and a flabby one, which cannot do as much work. Unused muscles lose their tone. Regular use of muscles gives them a healthy tone that enables you to do more without getting tired, and also helps you look and feel good. You can check this out yourself. Recall how you feel after a good swim or race or some enjoyable hard work. Compare that with how you feel hanging around with nothing to do or after being in bed for days because of an illness.

3-4 Skeletal Muscles and Tendons

There are three kinds of muscle tissue. One is made up of striped or striated (STRY ay tihd) fibers. Another has smooth fibers.

Heart or cardiac (KAHR dee ak) muscle, the third kind, consists of a combination of smooth and striated fibers.

Under a microscope, **striated muscle** fibers look something like banded peppermint sticks or barber-shop poles. Striated muscles are generally long and cross-banded. Some are found around the mouth and eyes, but most of them are attached to bones across joints. A special feature of striated muscle fibers is that they can contract rapidly and relax rapidly. This makes possible all the quick, graceful, and coordinated movements of the body.

Striated muscles are also called **skeletal muscles,** or **voluntary muscles,** which means they are more or less under conscious control. If you want one to contract, you just consciously decide to move a certain body part. Since we consciously control voluntary muscles, they can be strengthened by regular activity. Dancers can train to leap higher, basketball players to shoot more accurately, and runners to run farther and faster. All it takes is the right kind of practice and a strong desire to improve.

Skeletal muscles can pull but not push bones. They come in pairs. The muscles in a pair are usually attached to opposite sides of a joint. When one muscle contracts and shortens, the opposite one relaxes and lengthens. This moves a bone around a joint. To move a bone back to where it was, the opposite muscle contracts and the first one relaxes.

Skeletal muscles are attached to bones by tough, inelastic bands of connective tissue called **tendons.** They are largely composed of collagen fibers, the same substance that runs through the bones like reinforcing rods. Tendons are so strong that sometimes bones break before tendons tear. A tendon as thin as a pencil can withstand the pull of several tons' force without breaking.

Throughout the body, tendons slide against bones, ligaments, and other tendons. Where this happens—usually at joints, particularly freely movable joints—there is usually a **bursa** between the tissues that move against each other. A bursa is a small, fluid-filled, saclike tissue. Like synovial fluid in a joint, the slippery fluid within a bursa decreases friction between the adjacent tissues.

When a bursa becomes irritated or inflamed, it can be very painful. This condition, called **bursitis** (bur SY tuhs), commonly affects the knee, hip, shoulder, and elbow joints. Deposits of calcium in an inflamed bursa sometimes make bursitis worse.

Unfortunately, properly working bursas do not always prevent tendons from becoming inflamed, a condition called **tendinitis** (tehn duh NY tuhs). Tendinitis often results from working in cold weather without wearing warm clothing, or from doing strenuous exercise without any warm-up.

Tendinitis can also result from doing a job that one has great mental resistance to. Then the nerves, muscles, and tendons sometimes do not work together smoothly. Muscles can cramp, increasing the friction between the tendons and causing them to become inflamed.

Training muscles helps to develop thicker and stronger tendons as well as muscles that work better. The nerves that signal trained muscles also work better. Just what does "work better" mean, though? Training muscles one way can make them stronger, and training them in a different way can make them work for longer periods of time. What you do to build up strength and endurance are different.

A sprinter has to develop great speed very rapidly to win a short race. The strain on the thighs and calves is enormous. A long-distance runner has to just keep going and going and going, until perhaps at the end of the race, when a burst of speed is needed. Sprinters' training increases the size and number of fibrils in the muscle fibers of the legs. This is why most sprinters have large, muscular thighs and calves.

Long-distance runners generally have thinner legs. Instead of developing large leg muscles, their training increases muscle efficiency. This means their leg muscles work better in getting energy from stored energy supplies and in disposing of wastes. Physical-endurance training also increases the fatigue resistance of certain nerves in muscles.

When you train for both strength and endurance, your muscles cannot become both as strong as a sprinter's and as efficient as a long-distance runner's, because muscle fibers can only do one or the other. You have to settle for a compromise between the two. What sports do you think fall into that middle category? Are those the sports that you prefer?

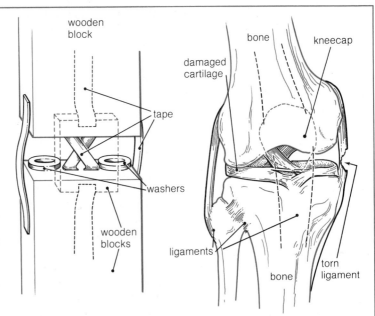

Health Frontier

Knee Woes

The knee is a very large and probably the most complicated joint in the body. Four strong ligaments hold the three long bones of the joint in place, and the largest synovial tissue in the body lubricates the joint. Two large cartilages and four bursas further reduce friction in the joint. The kneecap embedded in a tendon protects the front of the joint. Considering the protection of the knee joint, why do so many people have knee problems? A "trick knee," a dislocated kneecap, or "water on the knee" are just a few of many knee problems.

Even though the bones and connective tissues of the knee are strong and well protected against friction, it is a relatively fragile joint, because it represents a compromise between strength and flexibility. Knees support practically all the body weight, yet they also allow some freedom of movement. In daily activities, especially in sports, the knees are exposed to a lot of stress, and are often forced to move in ways they are not built to move.

The complexity and the fragility of the knee joint mean that many things can go wrong with it. Most knee injuries involve one or more of the two cartilages and four ligaments, par-

ticularly the external ligament in the back of the knee. The picture of the model of the knee joint—represented by two wooden blocks, tape, and washers—shows the ligaments and cartilages that are most often damaged.

If a ligament is slightly torn, an elastic knee tape or a special bandage is used to reduce movement of the joint, and the patient rests while the tissue slowly heals. More severe injuries may require surgery, for example, to remove torn cartilage, which is gradually replaced by scar tissue. Surgeons are developing very sophisticated techniques for repairing damaged knees. In fact, some surgeons are knee specialists and don't operate on other parts of the body. They have developed artificial knee joints to replace knees crippled by arthritis. And metal and plastic replacements for damaged ligaments or cartilage are also being installed now. After a period of time on crutches, the patient can usually learn to walk without help and without pain.

Equipment designers and doctors are also trying to prevent knee damage by devising a special athletic shoe with a movable heel, so the heel can move when the body pivots.

The Joy
of Moving

● **3-5 Investigating Your Muscles and Tendons**

In this investigation, you are going to locate some of the muscles and tendons in your hands, arms, feet, and legs. You will then observe how certain muscles and tendons work together when you move.

PROCEDURE

1. If you are wearing long sleeves, roll them up as far as possible in order to observe the muscles and tendons in your arms. Put your elbow and forearm on your desk, with the palm of your hand facing down. Curve your fingers as if you are playing a piano.

2. Keeping your fingers firmly on the desk, raise and lower your thumb several times. While you are moving your thumb, observe the movement of tendons and muscles in your hand, wrist, and arm. Using the fingers of your other hand, gently trace the moving tendons to where they join muscles. Also try to trace the other ends of the tendons to the bones they are attached to.

3. With your thumb and fingers firmly on the desk, raise each of your fingers, one at a time. Again observe the tendons and muscles that move. Trace the muscle origin and the bone attachment of each tendon.

4. Place your elbow on your desk, with your forearm bent up toward you and the back of your hand facing you. Bend your fingers so they touch the palm of your hand. Straighten them part way and then all the way. Do this several times, observing the movement of muscles and tendons in your hand and arm.

5. Turn your hand over and bend your fingers at the knuckles, so your fingers touch

Exertion makes muscles and tendons stand out on the body.

your palm. Observe the tendons and muscles in the palm of your hand and in your arm. Feel them with the fingers of your other hand. Feel what happens to the tendons as you slowly straighten and bend your fingers several times. Observe how far you can straighten your fingers.

6. With your elbow and forearm on the desk, palm up, straighten your fingers. Then move your hand up, bending the wrist, and observe the tendons and muscles that move. Then make a fist and observe whether or not the same tendons and muscles move. Feel the arm bones that move when you twist your wrist.

7. With the fingers of your other hand, locate the tendons on the inside of your elbow and try to trace them to where they join muscles. Observe the muscle and tendon movements in your upper arm as you bend and straighten your elbow.

8. Locate the Achilles tendon, just above your heel. Trace it up the back of your leg to the place where it originates in the calf muscle. Feel what happens when you bend your ankle to move your foot up and down.

9. Use the fingers of both hands to locate the hamstring tendons in the back of the knee. Trace the tendons to their origins in the thigh muscles. Feel what happens to the hamstring tendons as you bend your knee and then straighten your leg as far as you can. Try to determine how the contraction of a muscle affects a tendon.

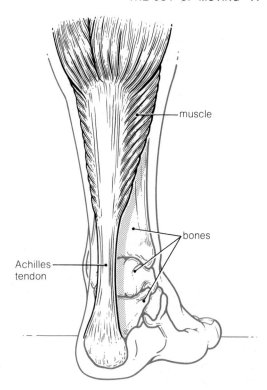

DISCUSSION

1. Based on your observations, how would you define a tendon?

2. How is the freedom of movement of a finger or limb limited?

3. How do muscle contractions affect tendons?

3-6 Smooth and Cardiac Muscles

Smooth muscle fibers have no light and dark bands like those of striated fibers, nor are they connected to parts of the skeleton. Smooth muscles control the movement of internal organs. The intestines, bladder, uterus (YOO tuh ruhs), stomach, veins, and arteries all have walls containing smooth muscles, usually of two types. An inner layer of smooth muscles runs in a circular direction while an outer layer of smooth muscles runs lengthwise.

The contractions of smooth muscles push food through the digestive tract and a baby through the birth canal. Smooth muscle contractions adjust the size of the pupils of the eyes, depending on light and dark. Tiny smooth muscles attached to hair follicles contract when you are cold or afraid, causing "goose bumps" on the skin. Smooth muscles in the walls of the arteries widen or narrow the vessels, depending on the nerve impulses sent to the muscles.

The contractions of smooth and striated muscles differ. Striated muscles generally contract faster, but smooth muscles can contract for longer periods of time without tiring. Smooth muscles can also contract so suddenly and completely that it hurts. You've probably had a knotlike feeling in your digestive tract at some time. What happened was that certain muscles contracted but did not relax afterward. This kind of locked-in contraction is called a **muscle spasm.**

Smooth and cardiac muscles are sometimes called **involuntary muscles** because they generally work without conscious control. You don't have to decide what your digestive tract muscles will do. Even if you wanted to, you could not decide to make them start or stop working. Or could you?

For centuries, people in India, Persia, and other countries in the Middle East and Far East have claimed that they could exercise a great deal of control over the workings of their internal organs. These people—many of them religious leaders and philosophers—said they could slow down or speed up their heartbeat rates, increase or decrease their blood pressure, change the temperature of any part of their body, and do other "miraculous" things at will. Western culture has been very doubtful about the claims of these people and unwilling to investigate them. Lately, however, many nonbelievers have been turning into believers. If you are interested in this subject, you may want to read the Health Frontier in Chapter 4. It discusses meditation and biofeedback training and tells about some techniques for controlling "involuntary" muscles.

The third kind of muscle is heart or **cardiac muscle.** It is found only in the walls of the heart. Cardiac muscle consists of a network of smooth and striated fibers bound

A barefoot villager in Spain carries a woman across burning coals during a celebration. His feet don't get burned. What "miraculous" control over his body does this man have?

together by connective tissues. The striated fibers give strength to the heart. They enable it to respond quickly to changes in body activity and to pump harder when necessary, resting only between contractions. The smooth fibers make the heart able to contract automatically and without conscious directions from the brain.

Cardiac muscle tissue can contract rhythmically even if it is removed from the body. A common biology experiment is to place a frog's heart in a solution of salts and oxygen. The heart continues to beat, just as though it were in the animal's body. The regular beating of the heart tissue occurs independently of the nervous system. The pacemaker coordinates the beating of the cardiac muscle tissue so that it all beats together rhythmically.

SELF CHECK

1. What are the most important functions of muscles?

2. How can you relax, rest, and sleep if you always have some muscle tone?

3. How are skeletal muscles, smooth muscles, and cardiac muscles different?

4. What is the function of a tendon? A bursa?

Working Muscles

3-7 **Muscle Energy**

Voluntary muscles are supposed to be under conscious control, but when they get tired, they also get stubborn. Your legs can feel so utterly tired out that they won't go another step no matter how much you want them to move.

That feeling of exhaustion or muscle fatigue can have several causes. The nerve impulses that cause contractions may not be getting through to the muscle. When nerves become fatigued, it feels as though the muscles are all tired out. Training can increase the ability of nerves to carry impulses to muscles for long periods of time.

Another main reason for muscle fatigue is that the muscles run out of energy. Then, like toys or flashlights with dead batteries, they stop working. All cell activities including muscle contractions run on energy contained in **ATP molecules.** (ATP is the abbreviation of the chemical name for a high-energy phosphorus compound.) Each ATP molecule is like a small battery full of stored electricity. The stored energy in the ATP molecule originally comes from digested food.

There is some ATP stored in muscle cells that have been resting. When a muscle begins working, the stored ATP provides the necessary energy. But there is only enough stored ATP for about ten seconds of work.

Muscle cells also have another form of stored energy: **glucose molecules.** Glucose can't be used directly the way ATP can, but the cells can "burn" it to make more ATP. The process is something like burning coal or oil in a power plant to make electricity. For muscle activities that last for a few minutes, the muscle cells depend on stored glucose to make ATP. What's stored isn't in the form of glucose, but in the form of great numbers of glucose molecules combined into large **glycogen** (GLY kuh juhn) **molecules.**

What happens after a few minutes of activity when the stored glucose (or glycogen) runs out? At that point the muscle cells rely on new supplies of glucose from the blood.

This glucose is called **blood sugar.** One of the main jobs of the blood is to carry glucose to all cells. During heavy exercise, the muscles use up blood sugar, so the liver releases more of it into the bloodstream. The liver is a storehouse of glucose (in the form of glycogen).

The last major factor involved when muscles use energy concerns oxygen. As glucose is broken down in cells, it turns into **lactic acid.** The lactic acid in turn is broken down into water and carbon dioxide. The complete breakdown of glucose to water and carbon dioxide releases 18 times as much energy as partial breakdown to lactic acid. But, and this is the key point, complete breakdown of glucose requires lots of oxygen. That is why heavy work makes you breathe faster and deeper. It can even make you painfully out of breath. Athletes sometimes get oxygen from tanks to help them recover from their exertion. The build-up of lactic acid in the muscles due to lack of enough oxygen causes the pain that usually goes with overworked muscles.

Muscles that are used a lot do a better job of taking in glucose and oxygen from the blood than flabby muscles. They also do a better job of breaking down glucose completely and getting rid of all the waste products. Finally, well-trained muscles manage all this activity with less heating up. There is always some wasted energy during muscle contractions. It takes the form of heat, enough to make you sweat sometimes. Well-trained muscles waste less energy. Besides, the attached tendons do not stretch as much, which leads to more graceful and exact movements.

Even well-trained muscles eventually reach a point where they can't keep up with the demands on them. They can't take in enough energy supplies, and they can't get rid of waste products fast enough. That's when muscle fatigue sets in.

When you stop and rest from a strenuous activity, you can be breathing very hard for a long time afterwards. All the products of the partial breakdown of glucose, such as lactic acid, still have to be further broken down. It doesn't matter that you're resting now. The chemical work the cells started has to be finished. The amount of oxygen it will take to finish the breakdown of lactic acid is called the **oxygen debt.**

Oxygen debt occurs because muscles can contract without receiving their full oxygen requirement. To run a short race requires about six times more oxygen than can be taken into the blood during the time it takes to run. The runner goes into oxygen debt and "pays" later. There is no oxygen debt during light exercise. You pay as you go, because you can take in enough oxygen during the time you are exercising. Lactic acid production and breakdown are in balance. Oxygen debt occurs only during strenuous exercise. Then you gulp air until the lactic acid is completely broken down. At that point, you have "paid" your oxygen debt.

● **3-8 Investigating Muscle Fatigue**

In this investigation you are going to find out how strenuous work affects your muscles. You will observe changes in the performance of certain muscles and in how they feel after resting and after repeating several exercises.

MATERIALS

stopwatch (watch or clock with second hand)
spring-type clothespin

PROCEDURE

1. Copy the table below.

2. Working in teams, take turns being timer, watching and counting, and doing the muscle-fatigue tests.

3. Place your right elbow and forearm,

NAME	CLENCHING FIST			LIFTING BOOK			OPENING CLOTHESPIN		
	Trial 1	Trial 2	Trial 3	Trial 1	Trial 2	Trial 3	Trial 1	Trial 2	Trial 3

Copy This Table on a Piece of Paper

palm up, on a table. While a partner watches and counts, open and close your fist as many times as you can for 10 seconds. Record the number of times you clench your fist in the table under "Clenching Fist" ("Trial 1"). Rest for 30 seconds, and then repeat the test for two more 10-second trials, resting 30 seconds between the trials. Try to exert the same amount of force during the second and third trials as you did during the first. Record your results in the table under "Trial 2" and "Trial 3."

4. Hold a book in your left hand against your side. Raise your arm straight out, parallel to the floor, as many times as you can in 10 seconds. Have a partner count the number of times you lift the book. Rest for 30 seconds, and then repeat the test for two more 10-second trials, resting 30 seconds between the trials. Record the results of your three trials in the table under "Lifting Book."

5. Using your right thumb and index finger, squeeze a clothespin completely open and release it as fast as you can for 10 seconds, while a partner counts the number of times you open the clothespin. Rest for 30 seconds and repeat the test for two more 10-second trials, resting 30 seconds between the trials. Record the results of your three trials in the table under "Opening Clothespin."

DISCUSSION

1. How did your muscles feel after doing the first trial of each muscle-fatigue test? Why do you think they felt this way?

2. Did you or your classmates perform faster on the second and third trials of any of the muscle-fatigue tests? If so, why do you think this happened?

3. Did you find that some people could perform better on the trials than others and experience less muscle fatigue? What reasons can you think of to explain their better performance?

4. Do you think most people have one hand and arm that is stronger than the other? Do you? If so, what might be the reason for this?

3-9 Overworked and Injured Muscles

There is a price to pay for too much activity as well as too little. It's pain. We have all paid the bill at one time or another, calling it stiffness, aches, soreness, strains, and a lot of other names. Muscles can be worked too hard for too long without a rest, or just too hard suddenly. Accidents can also injure muscles.

It's a good idea to build up muscles gradually. Muscles that do not work regularly lose their strength and endurance. There's a good chance that they will feel stiff and sore for a few days after being overworked. Healthy muscles can also be pushed too hard. To build up muscles, people have to work them harder than usual, but not suddenly or too strenuously. It's often difficult to know when to stop. By the time a muscle starts to hurt, you may have already gone too far. Stop *before* it hurts.

Scientists believe that muscle stiffness and soreness are caused by the build-up of waste materials from energy production. In the case of over-exertion, the waste materials and other fluids leak from the cells and collect in the muscle and make it swollen. Large amounts of waste materials, such as lactic acid, are harmful to muscles and nerves. The extra fluid also puts pressure on the nerves, which hurts. To add to the problem, the swelling reduces blood flow through the muscle. That slows down the removal of waste products by the blood and makes the pain last longer.

Stiffness and soreness in an overworked muscle—the kind of ache you can get from shoveling after the first snowfall, or pitching at the first practice, or staying in the same position for a long time—can be worked out. Try light massage, heat from warm baths, and gradually increasing muscle use.

When tired muscles sometimes go into spasm, they contract suddenly and uncontrollably. There can be a single contraction or repeated contractions, often occurring so rapidly that the muscle fibers are in continuous tight contraction. **Twitches** are mild muscle spasms, often of the facial and eye muscles. Twitches can be annoying but are not usually painful. They ordinarily stop after the muscle has had time to rest.

Painful spasms, called **cramps,** result from muscle fibers' contracting violently, sometimes into a hard knot. These are common in leg and arm muscles and often occur during sleep. Leg cramps are sometimes called "Charley horses." The cramp can last for only a few seconds, but the pain can last for hours. Muscle cramps can develop during swimming or other vigorous exercise. Rubbing the affected muscle or *gently* bending the leg or arm *with and against* the muscle contraction can sometimes relieve the pain.

Overstretching and partially tearing muscle fibers are other ways that people injure themselves. These muscle injuries are called **strains.** Twisting an ankle or lifting something too heavy using the back muscles are common ways that people strain muscles. Strained muscles need rest to recover.

Massage can work the "knots" out of sore and tired muscles.

Do some people give you a pain in the neck? Perhaps you unconsciously tighten your neck muscles when these people are around and giving you a piece of their mind.

Bruised muscles also need time to heal. A black and blue bruise can be caused by hitting a skeletal muscle. The colors come from bleeding within the muscle.

You don't have to work or play too hard to make your muscles hurt. Emotional stress will do it, too. Muscles contract the same way in either case. But we tend not to notice the contractions caused by emotions until we feel pain. After an argument you may find that your jaw, neck, or shoulder muscles ache.

A lot of people clench their teeth when they concentrate. Later they are surprised to find that their jaw hurts. Being upset or excited while eating can also affect the smooth muscles of the digestive system. Indigestion, stomach cramps, and heartburn often depend more on how you feel than on what you eat.

● 3-10 Relieving Tension

Many people have some sets of muscles tensed much of the time for emotional reasons. If your neck and shoulders feel tight, and if you notice that you frown much of the time, or if you are surprised to find that you walk around with your fists clenched, try this simple relaxing technique. It is not an answer to emotional problems, but it may help relieve muscle tension and discomfort.

PROCEDURE

1. Choose a time when you can be alone for about 20 minutes, and your surroundings are as quiet as possible. Lie down flat on your back, on a bed or rug, or sit in a comfortable position. Close your eyes. Put your arms at your sides and breathe slowly and deeply through your nose.

2. Begin to relax all of your muscles, starting with your feet and working up. Relax your feet until they feel as though they are sinking into the bed or floating off into space.

3. After your feet feel completely relaxed, relax your calf muscles. Continue all the way up to the muscles of your face. Try to keep your mind occupied with relaxing each set of muscles and with breathing slowly, rather than with worrying about

When you begin this activity, it helps to say to yourself, "I am at peace. No noise will bother me."

what might be bothering you. Repeating a word—any word—when you exhale might help you concentrate on relaxing.

4. After all your muscles feel relaxed, lie quietly and continue breathing deeply for a few more minutes.

5. CAUTION! When you finish this relaxation technique, give yourself a few minutes before standing up and going about your regular activities, or you may find yourself stumbling around. It's a lot like the awkwardness you feel when you get up in the morning, except that you won't feel sleepy.

If you are not successful in becoming relaxed, don't worry about it. Most people aren't successful the first time or even the tenth time they try. It usually takes practice before it works well.

Discussion

1. How did you feel afterward? Did certain muscles feel less tense? If so, which ones? Do you think these muscles might be ones you are in the habit of tightening up when you are under tension?

2. Did relaxing have an effect on your mood? If so, in what way did your mood change and why do you think it happened?

3. Would relaxing for a while once or twice a day make it easier for you to figure out ways of solving emotional conflicts?

Self Check

1. What is the source of energy for all cell activities?

2. Name the different sources of stored energy that muscles have, and describe how working muscle cells get energy from each source.

3. What are some causes of feeling tired? Of muscle soreness or stiffness?

4. Describe some ways to help relieve aching muscles.

5. What are some benefits of relaxing?

Chapter Summary

Keeping your body in good shape by exerting yourself physically and relaxing afterward is a source of pleasure and one of the most effective ways of enjoying a long life. Bones and muscles give the body its ability to move and its shape, and protect its internal organs.

Bones, composed of minerals, collagen, and water, are relatively lightweight in spite of their hardness and strength. Canallike networks within bones provide room for blood and lymph vessels. The red marrow inside bones produces most of the body's red and white blood cells. Bone tissue is constantly being broken down and built up.

The joints that make the skeleton flexible are fixed, partially movable, or freely movable. Where the ends of bones come together, synovial fluid and layers of cartilage prevent bones from rubbing. Joints are held together by ligaments. Strong as ligaments are, they can be torn, or sprained, if a joint is twisted beyond its ordinary limits. Joints often have bursas between tissues that have to move against each other.

Skeletal or striated muscles allow conscious control of movement. They are attached to bones by tendons. The contraction and relaxation of pairs of muscles around joints make possible the entire range of physical activities. Muscles, like bones, become stronger and work better with regular use. Physical activity improves muscle tone and circulation. There is a strong connection between feeling good emotionally and being in good muscular condition.

Smooth muscles control the activities of the internal organs. They are called involuntary muscles because they mainly function automatically. Heart or cardiac muscle is a combination of striated and smooth muscle. All muscles consist of fibers, which are made up of fibrils. Muscle contractions are triggered by nerve impulses.

Muscles get their energy from ATP molecules, glucose, and glycogen. When muscles are used vigorously, and do not get enough oxygen, lactic acid is formed and oxygen debt results. Overworked muscles become sore and may contract in painful spasms. Psychological conflicts and other emotional stress may also cause muscle tension and pain. Avoiding over-exertion and finding ways to relax help prevent or relieve injuries and soreness.

Chapter Self Check

1. What characteristics of bone structure enable it to be lightweight, strong, and hard?

2. How does regular and vigorous exercise affect the strength of bones?

3. Why do older people break bones more often than younger people do?

4. Describe two ways that bones are usually protected against friction at joints.

5. Give one or more examples of each type of freely movable joint.

6. Pain can protect you from serious injury. How does this statement apply to movable joints?

7. What is the most significant characteristic of muscle tissue?

8. What is the relationship between nerve impulses and muscular activity?

9. Describe the difference between a relaxed muscle and one with poor muscle tone.

10. How does regular physical activity improve conscious control over voluntary muscles?

11. What is a basic difference between the functions of striated and smooth muscles?

12. Describe how cardiac muscle is constructed.

13. How does training muscles for playing tennis differ from training them for lifting heavy weights?

14. Describe the process by which muscles use energy, and then rid themselves of waste products.

15. Why is it important to work up to strenuous physical activity gradually?

16. What are some causes of muscle pain?

17. Describe some effective ways of preventing or relieving sore or injured muscles.

18. How can emotional stress cause sore muscles?

Read More About It

Lenihan, John. *Human Engineering: the Body Re-examined.* New York: George Braziller, 1974. Comparisons of the functionings of human body systems and the workings of machines. Includes the skeletal and muscular systems.

Nilsson, Lennart, with Jan Lindberg. *Behold Man: A Photographic Journey of Discovery Inside the Body.* Boston: Little, Brown and Company, 1974. A collection of photographs of parts of the human body, including many of bones and muscles.

Nourse, Alan E., and the Editors of Time-Life Books. *The Body.* New York: Time Inc., Time-Life Books (Life Science Library), 1971 edition. Information about the human body, including the bones and muscles. Well-illustrated.

Silverstein, Alvin, and Silverstein, Virginia B. *The Muscular System: How Living Creatures Move.* Englewood Cliffs, New Jersey: Prentice-Hall, Inc., 1972. A comparison of the muscular systems in people and in other animals.

4

Self-Government

After completing the work in this chapter, you will be able to:

explain the structure and function of nerves, the brain, and the spinal cord.

describe some of the activities of the cerebral cortex.

list several functions of the voluntary and the autonomic nervous systems.

describe how sensory information is received and interpreted.

compare the ways the nervous and endocrine systems coordinate the workings of the body.

The United States Pavilion at Montreal, designed by Geometrics, Inc. and R. Buckminster Fuller. This beautiful structure is built of simple, repeating units: hexagons. The brain is a vastly more complex structure. But it, too, is mostly built of relatively simple, repeating units: nerves.

Acting in Control

The best part of Alicia Lee's bike ride home from school was going down Bobsled Hill Road. To build up speed, she pedaled part way down the hill. Then when she was really flying, she coasted. Near the bottom of the long hill she gradually put on the brakes. She had to stop herself because of the traffic light at the bottom of the hill. But this time when she pressed down on the pedal, the brake gave way.

Alicia knew she was in danger.

Instead of slowing, the bike kept going faster and faster. She started getting panicky. "What am I going to do?" she asked herself. No one answered. She was whipping by the parked cars on the road. Her heart pounded, and her palms began sweating. Her mouth was so dry she couldn't swallow. She was covered with goose bumps.

At the moment Alicia knew she was in danger, a built-in set of emergency responses went to work. Part of her nervous system sent nerve impulses to her adrenal glands. The adrenal glands then rushed chemicals into her bloodstream that reached the liver and signaled it to quickly send more glucose into the blood. Another part of her nervous system made her heart beat faster to pump this vital energy supply, the glucose, to the cells. And her breathing increased rapidly to get more oxygen to the cells, too. At the same time, her digestive system and kidneys shut down, allowing more blood to flow to her brain, muscles, heart, and lungs.

In short, without conscious effort, Alicia's energy systems and muscles got ready to cope with the emergency.

She suddenly had an idea—really an image: pressing her sandaled foot against the tire to slow it down. She tried it but nearly lost control of the steering. She was getting close to the traffic at the bottom of the hill.

There were butterflies in her stomach, and her heart was pounding faster.

"I've got to turn into that driveway," she thought, "and try to fall on the grass, not the pavement." Thousands of nerve impulses shot out to dozens of muscles. She swerved sharply to the right, took the bumps, and leaned way over. She put her arm down to break the fall and to protect her head. The pedal dug into the lawn, the bike skidded on its side, then stopped.

After a few seconds Alicia untangled herself from the bicycle and stood up. Her legs felt trembly and weak. She was sweating, but her heart wasn't beating as fast.

"If I hadn't been able to stop in time!" she thought. "I'm lucky that my brains didn't get scrambled." When she realized how close she had come to a bad accident, she felt sick and quickly sat down. She glanced at her hand, which had suddenly begun to hurt. There was a scrape with some blood coming out of it. Her ankle hurt too.

Alicia's nervous system began to reverse the set of automatic emergency responses that got her through the experience. It slowed down the flow from her adrenal glands. Nerve impulses signaled the liver to remove excess sugar from the blood and store it. Her breathing and heartbeat rates returned to normal. And her kidneys and digestive system resumed their activities.

Feeling very lucky and only slightly bruised, Alicia picked up her bike and pushed it home.

The Nervous System

4-1 Organized Commotion

Stop and think about what's happening right now within your body. From the first three chapters, you've learned that there is a lot going on inside you all the time. Each body system is carrying out different functions. Besides that, the actions of each tissue and system—all the cells in your body—are being coordinated with each other. None of the cells is a loner. But how does it happen that each one "knows" what the others are doing?

We say that the organs and systems mostly work automatically or without any conscious effort on our part. That doesn't mean that life goes on by chance.

Alicia's sense of danger immediately set off automatic emergency-response activities in her body. You might look back at the story and see how many changes were mentioned. She skillfully avoided having a serious accident—perhaps by being able to ride her bicycle better than ever before. Then another set of automatic responses quickly returned Alicia's body activities to normal. This is just one example of the way certain nerves and glands work together to keep all the parts of the mind and body in touch with each other. (A **gland** is any organ that produces some substance and releases it to another part of the body.) The nerves and glands, working together, also control growth, sexual development, sensations from outside and inside the body, and influence emotions, thoughts, and memories.

The **endocrine** (EHN duh krihn) **system** consists of endocrine glands that send chemicals called hormones directly into the bloodstream. Each gland puts out different hormones that affect specific organs and tissues. Hormones travel through the bloodstream until they reach the target organs, then go to work. Some hormones have short-term effects, such as speeding up the heartbeat rate. Others have long-term effects, such as regulating the growth of the skeleton.

The **nervous system** includes the brain and the nerves. It responds to stimuli from both inside and outside the body. Messages called nerve impulses are transmitted from one nerve cell to the next. The nerve impulses consist of electrical and chemical changes in nerves.

Nerves and glands make up the body's two systems for self-government.

If you think about Alicia's story, you will probably conclude that the nerves and endocrine glands work together. You're right. Both affect all parts of the body and work together to control everything that happens in it. Nerve impulses race along nerve pathways in an instant. Hormones carried by the blood take longer to reach their targets. Even so, some hormones produce their effects in less than a second. Others take several minutes or even hours to cause changes.

Even though the nervous system and the endocrine system work together, it is easier to understand how each one works by studying them separately. For this reason, the beginning of this chapter will discuss the nervous system. The end of the chapter will discuss the workings of the endocrine system.

4-2 The Head of the Organization

Everything depends on **nerve impulses**—everything we do, think about, feel, and remember. These tiny electrochemical impulses flicker along nerves throughout the nervous system, carrying information and orders. The nervous system consists of all the **nerve cells** in the body: in the nerves, the spinal cord, and the brain.

A nerve cell is called a **neuron** (NOOR ahn). Each neuron has three main parts: the **cell body,** the **dendrites** (DEHN drytz), and the **axon.** Dendrites gather "information"

Nerve impulses travel from the axon—across the synapse—to the next neuron's dendrites.

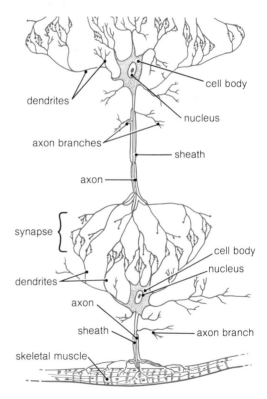

and carry it to the cell body. The cell body sends the information along the axon to the next neuron, or a muscle fiber, or a gland, to be stimulated.

Nerve pathways are made up of many neurons. The neurons do not touch each other. Instead, the branches of the axon of one neuron mingle with some of the dendrites of the next neuron. This leaves a microscopic gap, called a **synapse** (SIHN aps), between the fibers of the neurons. When a nerve impulse reaches the tip of an axon, the electric effect stops for an instant. The tips of the axon release a chemical that stimulates the dendrites of the next neuron. This chemical action starts a new electric impulse traveling in the next neuron. The electrochemical process is repeated until the nerve pathway ends.

Most nerves can carry impulses only in one direction between the brain and other parts of the body. Once a nerve is stimulated, or an impulse is set off, the nerve carries the impulse with the same strength along its full length. A stronger stimulus won't cause a stronger impulse. It will just stimulate more nerves.

Nerves spread out from the **spinal cord** like roots, reaching every part of the body. And like a large flower on its stem, the **brain** sits on the bundle of nerves that makes up the spinal cord. The brain is the head of the organization. It coordinates everything that happens within the body. But don't think that the brain simply bosses the rest of the body around. It is as much a "super servant" as a leader. Think, for example, how hard the brain works to keep the body supplied with energy and warmth. When your blood sugar level drops, you may not be

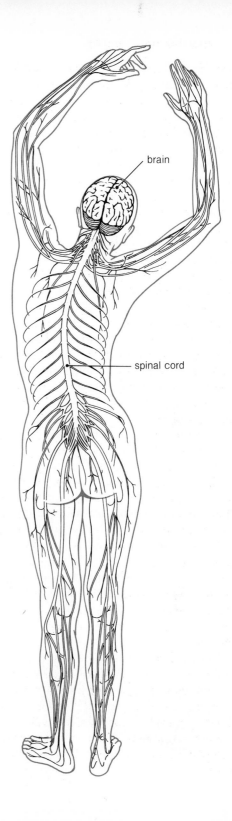

brain

spinal cord

The nervous system connects the brain with every part of the body.

able to think of anything but food. When your hands are freezing, you concentrate on trying to get them warm.

The more we learn about the brain, the more mysterious it seems. It makes us aware of touch, pain, and other sensations. But it feels no sensations itself. Its energy needs are amazing. It accounts for only two percent of body weight. It sits motionless in the skull, and its cells don't divide. Yet this mass of 10 billion nerve cells requires 20 percent of the body's blood supply and 25 percent of all the oxygen in the blood-stream. And perhaps strangest of all, the size of the brain has nothing to do with a person's ability, intelligence, or accomplishments.

The brain and the spinal cord—the **central nervous system**—are the most protected parts of the body. Otherwise, they would be easily damaged, and damage to this system can be crippling or fatal. The strong skull protects the brain and certain sense organs. The vertebrae and cartilage of the backbone protect the spinal cord. Within this body armor, the central nervous system is further protected against bumps and quick move-ments by three layers of membranes and a special fluid. The fluid acts as a cushion and also removes waste materials and harmful substances produced by disease-causing organisms.

Do you know why doctors, nurses, and people trained to give first aid work so hard to get a person's heart beating again if it stops? The brain needs a constant supply of oxygen-rich blood. If the blood supply to the brain is cut off, a person loses con-sciousness in seconds. After about four minutes without blood flow, the brain is permanently damaged. Acting as a guard against this, the major arteries of the brain are interconnected. If one artery gets blocked, some blood gets rerouted to the others.

If the chief arteries that carry blood from the aorta to the brain are partly blocked, however, there is no back-up system. In some older people the arteries often get clogged with fatty material. If a large part of the entire system of arteries in the brain gets clogged with these fatty materials, physical and mental abilities may suffer.

The brain is soft tissue—about 85 percent water—made up of two kinds of cells. There are billions of nerve cells. But they are far outnumbered by another kind of cell that surrounds them. These other cells provide support and form scar tissue if nerve cells are destroyed by disease or injury. Many scientists believe that these other cells may also help the nerve cells by providing them with energy and by carrying materials to them from capillaries. These cells are also believed to be involved in certain brain functions, such as memory.

People are probably born with all the nerve cells they will ever have. Nerve cells grow, and some can repair themselves. But they don't seem to be able to reproduce. When a nerve cell in the brain dies, it is not replaced. Even though your brain will never have any more nerve cells than it does now, you'll have more than you need, even if you live to be over 100. Eyesight and hearing may become less keen in older people, but their mental capabilities do not necessarily wear out. If anything seems to be true, it is that we rarely make use of all the mental capabilities we have at any age.

4-3 The Rooms of the Mind

How do you feel right now? Not what kind of mood are you in, but what is your body telling you about itself and your surround-ings? Do you feel warm, cold, or just right?

Having a lively mind comes from being interested in many things; it doesn't depend on age.

Are you hungry? What do you see? Close your eyes and pay attention to other kinds of sensations. What do you hear? Focus on your muscles and then your skin. Perhaps while you are taking stock of yourself you are also thinking about some other things you have to do or you're remembering past experiences. Many kinds of mental activities go on within us at the same time.

All these thoughts and sensations take place in the outer layer of the **cerebrum** (suh REE bruhm) called the **cortex** or **cerebral cortex.** If you could look inside a skull, you would see the deeply wrinkled, pink-ish-gray surface of the brain. That's the cortex. It is the brain's center for the most highly developed human traits, such as speech, reasoning, memory, and creativity. Special areas of the cortex also enable us to decide to move, and then to do it. Other areas of the cortex receive nerve impulses from the senses.

Still other parts of the brain are involved with muscular coordination and experiencing emotions. In other words, nerves are specialists that live apart in separate rooms.

Scientists and surgeons have learned a lot about the rooms of the mind. A person can

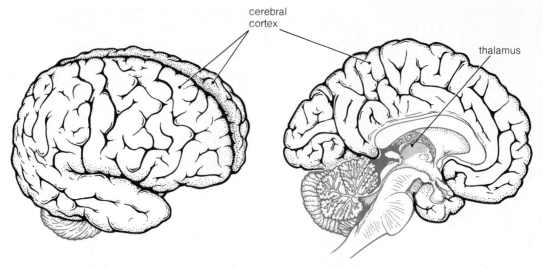

The wrinkled surface of the brain is the cerebral cortex.
The thalamus is deep inside the brain.

be awake during many kinds of brain surgery, since most brain cells don't feel pain.
Before such an operation, the patient is
given a local anesthetic to deaden pain from
having the scalp cut. Then, after exposing
the brain, the surgeon carefully touches
different areas. Touching one place can
make a patient remember a forgotten experience or an old song. Or a hand or foot may
feel as though it's being tickled. Or the patient may feel some other sensory organ at
work when it really isn't. As soon as the
surgeon stops touching the brain, the sensation stops. The functions of different specialized areas of the cortex and some other
parts of the brain have been pretty well
determined in this way.

One part of the brain that assists the cortex in sorting out sensations is the **thalamus**
(THAL uh muhs). It lies under the cerebrum. All body sensations are first sent into
the thalamus. Some arrive by way of the
spinal cord. Other impulses come directly
from sense organs in the head, such as the

nose, tongue, and ears. The network of
nerves in the thalamus organizes these sensations, and then sends them to the appropriate parts of the cortex. The thalamus is
also the center for feeling pain.

No one understands how the electrical
currents within the brain come to be felt as
pain, pleasure, or affection. No one understands how these same currents work when
we solve a problem, or remember a short-
cut, or recognize a flower. All that is certain
is that mental activities depend on nerve
impulses.

● 4-4 **Taking Sides**

Close your eyes and try to get a sense of
your body. How does the left side feel compared to the right side? Do they feel the
same or different? Now try to answer the
questions on the next page. First read a
question, then close your eyes and see what
you think the answer is.

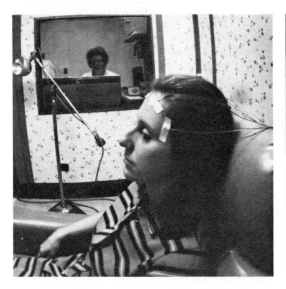

The patient with electrodes taped to her head is having her "brain waves" painlessly measured. The machine draws an electroencephalogram (**EEG**) of the tiny electrical currents in the brain.

1. Which side of you feels more active?

2. Which side seems more passive?

3. Which side feels heavier?

4. Which side seems lighter?

5. Which side seems more mysterious?

6. Which side feels more artistic?

7. Which side seems more logical?

These questions are based on the work of Robert Ornstein, a psychologist interested in how the mind works. You will understand the significance of your answers better after you read the next section.

4-5 The Double Brain

Many body parts come in pairs: eyes, legs, kidneys, and so on. Research has shown that the human brain is also, to a certain extent, a pair of brains.

The cerebrum is divided into halves, or **hemispheres,** from the front of the head to the back. Each hemisphere has its own control centers that regulate body functions and behavior. Nerves connect each hemisphere with the other as well as with all the other parts of the brain. And both sides are connected by nerves to the brain stem that joins the spinal cord. But each hemisphere is primarily connected with the opposite side of the body and is involved with different activities.

Nerve impulses travel back and forth from the left side of the cerebrum to the right side of the body and vice versa. The left leg is linked with the right side of the cerebrum; the right leg with the left side. Impulses from the eyes go to both sides of the cerebrum, but not in the way you'd expect. The right side of the field of vision of *each* eye sends impulses to the left side of the cerebrum. Impulses from the left side of the field of vision go to the right cerebrum.

A lot of the information that follows is based on recent research. Many people, even many doctors, don't know about it.

Although each half of the cerebrum has many of the same functions that the other has, each one is also specialized. For right-handed people, the left hemisphere usually controls language skills such as reading, writing, and talking. It tends to process small bits of information one at a time. In this way it is specialized for logical reasoning and step-by-step problem-solving. When you silently talk to yourself, the left hemisphere is probably the talker and listener.

The right hemisphere is primarily not verbal. It is specialized for keeping us aware of our overall physical position. This side of the cerebrum seems also to be responsible for many artistic, creative, and intuitive experiences. These experiences depend on seeing patterns, not on having separate impressions or thoughts. The right hemisphere also controls some of the ways we communicate without words, such as our facial movements and tone of voice.

This left-right organization applies to right-handed people, but not necessarily to lefties. Some of them have reversed sides of the cerebrum, some the same sides as right-handed people. And some have a mixture, with language abilities on both sides of the cerebrum.

Although each hemisphere tends to specialize in certain functions, each has the potential for doing the other's jobs. If part of one hemisphere is damaged, the other hemisphere is often able to take over the function of the damaged part.

Some people think the left hemisphere is the more important one because most aspects of our society seem to be based on language. Which hemisphere is dominant depends on what you are doing. You can be so busy with a math problem that you are unaware of sitting in a chair. Or so moved by a sunset, a painting, or a touch that you are at a loss for words. Our finest achievements often combine logic with intuition.

Having a "double brain" sometimes seems to affect consciousness in strange ways. You've certainly had the experience of making a logical decision to do something but being nagged by doubts at the same time. Your "head" seems to say one thing. Your "gut reaction" says something else. Or another way to put it is that your reasoning and intuition disagree. Some scientists believe that to some extent the structure of our brains sometimes causes us to "be of two minds." (Notice how many ways we have of referring to these mental conflicts.)

Each side of the cerebrum is connected by nerves to the opposite side of the body.

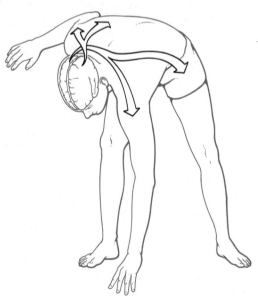

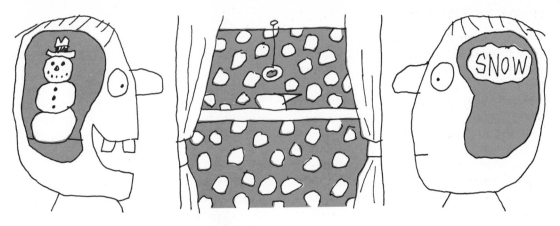

Avoid being a half-wit: use both halves of your wits.

Here are two helpful hints for using your double brain when you have a problem or conflict: Don't let your left hemisphere talk your right hemisphere into doing something it feels uncomfortable about just because it can't talk back. The right hemisphere may have its reasons even though it can't discuss them. Maybe your body has "noticed" something your reasoning has missed. Re-examine the situation. And try this strategy sometime when you are stumped by a problem you've been turning over in your mind: Stop thinking about it. That is, stop talking about it to yourself over and over in your most logical fashion. Go for a walk or just close your eyes and be silent for a while. The solution may then just come to mind all at once, a gift from the pattern-finding side of the cerebrum to its step-at-a-time partner. (Such solutions should then be analyzed for practicality.)

4-6 Doing Things Without Thinking

If we had to be constantly thinking about everything that goes on in our bodies, we'd never get any other thinking done. Imagine having to keep reminding yourself to breathe, have heartbeats and stomach contractions, and even to sweat. Worse yet, imagine that during an emergency you had to consciously speed up some of these internal activities and slow down others while you were also trying to think your way out of a jam!

Fortunately, the nervous system is made up of two different parts or systems. The **voluntary nervous system** is mostly under conscious control. It controls the skeletal muscles and senses. It thinks, remembers, and is aware of things. The **autonomic nervous system** is made up of different nerves and parts of the brain. This system works, for the most part, without conscious control. The nerves in the autonomic nervous system branch out to all the internal organs, to the smooth and cardiac muscles, and to all the blood vessels.

The autonomic nervous system is divided into two parts. One part acts like an accelerator and speeds things up. The other part puts on the brakes. The two parts control the speed of body functions by working in opposition to each other. The accelerator part prepares the body to act during excitement, challenge, fright, or anger. Working with endocrine glands, it gets body functions such as heartbeat, breathing, and the release of glucose into the bloodstream going at high speed.

The braking part of the autonomic nervous system does the reverse. Again working with the endocrine system, it calms the body down. After the challenge or excitement passes, it slows down the breathing and heartbeat rates and relaxes the muscles. It also gets working again some body functions, such as digestion, that stop during great excitement.

Most of the control of the autonomic nervous system is carried out by the **hypothalamus** (hy poh THAL uh muhs), a tiny part of the brain. It directly controls the nerves in the autonomic nervous system. It also controls the rates of some body functions indirectly by affecting the nearby **pituitary** (pih TOO uh tehr ee) **gland,** an important part of the endocrine system. You'll read about it later in the chapter. Directly or indirectly, the hypothalamus regulates temperature, thirst and water intake, and the body's use of food. It also plays an important part in feeling hunger and sexual desire, and in reproductive and wake-sleep cycles.

Since the hypothalamus helps the body to automatically react to exciting situations, it should not be surprising that the hypothalamus and some nearby organs are also the locations of strong emotions such as pleasure, rage, and fear. These, too, are aspects of life that we have limited conscious control over. Emotions seem to happen to us, often in spite of ourselves. No one knows if some people have more active hypothalamuses than other people, but it certainly seems so.

Other parts of the brain in between the cerebrum and the spinal cord are involved with automatically regulating body processes. They are also connected to the hypo-

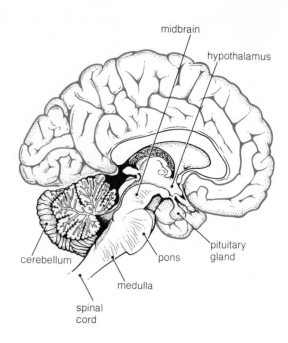

These parts of the brain are involved in doing things without having to think about them. They are part of the autonomic nervous system.

thalamus by a network of nerves. These parts of the brain—the **midbrain, pons,** and **medulla**—are highly complex in people and other animals. What sets people apart from other animals is how much more complex their cerebrums are.

You should not think of the voluntary nervous system and the autonomic nervous system as completely separate and independent. They have some of the same functions and many nerve connections. Some people, for example, develop considerable control over their breathing rate and even their heartbeat rate.

It would also be a mistake to think that the voluntary nervous system operates only by conscious attention to each and every detail of action. People do many things "unconsciously" or so automatically that they are unaware of controlling certain muscles. You probably don't pay much attention to walking unless you jump over a puddle or have a sore leg. Driving a car requires a lot of complex muscle coordination, in addition to handling sensory information. But once you learn to drive, most of your attention is on looking and listening rather than on controlling muscles. The reason is that another part of the brain, the **cerebellum** (sehr uh BEHL uhm), is helping out the cerebrum. This part of the brain helps coordinate muscle actions. When you pick up a pencil, drive a car, or even turn a page, the cerebellum coordinates hundreds of muscle actions. The cerebrum gives the orders, but the cerebellum sees that the orders are smoothly carried out.

Since the cerebellum coordinates muscular activities, it would also seem like the logical place in the brain to control balance. It does, with the help of structures in the inner ears called **semicircular** (sehm ih SUR kyuh luhr) **canals.** The semicircular canals are filled with fluid. When you move in one direction, the fluid moves in the opposite direction. That exerts pressure on hairlike nerve cells in the canals. The nerves send impulses to the cerebellum and cerebrum. In this way you become aware of the sensation of motion, and the cerebellum automatically adjusts the right muscles that allow you to keep your balance. If you whirl around fast or shake your head fast, the nerve cells get over-stimulated. That makes you feel dizzy. And while you are dizzy, the cerebellum has difficulty coordinating certain muscle actions.

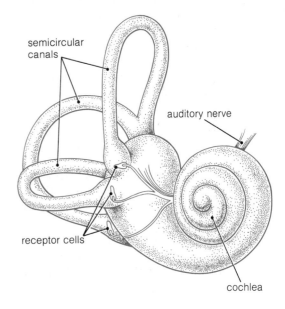

If the tightrope walker starts to lean over, the fluid in his semicircular canals moves, and gives his brain a warning signal.

● 4-7 **Investigating Your Learned Behavior**

Most of the things we know, we had to learn. And we learn many things so well that we don't even think about them. They have become habits, such as the ways we walk, get dressed, and even the ways we go about solving problems.

Choose one of your habits and answer these questions.

1. How did you come to develop this habit? Were there any outside influences on you, or did you develop it on your own?

2. Is this habit helpful, or are you "in a rut"?

3. Can you change it if you want to? (Try it for a day or two.)

Many of the skills you have learned are quite complicated. Dancing, skiing, driving a car, or playing the guitar involve learning many steps and thinking about several things at once. But these skills become "second nature" after a while.

Think about a complicated skill you have mastered. Then answer these questions.

1. How did you feel the first time you tried it?

2. What step was hardest to learn?

3. Did more than one person teach you? Did that make it harder or easier to learn the skill?

4. How much of your learning was trial and error? Reasoning? Natural ability?

5. How would you help someone else learn this skill?

6. What skill are you now trying to learn? What would help you learn it faster or better?

Health Frontier

Controlling the Uncontrollable

Our thoughts and feelings are more controlled by certain body processes than we ever imagine. When the stomach muscles contract, for example, we think of food. But the conscious part of the brain doesn't seem to be able to intentionally control internal body processes.

Many people are beginning to believe that some of the body processes usually considered uncontrollable can be controlled after all. With the right training, some people have learned to change their blood pressure and heartbeat rates at will. They can change their body temperature and even affect how much oxygen their bodies are using. More important for many people, they can put themselves into a relaxed or peaceful mood. They can turn off a headache, relieve aching muscles, and get rid of anxieties. What they have learned is how to gain more control over their emotions and behavior.

There are many techniques for controlling body functions that usually seem automatic. You've probably heard of some forms of yoga. Two other techniques are becoming very popular: meditation and biofeedback training.

There are many ways to meditate. Meditation usually involves a way of concentrating without straining. Meditators can concentrate on a word, an idea, a problem, or even a special syllable that has no meaning. There are many paperback books that describe various kinds of meditation you can learn how to do on your own.

You can learn to meditate almost anywhere.

One of the most powerful and interesting results of most kinds of meditating seems to be that a person learns to quiet the verbal half of the cortex during meditation and senses things more through the nonverbal half of the cortex.

You have to persist to learn how to meditate effectively. Doing it once or twice won't get you very far.

Biofeedback training involves the use of special equipment. One type of machine converts muscular activity into a tone. A person learns that the tone rises when the muscle contracts and falls when the muscle relaxes. After a period of training, the individual may be able to relax at will.

EEG machines are also used. Electrodes are taped to the forehead, and the EEG shows different types of mental activity. Alpha waves produced by the brain appear during relaxation and disappear when the individual is experiencing a strong emotion or is concentrating. Somehow—no one knows exactly how—people can learn to increase the amount and duration of alpha waves. In other words, they can learn to relax.

If a person trained in biofeedback gets a headache from nervous tension, he or she can increase alpha wave production and end the headache. Biofeedback training has also been used to help people reduce their blood pressure and relieve the symptoms of asthma.

Perhaps producing alpha waves will become an important way for people to stay healthy. Maybe it will turn out to be just a way that people can relax at will. The research on biofeedback training is still new, limited, and controversial.

4-8 The Spinal Cord

At the base of the medulla, or brain stem, the spinal cord runs downward through an opening in the bottom of the skull. Connective nerve fibers run up and down the spinal cord. The ascending fibers carry sensations collected by the **spinal nerves** upward through the brain stem to the cortex. The descending fibers carry directions from the cortex down through the brain stem to various spinal nerves, then to muscles of the legs and arms and to internal organs. The parts of the brain involved in autonomic control also send and receive impulses along spinal nerves.

Nerves from the lowermost section of the spinal cord, going down through the hips into the legs, are among the longest and largest in the body. Straining the lower back or injuring any section of these nerves is common and painful. A slipped disk, for example, will press on a spinal nerve and cause pain, usually in the lower back, that often spreads down one or both legs. You should always go to a doctor for treatment of a serious backache.

Orders from the brain aren't necessary for everything. Many spinal nerves provide limited control for certain body parts they are linked with. For example, if you've stood in the same place for a while, particularly with your feet close together, you may have noticed that you swayed slightly from left to right or forwards and backwards. Leaning one way or another stretches muscles on the opposite side of your legs, causing a nerve impulse to go to the spinal cord. Spinal connections with other nerves cause the stretched muscles to contract, pulling you back to a straight position again. At the same time impulses are carried to the brain, which registers the sensation. But the muscle reaction occurs without the brain's direction.

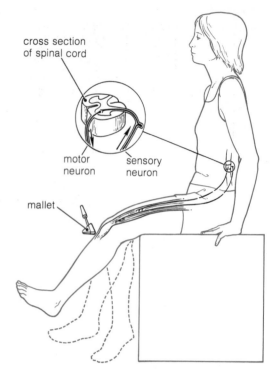

cross section of spinal cord

motor neuron

sensory neuron

mallet

A sensory neuron senses a tap; a motor neuron makes the knee jerk in this simple reflex arc.

This kind of nerve pathway to and from the spinal cord that bypasses the brain and works automatically is called a **reflex arc.** Because they work automatically and quickly, the many reflex arcs between body parts and the spinal cord greatly increase the efficiency of the human nervous system.

4-9 Dead or Alive?

You have probably heard of people who have had a serious accident or illness and are kept alive by machinery in hospitals. Their EEG's show no cerebral activity. Special equipment keeps their hearts, lungs, and kidneys working. The thinking, talking, and reacting parts of their brains are not functioning. But automatic parts of the nervous system still work. Liquid food, dripping directly into the bloodstream, or by tubes into the stomach, is absorbed in the body cells.

Whether a person in this condition should be considered alive is a question that arises more often now. Today medical science has new ways of keeping the automatic body systems working even after people lose much of their brain function. This question concerns everyone, not only doctors and lawyers. How would you feel if someone you knew were in this condition? What do you think people should consider in deciding whether or not a person should be kept "alive" by machinery?

SELF CHECK

1. How do nerve cells transmit information?

2. In what ways does your brain control your body?

3. What are some special functions of each hemisphere of the cerebrum?

4. Describe a situation in which the two parts of the autonomic nervous system are involved.

5. Describe a reflex arc.

The Senses

4-10 Perceiving the World

Imagine being alone in a dark and soundless place, completely cut off from the outside world. Perhaps, for a while, having no outside interference would feel good. But you would soon become bored and eager for stimulation of your senses.

Sensory **receptors** can be nerve endings, special cells, or sense organs such as the eyes. Each responds to different physical stimuli. The skin has millions of nerve endings. Each one responds to a certain type of stimulus such as pressure, heat, or pain. Muscles, ligaments, and tendons have nerve endings that react to stretching and contracting. Specialized cells in the nose, the mouth, and the tongue react to certain chemicals. Complicated sense organs such as the eyes and ears respond to light and vibrations in the air. These and other sensory receptors give you information about happenings inside and outside your body.

The information the senses provide is limited. We never sense the entire world. For example, we can only hear a certain range of sounds. Dogs and bats hear sounds we can't hear. Our eyesight is limited to a narrow range of electromagnetic energy. Outside that range are heat rays, X rays, and radio waves—wavelengths we can't see. The other senses have similar limitations. Some animals, such as birds, also seem to have kinds of sense receptors we don't have at all, such as receptors that sense the earth's magnetic field.

All the impulses that reach the cerebral cortex from the sensory receptors are electrochemical signals, but the particular sensation that is perceived depends on the part of the cortex the impulse reaches. The part determines whether the brain "sees," "hears," "feels," "tastes," or "smells."

The cortex does a lot more than just register sensations. It analyzes and interprets sensations, partly in terms of past experiences. It can tell one sensation from another and combine sensations from different sensory receptors. It can focus attention on some receptors and ignore others. It can even make you see or hear things that aren't there. So, perceiving the world is actually a very active process, not a passive one of just taking in information. People create their own awareness of the world.

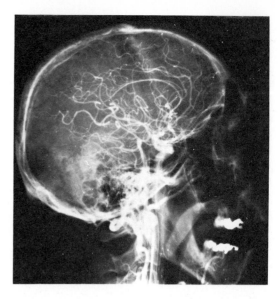

X-ray machines, microscopes, telescopes, and other devices extend the range of our senses.

A mask, a woman, or something else? What you see depends on your experience, not just on your eyesight.

4-11 Taste and Smell

Taste and smell are closely related senses. You can probably remember being so stuffed up from a cold that you had almost no sense of smell. Can you remember how food tasted then? You can also probably think of many foods that you enjoy a lot because of the combination of how they taste and smell.

Receptors for taste and smell respond to certain kinds of chemicals that touch them. The sensation of a taste or odor depends on the particular combination of neurons that react to it. Smell is a long-distance sense because air can carry chemical particles from long distances to the receptors for smell. But taste requires actual contact of a material with the tongue and mouth. The receptors for smell are in the mucous membrane in the upper part of each nostril where not much air ordinarily reaches. That is why people have to sniff strongly to pick up faint odors. Even so, people have a more delicate sense of smell than of taste.

Since the nostrils are connected to the throat, particles that escape into the air from food in the mouth enter the nasal passages and also stimulate receptors for smell. The reverse is true also. Particles that enter the nostrils go to the mouth by way of the throat and often stimulate receptors for taste. Some smells seem so strong you can just about taste them. And the smell of onion certainly affects its taste. Receptors for taste and smell work together in determining how something smells or tastes.

Receptors for taste are special cells called **taste buds,** that are clustered in tiny barrel-shaped folds of the tongue. Other taste buds are in the lining of the mouth and throat. Taste buds are microscopic, but you can see the bumps on your tongue that hold them.

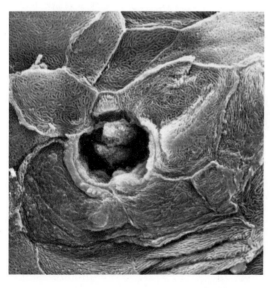

A highly magnified view of a human taste bud.

The tongue and mouth have specialized nerve endings that react to heat, cold, and touch stimuli also. They sense the texture and temperature of food. The combination of all these different sensations, including information from the receptors for smell, produces the different tastes of foods.

4-12 Sight

Vision provides most people with perhaps 75 percent of the information they get about their world. Eyes receive light stimuli that the brain interprets as shapes, colors, relative brightness, and distance.

Light receptors are in layers of special cells that form the inner coating, or **retina** (REHT uhn uh), of the eyeball. Light receptors undergo chemical changes when light hits them, similar to the way the film in a camera works. However, the retina is not made of a single-use film. The light receptors are alive and can usually restore their light-sensitive chemicals almost immediately after being exposed to light.

The retina has two types of light receptors, called **rods** and **cones.** Cones enable you to see color, but they do not work in dim light. Rods, which are more numerous, contain a chemical that reacts to much less light than the chemical in the cones does. You've probably noticed that after sunset you can see less detail and almost no color. As it gets darker, the cones gradually stop reacting, and you are only getting visual information from the rods. Rods respond only to white and shades of gray. During the day, or in bright light, there is enough light to stimulate the cones. They react to the whole range of colors that make up visible light. Another layer of cells just below the rods and cones reduces reflections within the eyeball that would blur vision.

There is a place in the retina where all the nerve fibers from different parts of the retina come together. They pass through the inner wall of the eyeball and form the **optic nerve,** which goes to the vision center of the brain. Blood vessels also enter the eye through this opening. Since there is no room for any rods and cones in this area of the retina, it is called the blind spot. Under ordinary conditions, the blind spots in the two eyes do not interfere with vision. The blind spot for each eye is in a different part of the field of vision, so each eye makes up for the other's blind spot.

Since the eyes are over an inch apart, people see from two slightly different angles. The eyes actually have slightly differ-

ent fields of vision. These two fields of vision provide two different images that are blended into one by the brain. The brain learns to judge distance by comparing the two images it receives. If an object is far away, the two images are almost the same. But if an object is close, the two images are very different. Some people have only one eye that works. Even so, they can learn to make good judgments of distance. They can see objects in three dimensions, although not as well as a person with two healthy eyes.

Most of the eyeball contains a transparent, firm jelly that helps focus light and gives the eyeball its shape. The **lens** is embedded in the front part of this jelly and is

What you expect to see can make it difficult for you to see the unexpected . . . until it's too late.

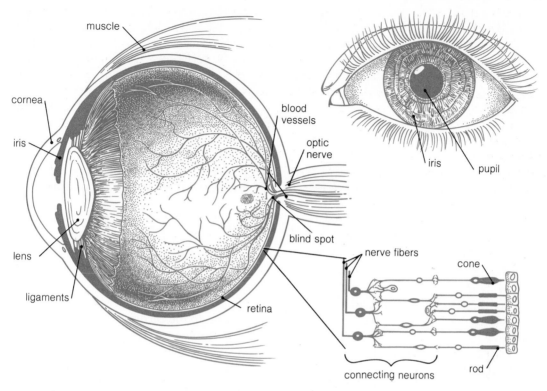

A cut-away view of the eye shows that it is somewhat like a camera. Both have lenses that focus light. The retina is a thin sheet of nerve tissue that serves as a light-sensitive film.

held in place by fine, threadlike ligaments. The front of the eyeball has a transparent cover, called the **cornea** (KAWR nee uh). Between the cornea and lens, there is another watery liquid. This also helps hold the lens firmly in place and maintain the shape of the eyeball.

The eye regulates the amount of light that enters it. The opening of the eye, called the **pupil,** is surrounded by the colored part of the eye, the **iris** (EYE rihs). The iris contains tiny muscle fibers. In bright light, the muscle fibers relax and the iris expands. This makes the pupil only a small opening

through which light can enter the eye. In dim light, the muscle fibers in the iris contract, and the pupil enlarges as the iris shrinks. It takes the iris a while to adjust when we go from brightly to dimly lit places or the reverse.

The other adjusting system of the eyes, the lens, allows us to see near and distant objects. The lens is elastic and can be stretched or relaxed. When we look at distant objects, eye muscles contract and the attached ligaments pull the lens into a flat shape. When we look at close objects, the muscles relax, allowing the lens to bulge. In

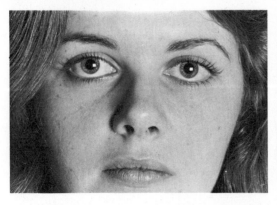 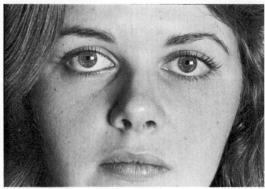

People communicate with their eyes, as well as see. Being interested in someone makes the pupils widen. Most people find the face with the wider pupils to be warmer looking.

this way the lens changes the way it bends light and focuses it on the retina, and allows us to see both distant and close objects.

Nearsightedness results when the eyeball is too long. The lens bends the light rays so that they come to a focus before they reach the retina. Nearsighted people can see close objects but have trouble seeing distant objects. In the case of **farsightedness,** the eyeball is too short, and light rays would focus behind the retina. In the case of **astigmatism** (uh STIHG muh tihz uhm), incoming light rays focus at more than one point because of uneven curving of the cornea. Nearsighted or farsighted people may also have astigmatism.

4-13 Hearing

In addition to sight and touch, hearing is probably the other sense that we are most aware of. The only part of the structures for hearing that you can see is the **outer ear.** The actual sound receptors are well protected deep within the skull.

The outer ear receives vibrating air, and funnels it through a curved channel—the **ear canal**—to the **eardrum.** The eardrum is a thin membrane, stretched tightly across the inside of the ear canal. It vibrates like a drumhead when air waves hit it. The **middle ear** is an air-filled cavity, with three tiny bones that pick up and increase the strength of the vibrations of the eardrum. These little bones carry the strengthened vibrations to a membrane in the **inner ear,** called the oval window. It covers part of the **cochlea** (KAHK lee uh), a liquid-filled organ lined with hairlike sound receptors. When the liquid vibrates, it stimulates the sound receptors, and they send impulses along the **auditory nerve** to the brain. When different combinations of sound receptors are stimulated, you hear different sounds.

Have you ever felt your ears pop when you traveled up or down in a fast elevator? Or when you've been stuffed up from a cold, have you felt uncomfortable pressure in your ears? The **Eustachian** (yoo STAY shuhn) **tube** connects the middle ear and the throat. It keeps the air pressure the same on both sides of the eardrum. If the air pressure changes rapidly in the ear canal outside the eardrum, the narrow Eustachian tube sometimes does not equalize the pressure quickly enough. Then the ears feel stuffed up. But the tubes soon open and close automatically. Then you feel your ears pop. When you feel pressure on your eardrum, you can help the Eustachian tube equalize the pressure by swallowing or yawning a few times.

The eardrum is protected by hairs and glands lining the ear canal. The glands produce wax. The hairs and wax help to keep out dirt and dust that would interfere with hearing. Unless wax accumulates deep inside the canal, it does not have to be scraped or dug out. You can easily damage

Very loud noise can cause permanent damage to the ears and a loss of hearing.

The bones in the middle ear amplify sounds picked up by the outer ear.

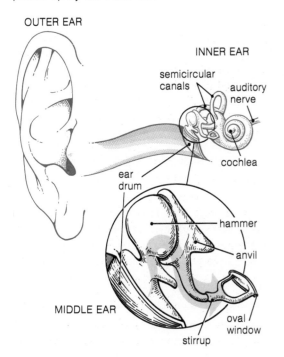

OUTER EAR

INNER EAR

semicircular canals

auditory nerve

cochlea

ear drum

hammer

anvil

MIDDLE EAR

oval window

stirrup

the ear canal and eardrum by picking or scraping wax out of the ear.

Not only are the human hearing structures sensitive enough to detect the sound of a mosquito in the room, they are also strong enough to withstand the crash of thunder, the roar of a jet engine, or the loud blast of an explosion—for a while. There are limits to what the ear can take. High-pitched sounds can make the ears hurt. Extremely loud sounds can injure the ears. Many people who often listen to very loud sounds lose part of their hearing ability.

Do squeaky sounds or too much noise ever make you feel tense or irritated? What noises bother you? What are some that make you feel good? Almost all sensory information causes emotional reactions. Scratching one's fingernail along a chalk-

To perform under stress you need the help of certain endocrine glands. Weight lifters depend on their adrenal glands as well as on their muscles.

board bothers a lot of people. Other sounds may be soothing or exciting. Music, with or without words, is mostly emotional communication.

Colors can also affect emotions in various ways. Red makes some people feel uncomfortable. Soft shades of blue and green relax some people. Seeing a friend or smelling food can create other emotions.

The opposite case is true, too. Your emotional state will affect how you sense your surroundings. You may be intensely aware of the environment or hardly aware it exists. These are other instances of just how complex the sensory processes are.

SELF CHECK

1. Describe how a sensory stimulus is received and interpreted.

2. Suggest some ways to prove to yourself that the senses of taste and smell are related to each other.

3. What types of light receptors are in the retina of each eye? What is the function of each type?

4. How does the eye regulate the amount of light entering it?

5. How does sound travel from its source to the auditory nerve?

The Endocrine System

4-14 Chemical Controls

Frightened people can be amazingly strong or able to run extra-fast. When some people are excited, they also have keener perceptions and can think faster. You may remember that under stress, Alicia in the opening story avoided an accident by handling her bicycle particularly well. The reason for these unusual abilities is that during excitement or fright the autonomic nervous system works with certain **endocrine glands.** Both the nervous and the endocrine sys-

tems mobilize the body's energy supplies, which the body uses to cope with an emergency. The endocrine glands also help calm the body down after an emergency passes, and influence nearly every other aspect of a person's life, just as the nervous system does.

The **hormones** produced by the endocrine glands and released into the blood are powerful chemicals. Although the amounts are small, they make a great difference in the way the body works. Hormones trigger, speed up, slow down, or stop body functions. Sometimes a hormone's effect on an

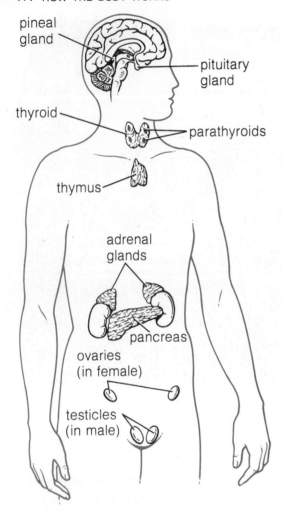

pineal gland

pituitary gland

thyroid

parathyroids

thymus

adrenal glands

pancreas

ovaries (in female)

testicles (in male)

The glands of the endocrine system control the body through hormones.

organ may directly influence almost every cell in the body. Or only a single organ or another of the endocrine glands may be affected.

A hormone is released only in response to a particular signal. The signal may come from the nervous system, from another endocrine gland, or from materials in the blood. When enough of a particular hormone has been released, there is always an automatic shut-off signal. This prevents too much of a hormone from entering the bloodstream. Another way to think of this process is that information about the effects of hormones already released is *fed back* to the gland to control its future action.

A good example of one type of so-called *feedback control* is the body's alarm system. Two **adrenal** (uh DREE nuhl) **glands,** one covering the top of each kidney, are part of the alarm system. When people are under stress or are frightened or excited, the nervous system stimulates the inner tissues of the adrenal glands. They respond by releasing two hormones. Both hormones are quickly carried by the blood to the body's energy-supply systems, preparing the body to react. When the nervous system senses that enough of the hormones have entered the bloodstream, nerve impulses to the adrenal glands shut down the release of these hormones.

The **pituitary gland** is only about the size of a pea—slightly larger in women than in men. It is one of the most important glands of the endocrine system. Since this gland affects a large number of important body functions, it is sometimes called the "master endocrine gland." It is deep within the brain, attached to the hypothalamus by a thin stalk of nerve fibers and capillaries. This direct connection to the hypothalamus helps to coordinate the nervous and endocrine systems. The pituitary releases several different hormones. Some of the pituitary hormones trigger the activities of other endocrine glands. Other pituitary hormones control growth, blood pressure, and the body's water content. The pituitary growth hormone affects how fast you grow, your height, and your body build. It affects the activities of cells, such as food breakdown and the making of new cell parts.

Like any chemical factory, the endocrine system has feedback controls that measure and regulate the amount of chemicals that are produced.

Another pituitary hormone stimulates the **thyroid** (THY royd) **gland** to produce hormones, which also affect cell activities. The thyroid is one of the largest human endocrine glands. It is located in the front of the neck, just above the breastbone. Thyroid hormones speed up the change of food materials into energy within the cells. Thyroid hormones work with the growth hormone produced by the pituitary. In addition, thyroid hormones also affect growth rate, the body's water content, and other functions.

A healthy thyroid adjusts the rate at which body cells produce energy, according to a person's age, body build, and amount of activity. Too much of one thyroid hor-

mone, thyroxin (thy RAHK sihn), can make people overactive, nervous, and unable to sleep soundly. They might eat more food but still lose weight because their cells are burning up food too fast. Too little thyroxin can produce opposite effects, such as drowsiness, fatness, and an inability to keep up with work and social activities.

Clusters of cells in the **pancreas** also produce hormones that affect the production of energy within the body cells. These hormones are **insulin** and **glucagon** (GLOO kuh gahn). Insulin regulates the amount of glucose that gets through the cell membranes into the cells. Insulin also stimulates the liver to store glucose in the form of glycogen. People who have **diabetes** don't produce enough insulin. Their cells cannot use glucose properly. Nor can the liver build up energy reserves. Diabetics can be helped by eating a special diet, taking doses of insulin, and exercising.

The other hormone produced by the pancreas has just the opposite effect on the liver that insulin has. Glucagon stimulates the liver to change glycogen back into glucose and to release it into the bloodstream. Both insulin and glucagon are examples of hormones that are released in response to chemicals in the blood. When there is too much glucose, insulin is released. When blood sugar levels become too low, glucagon is released. In that way blood sugar levels are maintained according to the body's need for energy.

The **ovaries** in women and **testicles** (TEHS tih kuhlz) in men produce sex cells and sex hormones. When and how much depends partly on the pituitary gland. Female sex hormones change girls into women. Male sex hormones change boys into men. These changes do not occur at the same time in all individuals. Girls tend to mature earlier than boys. The changes do not always proceed on a smooth schedule. A boy may have a deep voice at the age of 14 but no sign of whiskers. A girl may menstruate (MEHN stroo ayt) but notice that her figure has not yet developed. It takes several years for the complex production and interaction of sex hormones to result in physical maturity.

Another tiny gland, the **pineal** (PIHN ee uhl) **gland,** seems to affect the rate at which sex hormones work. The pineal gland is connected to the optic nerve and is affected by the amount of light that strikes the eyes. In Spring, when the number of hours of daylight increases, the pineal gland produces more of a hormone that increases the action of the sex hormones. The result is "Spring fever." Another pineal hormone seems to affect the wake-sleep cycle. Do you wake up fast and bounce out of bed ready to go? Or do you wake up slowly and not get into high gear until mid-morning? Scientists believe that the pineal gland to some extent regulates people's daily rhythms, or, as they are sometimes called, biorhythms.

The **thymus gland,** in the chest above the heart, is relatively large at birth, and then slowly shrivels. Its exact functions have not been determined, but it is believed to help the body fight disease-causing organisms.

The endocrine system is very complicated. Many aspects are still not understood. For example, a group of chemical compounds called **prostaglandins** (prahs tuh GLAN dihnz) affects many body functions. Scientists do not completely understand how these compounds work. But they are thought to be hormones. Some of these compounds reduce blood pressure and decrease heartbeat and breathing rates. Others affect the speed of nerve impulses to and from the brain. Some are believed to affect the contraction of smooth muscles. Like hormones, prostaglandins circulate in the blood. But they are produced by many tissues of the body, not just by endocrine glands. Scientists are studying prostaglandins to learn how they work and perhaps how to use them to help people with certain diseases.

In studying the different body systems, you've probably concluded that we can't point to one system or to one body part as the most important. You're right. No one gland or organ serves as the one controller of the body. The nervous and endocrine systems harmonize all the other systems. But the music would lack its full effect without the whole orchestra playing.

Everybody knows that plants are affected by the seasons.
People are, too. Increasing hours of daylight set off Spring fever.

1. Why is the pituitary gland called the master endocrine gland?

2. What are some signs that someone's thyroid gland may be producing too much hormone or too little hormone?

3. How do hormones from the pancreas control the amount of sugar in the blood?

4. What endocrine gland indirectly regulates the production of sex hormones?

5. How is the on-and-off action of the adrenal glands regulated?

Chapter Summary

Together, the nervous and endocrine systems coordinate and control the body systems. The nervous system transmits information back and forth from the brain and spinal cord to every part of the body by electrochemical impulses. The endocrine glands produce hormones and release them into the bloodstream. Hormones are substances that regulate body functions, including the activities of other glands.

The brain both controls body functions and enables you to choose and control your activities. The brain requires a constant supply of blood and oxygen to keep functioning. It is more protected than any other part of the body—by the bony skull, membranes, and fluid. The cortex is the center of the most highly developed human traits, including speech, reasoning, creativity, and memory. Other areas of the brain control digestion, heartbeat rate, circulation of the blood, and other largely involuntary activities.

Nervous control of the right half of the body is centered in the left cerebral hemisphere, and vice versa. Although the two halves of the cerebrum are connected, each half seems to have some specialized functions. In most people, the right hemisphere seems to be responsible for some creative and intuitive experiences, and the left hemisphere seems to be the focus for language skills.

Nerves are divided between the voluntary and the autonomic nervous systems. The systems have some of the same functions. Voluntary activities that are repeated tend to become automatic, or habits. Some people trained in meditation and biofeedback have learned to relax at will and to control "automatic" body functions.

The brain is also the center for registering and interpreting sensations. Your sensory receptors give you information about the inside of your body and about stimuli from outside. Your eyes, ears, and skin tell you the most about the outside world, but the senses of taste and smell also give you information. Not only does the brain combine sensations in many different ways, but the senses and emotions also influence each other.

Hormones produced and released by the endocrine glands set off, speed up, slow down, or halt specific body functions. An endocrine gland may react to a signal from another endocrine gland or from the nervous system. The pituitary gland influences more body activities than any other endocrine gland. Some endocrine glands produce hormones that counteract each other, and release the hormones at different times according to the body's needs. Long-term activities, such as growth and the development of sexual characteristics, are regulated by endocrine glands.

Chapter Self Check

1. In what ways are the nervous system and endocrine glands both controllers and workers in the body?

2. Explain similarities and differences in the ways the nervous and endocrine systems work.

3. How do impulses travel along a nerve?

4. What information does an EEG give about brain activity?

5. Which of these parts of the body would you expect to be controlled by a larger area of the cortex: toes or fingers? Why?

6. If the right side of the brain were damaged, what parts of the body would you expect to be most affected?

7. Explain the difference between the voluntary and the autonomic nervous systems.

8. What structure in the brain makes it possible for learned activities to become practically automatic?

9. What parts of the brain might be involved in the following health problems: (a) constant hunger in spite of eating a lot; (b) a tendency to fall asleep several times during the day; (c) loss of ability to hold a pen; (d) loss of a sense of balance.

10. People who are injured or have had a serious illness sometimes cannot regain consciousness. Which parts of their brains are still working? Which are not?

11. What parts of the body are reached by spinal nerves?

12. Explain the complaint, "My back hurts. I must have a slipped disk."

13. What is the function of a sensory receptor?

14. Pain has been called a protective device for the body. Give examples that support this statement.

15. In what part of the eye are light receptors located?

16. What is the function of the Eustachian tubes?

17. Describe how the parts of the middle and inner ear function.

18. What would happen if a person's pituitary gland produced too little growth hormone or too much?

19. Explain the term "feedback control" as it relates to the adrenal glands and the nervous system.

20. Name two or more functions of the thyroid gland.

21. What are the differences between the ways nerves and endocrine glands control and coordinate body functions?

Read More About It

Riedman, Sarah R. *Hormones: How They Work.* New York: Abelard-Schuman, 1973. How hormones affect the body and each other, and their importance to health. Discusses research leading to the discovery of hormones and the need for further research.

Silverstein, Alvin, and Silverstein, Virginia. *Bionics: Man Copies Nature's Machines.* New York: McCall Publishing Company (E. P. Dutton & Company, Inc.), 1970. How the structures of various organisms have provided models for traffic-control systems, sonar detection systems, computers, and other devices.

Stevens, Leonard A. *Neurons: Building Blocks of the Brain.* New York: Thomas Y. Crowell Company, 1974. The neuron, the importance of technology to what is known about the neuron, and difficulties encountered in neuron research.

Ward, Ritchie R. *The Living Clocks.* New York: Alfred A. Knopf, Inc., 1971. How biological "clocks" affect human behavior and the behavior of other organisms.

Unit 2 TAKING CARE OF YOURSELF

5

Keeping Fit

After completing the work in this chapter, you will be able to:

explain what fitness means.

describe several factors to consider in selecting physical activities.

list at least six beneficial effects of regular physical activity.

describe several ways to protect yourself against sports injuries.

discuss some of the physical and mental activities that go on during sleep.

The Prehistoric Button-Pusher

Here's an idea for a new situation comedy written for television:

A caveman and a cavewoman are standing in front of a shiny machine. It is something new to them, and they look at it full of curiosity. They are an intelligent pair with rugged bodies. Both of them are good hunters, always on the alert against wild animals and strangers from the other side of the mountain. They are cautious about the machine but finally get around to touching it.

It turns out to be a time machine. In an instant, they are transported to the twentieth century. The caveman is sitting at a desk, wearing a business suit. His job is to make decisions, talk on the phone, push buttons, and listen to his boss shout at him. His mate is wearing a dress, not the skin of a deer she killed. She must spend a lot of her time hunting in the library for information that will help her defend her client in court. Their cave has become an apartment filled with confusing gadgets.

A television program about a caveman and a cavewoman trying to manage in the modern world could be more than a comedy. It could also be a sad story. Would they really be able to manage? How would

their superb bodies react to being confined most of the time? How would they handle the stresses and anxieties of a technological society?

How do *you* do it? Humans are pretty much the same as they were 40,000 years ago. Only the world has changed. We still have the physical capabilities and needs of a cave-dweller. How do you satisfy those needs for a vigorous, physically active life? What are the effects of not satisfying the caveman or cavewoman in you?

The Active Life

5-1 You're Better Than You Think

Many other animals can outperform people at specific tasks. Dogs have a keener sense of smell, deer can run faster, and flies can walk upside-down and fly. Except for our mental capabilities, almost anything we can do, some other animals can do better. Because of this, many people believe that human beings make up an inferior kind of animal. It is said that we survive in this world only because of our brains. In fact, that isn't true.

No other animal on Earth can match the overall physical performance of a healthy man or woman. We combine excellent sensory abilities with muscular strength, endurance, agility, and gracefulness in ways that no other animal does. While most other animals specialize in one or a few skills, people do remarkably well with their entire bodies. For example, dogs have a better sense of smell, but people have better eyesight and tactile senses. (We also have a pretty good sense of smell.) Deer and horses can outrun people for short distances, but Indian hunters used to run these animals down on foot by chasing their prey for a day or two until it collapsed from exhaustion. A trained jogger or marathon runner could probably do as well today. And while we can't fly or walk upside-down, the human hand can perform a combination of feats that no other animals can match.

Acrobats, gymnasts, dancers, boxers, and divers can flex their muscles and bend their joints in more ways than most other animals can, and often with grace as well as skill. So can most children.

Human skin is a rugged covering. It isn't as thick as cowhide or as hard as turtle shells. But many groups of people live their whole lives in harsh environments without shoes or clothing. And what skin lacks in toughness, it more than makes up for in sensitivity and in ability to adjust to heat, cold, and rough surfaces.

People can eat a tremendous variety of plants and animals for food, or live on plants only or animals only. Our teeth and the rest of our digestive system give us great freedom of diet, perhaps more than any other animal has.

You probably know that most animals are adapted to living in specific types of environments. They have special requirements for food, temperature, shelter, light, and other things. They are specialists, while people are generalists. We lead healthy lives in every continent and climate on Earth. Add human intelligence to all our physical capabilities and it is easy to see that people are the most versatile and capable animals

There are few places on Earth where you can't find people.
Where we don't adapt naturally, our equipment helps us out.

on Earth. (Of course, that doesn't give us a license to treat the other living things in our environment with contempt. Doing so is neither fair nor sensible, as it can endanger our own survival.)

Physically fit men and women are the pride of the planet. Our physical capabilities are great, perhaps unknown. If you are healthy, the things you can learn to do and enjoy are practically unlimited.

5-2 Fitness

Some people think being fit means developing bulging muscles and a strong grip. Other people think it means being athletic and skilled in a lot of sports. Still others think it means feeling good and being able to do the activities you enjoy.

There is no one standard of **fitness.** There are different levels of fitness, but fitness has some basic characteristics at all levels. Fitness is a combination of physical and emotional health. It involves all of you: body, thoughts, and feelings. If you are fit, you can meet the physical and emotional demands of everyday life. If you are fit, mild exertion does not leave you gasping for breath, exhausted, and full of aches and pains. When you are fit, you do not feel tired, nervous, edgy, or tense most of the time, and you sleep well.

You can choose the level of fitness that you want to achieve. It all depends on what you want to do with your life. You can decide that you want to lead an active, but not very strenuous life. Or you can decide that you want to reach the limits of your physical and mental capabilities. Or you can try to be somewhere in between.

You don't have to be a husky lumberjack or an Olympic athlete to be fit. And you don't have to do calisthenics (kal uhs THEHN ihks) or compete in sports, although your version of becoming fit might involve those things. It all depends on the limits you set for yourself.

5-3 What Shape Are You In?

This is a checklist to help you decide whether you are fit (or healthy). You don't have to write down the answers. Just think about the questions and make your own decisions.

1. Do you exert yourself often?

2. Can you exert yourself when you want to or need to without total exhaustion and aches and pains? Does your heartbeat slow down quickly after exercise? Do you get your breath back right away?

3. Do you regularly do activities that give you a sense of vitality and accomplishment?

4. Do you feel tired, nervous, edgy, or tense most of the time?

5. Can you relax when you want to?

6. Do you sleep well? Do you feel rested after a night's sleep? Do you get sleepy during the day?

If your answers to this checklist show that you are not fit, you need to work on improving your health. Try to get help in becoming fit. Find out what you can do. The next section may give you some ideas.

5-4 Choosing Physical Activities

To become fit and stay fit you should be physically active all year long. You do not have to be an athlete or do calisthenics. There are many non-sports activities that you can enjoy that will help you stay fit. You do not have to restrict yourself to the activities offered in physical education class in school. Many activities can be enjoyed outside of school. For variety, you will probably want to have several activities for different times of the year.

For a lot of people, "get some exercise" sounds like "take your medicine." They think of sit-ups, push-ups, and chin-ups—which they've tried and disliked doing—and they make a face. Maybe you think of "exercise" in the same way. In that case, you shouldn't "exercise." Your goal should be to choose physical activities you can enjoy doing. When choosing an activity, consider your size, strength, abilities, interests, the cost, and the available facilities. There is a large variety of activities. They involve teams, opponents, or single individuals. And don't rule out any activities just because of your sex.

If you like being involved with a group and enjoy competition, you might be interested in team sports. Most team sports are fast games, many involving body contact. They usually require special organization, equipment, and facilities. You will usually have to play them at school or at some other community facility.

Opponent sports usually require less organization, less equipment, and less costly

Labor-saving devices also limit opportunities for exercise.
If you were in these pictures, which way would you travel?

facilities than the team sports do. As a result, if you enjoy competition and perhaps don't enjoy group activities, opponent sports may be for you. You do not have to stay at school to play most of these sports. You can play many in a lot, field, backyard, or community recreation area. Some opponent sports, such as wrestling and boxing, involve body contact. Combative sports from the Orient are becoming quite popular. These include aikido, judo, karate, kendo, and kung fu. Other opponent sports allow competition without body contact. These include tennis, handball, fencing, and paddleball.

You decide the amount of time, energy, and skill you put into an opponent sport and the enjoyment you receive. Instead of depending on team members, you are able to test only yourself against a single opponent. You can find out how you alone stand up in competition.

Team or opponent sports are usually fairly strenuous. They can force you to push yourself harder than you might ordinarily push yourself in an activity because of the challenge of your opponent or the expectations of your teammates. Competitive sports are a social activity and allow people with similar interests to get together and share those interests. These sports help you meet people and make new friends. Competitive sports also help you learn to get along with other people.

If you do not enjoy competition, there are many sports that you can do alone or with others without competing. You can set your own standards or goals that you want to achieve; you do not have to beat an opponent. You compete only against the goals you set for yourself. Some of the individual sports that can be done non-competitively include gymnastics, skiing, swimming, weight lifting, bicycling, and hiking.

Are there any activities here that you might like to try?

TEAM SPORTS	OPPONENT SPORTS	INDIVIDUAL SPORTS (CAN BE DONE COMPETITIVELY)	OTHER ACTIVITIES	
baseball	aikido	archery	aerobic exercises	jogging
basketball	badminton	bowling	backpacking	jumping rope
curling (ice bowling)	boxing	cricket	ballet	kayaking
field hockey	fencing	croquet	bicycling	mountain or rock
football	handball	diving	calisthenics	climbing
ice hockey	horseshoes	golfing	camping	parachuting
lacrosse	judo	gymnastics	canoeing	roller skating
netball	karate	skiing (downhill and	dancing	rowing
polo	kendo	cross-country)	fishing	running
roller hockey	kung fu	swimming	gardening	sailing
rugby	paddleball	target shooting	hiking	skin diving
soccer	ping-pong	track and field	hunting	sledding
softball	shuffleboard	trampoline	horseback riding	surfing
speedball	squash	weight lifting	ice boating	walking
volleyball	tennis		ice skating	water skiing
water polo	wrestling		isometrics	yoga

Do you do any exciting sports activities?

Some sports that are fun to do are not very challenging to the body. Golf and sailing fit this category. They often involve less exertion than many other sports. Because of that, they may have to be done more often or for longer periods of time to have beneficial effects on the body. Being outdoors and having a change of pace, however, is good for you regardless of the amount of exertion.

Regular physical activities do not have to be expensive. Many indoor and outdoor activities require inexpensive equipment or no equipment at all. Some of these activities include basketball, swimming, walking, and jogging. In addition, you can find facilities that cost little or no money. Some school sports facilities are open before and after school hours. The YWCA and YMCA have gymnasiums and pools, often available to students at low cost. Some communities have free recreation centers that include tennis courts, indoor and outdoor pools, playing fields, and playgrounds. Many of these facilities are open during the evening as well as during the day. Sometimes churches and synagogues provide free recreation facilities. Some communities set aside play streets. Often just an empty field or driveway works well for softball or basketball.

Whatever physical activity you choose, it should be fun for you, and you should find yourself relaxed afterwards. The most important thing to keep in mind is that during activity you must exert yourself and increase your heartbeat and breathing rates. Regular exertion ensures that you will stay fit. Once you get into the habit of regular physical activity, you will feel good and enjoy being fit all your life.

5-5 The Advantages of Being Active

Being active is not just a way to improve an already healthy body—to become stronger or more attractive, for example. The fact is, if you are not regularly active, you don't just stay the same. Your health actually goes downhill.

Constantly inactive muscle fibers become smaller, and they store less energy. They exert less tension for a task, and they tire quickly. When inactive muscles are overworked, they often feel stiff and sore for a few days afterwards. Unused joints become stiff and less flexible, and can become sore if moved too far or too fast. A lack of stress regularly exerted by muscles makes bones eventually become softer and more easily broken.

The effect of regular exercise is to make muscles and joints stronger and more flexible. Tendons and bones also become harder and stronger. Well-used muscles do not tire as quickly as flabby muscles do, even though they do more work. This is because trained muscles can take up and use glucose and oxygen from the blood at a faster rate. They also get rid of waste products faster. And trained muscles are also more efficient at turning food energy into work.

The heart is the most hard-working and efficient muscle in the body. Like other muscles, it is strengthened and enlarged somewhat as a result of regular activity. The number of its capillaries and the amount of

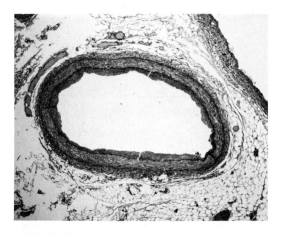

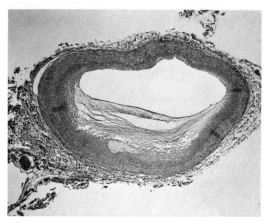

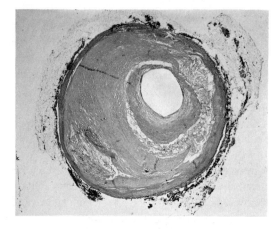

A normal artery (top) can become narrowed and then nearly closed off with fatty materials.

Being a "weight lifter" by carrying extra weight doesn't build muscles or improve a person's physical condition.

blood flowing into the heart also increases, as does the amount of energy it stores. A trained heart beats slower at rest and has more resting time between heartbeats. It does not have to work as hard as the untrained heart does. All of these factors make the trained heart more efficient than the untrained heart. Even people who have suffered heart attacks are usually advised to get light, and then moderate, exercise.

Regular activity also improves the condition of the blood vessels. It helps prevent or slow down the build-up of fatty materials on the inside of artery walls. If the passageways become smaller and the artery walls become harder, the heart has to work harder to force blood through. This is a major cause of heart attack. Regular exercise also reduces blood pressure at rest, so the heart does not have to work as hard.

Regular, strenuous activity increases blood volume and the number of red blood cells. As a result, more oxygen, food materials, and wastes are transported more efficiently. Also, the number of blood vessels in the muscles and the amount of blood the muscles receive increase.

Since the walls of veins have little supporting tissue, good circulation depends on the movement of the muscles through which the veins run. Movement of the limbs helps move the blood through the veins from the lower parts of the body back to the heart. Patients who must spend long periods of time in bed are often given gentle leg exercises to prevent blood from clotting or pooling in their veins.

The respiratory system also benefits from regular activity. Exercise increases the lungs' ability to take in oxygen from the air and makes the movement of oxygen and carbon dioxide between the air and blood more efficient.

Weight and overall appearance are greatly influenced by regular activity. Dieting without regular activity is a hard way to lose weight. Overweight people sometimes think that exercise will not help them lose weight. They think that it will only make them hungrier. Just the opposite is true. Physically active people usually automatically adjust their food intake to energy needs. They are seldom overweight. They use up all the energy they take in and do not accumulate fat. An inactive person loses the automatic balance between energy intake and output. It is the combination of too little exercise and too much food that produces fatness.

Another aspect of appearance that is affected by activity is posture. Strong abdominal, back, and limb muscles produced by regular exercise hold the body together in a natural and healthy position. You do not have to think about how you look. You have a smoother and livelier walk, and you are not slumped over or pot-bellied. Your body is flexible, and you have no stiffness or strain. That makes you comfortable and more attractive. Inactivity usually results in a cramped, unhealthy, and uncomfortable posture.

Do you often feel tense because of all the things going on in your life right now? Emotional stress arouses the nervous and endocrine systems. Muscles contract, and the body is ready for action. The result is sore muscles, often in the jaw, neck, shoulders, or abdomen, if you hold back and have no way to use those muscles. Regular physical activity can help. It actually results in relaxation—lets you "unwind" or "blow

This is one way that you could exercise to let off steam.

off steam." Activity won't solve your problems, but it will give you a break and put you in a better frame of mind to handle them. It will also help you sleep better. Constant inactivity can result in continued tension, fatigue, and inability to sleep.

Some activities, such as weight lifting, tennis, or yoga, require intense mental concentration as well as physical effort. When your mind and body are totally involved like this, you feel a sense of well-being. Other activities require less mental concentration. But they are still pleasing and can make you feel good. Doing either type of activity will give you a sense of achievement and self-confidence.

5-6 Protecting Yourself

The best protection against being seriously injured during physical activity is to be in good condition. When you first take up any strenuous activity, you should work up to it gradually. Your body needs time to build itself up to handle the new demands you are putting on it. Otherwise you are likely to injure yourself. Muscles need training before they can work at their top capacity and give you strength and stamina in physical activities. Strong muscles and ligaments guard joints against sprains and bones against breaking. They also help guard the liver, spleen, kidneys, and other organs from injury.

Each time you work out, first do warming-up and loosening-up exercises to prepare your muscles for activity. Choose the exercise routine that makes you feel good or one that your coach recommends. Many people in good physical condition are injured because they neglect to warm up before exercising vigorously.

Warming up should always be part of your exercise routine, whether a coach is there or not.

Before first taking up a strenuous activity, it is a good idea to have a medical examination. A doctor should also review your medical history to make sure that no past illness will affect your performance or create a health problem. Most high schools require a medical examination before taking part in organized competitive sports. If you are injured or become ill during the sports season, you should have a doctor check you before you return to competition.

Following the rules of the game and the advice of your coach, both in practice and in competition, is important in preventing injuries. Many of the rules in sports were

Professional athletes wear protective clothing because they want long, healthy careers.

created to make the games safe. Injuries often occur when people break the rules or horse around during practice.

If a sport or activity calls for special clothing and protective equipment, always use them, even in practice. Playing without them increases the risk of injury. Many injuries occur when people do not use protective equipment during practice. To prevent infections, clothing and equipment should be cleaned and dried often.

Don't try to work or play hard after a big meal. Heavy exertion interferes with digestion. You will feel better if you eat only a light snack before working out.

Although the body can wait for food, it cannot manage very long without water. During vigorous exercise, the body loses water and salt, mostly through perspiration. Since the body needs to have this water and salt replaced, you should drink a little fluid at least every hour during exertion. If you drink a lot, you'll feel bloated. A coach or teacher may supply salt tablets or remind the players to take extra salt at mealtime. Heat exhaustion or a heat stroke, which is much more serious, can follow strenuous physical activity in the heat if the body does not have enough salt and water.

● **5-7 Relaxing**

What do you do to relax? Do you take long walks, talk with friends, listen to music? There are many pleasant things to do to break a day's routine and help you unwind. The best relaxation often comes after muscular exertion—as in the following activity, for example.

PROCEDURE

Begin this activity with a brief warm-up, such as running in place, jumping, or hopping for about a minute. After the warm-up lie flat on your back and get as comfortable as possible. Lie on a mat or blanket.

1. As you bend your knee, slide your right heel to your buttocks and let it slide back down to the starting position quickly.

2. Slide your right heel to your buttocks again, but this time let it down to the starting position very slowly. Let your foot feel as though it is floating away and imagine that your leg is getting longer and longer.

3. Repeat steps 1 and 2 with your left heel.

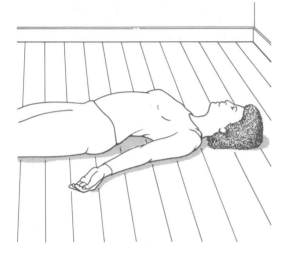

9. Squeeze your shoulders down hard on the floor again. Release them slowly until your back seems to go right into the floor.

10. Press the back of your head down until your shoulders are raised slightly off the floor. Let your shoulders down quickly.

11. Press your head down until your shoulders are lifted off the floor again. Let your shoulders down slowly until the back of your neck seems to go right into the floor.

12. Take a deep breath, in through your nose and out through your mouth.

13. Imagine that you are floating away on a soft carpet.

SELF CHECK

1. How do you define fitness for yourself?

2. What activities would you choose to keep fit all year long?

3. Why do only regular, vigorous activities result in fitness?

4. In what ways is the body affected by lack of regular physical activity?

5. How can physical activity make you feel better emotionally?

6. Why is a medical examination important before you take part in a strenuous competitive sport?

4. Squeeze your buttocks muscles together tightly on the floor. Release the tension all at once.

5. Squeeze your buttocks together again but release the muscles slowly, ever so slowly, feeling your buttocks flatten out on the floor.

6. Arch your back 6 to 8 inches (15 to 25 centimeters) off the floor. Release it all at once.

7. Arch your back again but let it return to the floor slowly. Imagine that your back is going down into the floor.

8. Squeeze your shoulders down hard on the floor. Release them quickly.

To Sleep . . . To Dream

5-8 Why Sleep?

Some people sleep only two or three hours a night. Infants and children sleep many more hours than you do. High school students average about eight hours a night, but this is not a magic number. You may find that seven hours is all you need or that you can't get along on less than ten. When you feel a lot of emotional stress, your sleep needs may go up. Some people sleep less during the week and catch up on the weekends. Some people do the reverse.

There is no general agreement among scientists as to why people sleep. The reasons are many and complex. Some theories say that sleep is necessary so the body can dispose of waste products built up during the day. Perhaps we sleep, at least in part, so that we can dream. In any case, to say that people sleep because they need rest is no explanation at all. It merely restates the problem. A satisfactory theory will also have to explain why some people function well with very little sleep. This much is sure, most people find sleeping pleasant.

No one knows the full answer to why people sleep. What is known very well, though, is what happens when people don't get enough sleep. They begin to work less efficiently, mentally and physically. They become irritable and accident-prone. After a long sleepless time, they become confused and have hallucinations (huh loo suh NAY shuhnz). That is, they seem to experience things that aren't really there. In time, a person deprived of sleep can suffer a complete breakdown and maybe even die.

5-9 The Cycles of the Night

Sleep is a surprisingly busy time for the brain. There are four distinct stages of sleep. These stages occur in cycles that each go from stage 1 to stage 4 and back through stages 3 and 2 to stage 1. Each of these cycles lasts about 90 minutes in all; then a new cycle begins for another 90 minutes—all through the night. An average night's sleep has five or six of these cycles.

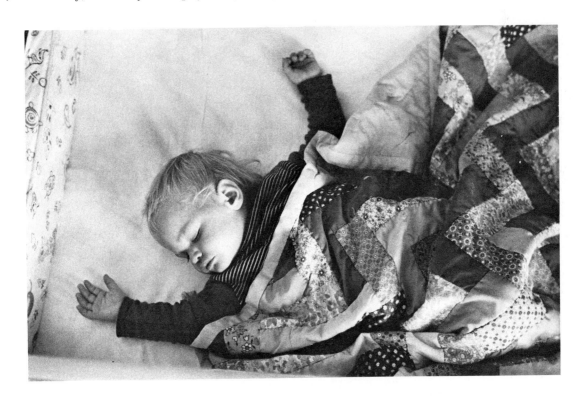

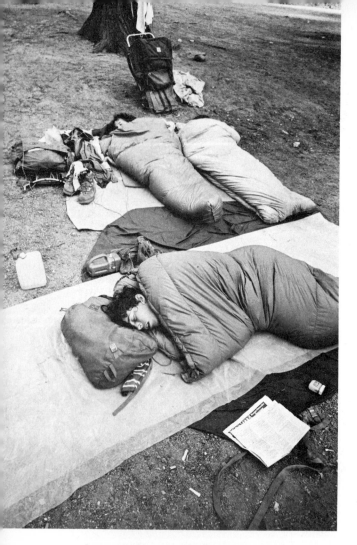

Some people can fall asleep anywhere, anytime, and in any situation.

The four stages of sleep progress from the lightest sleep (stage 1) to the deepest sleep (stage 4). Stage 1, when recorded on an EEG, results in brain waves that look fairly close to those of the waking state. Stage 4 sleepers produce brain waves similar to those of people in a coma. As sleep deepens, brain waves, heartbeat rate, and breathing rate become slower, and there is less body movement. Also, body temperature drops

and blood pressure falls, until the next cycle starts up.

The first stage 1 of the night is just a descent into sleep. Starting with the second sleep cycle and for the rest of the night, however, stage 1 sleep is often referred to as **REM sleep.** It is called REM sleep because during this 10–15 minute stage, the sleeper's closed eyes show Rapid Eye Movement. People are not easily awakened during this stage. When people who volunteer for sleep-research experiments are awakened during REM sleep, they usually report that they had been dreaming. Dreaming also occurs during the other stages of sleep, but eye movements are slower then. And dreams in the other stages are less vivid and interesting, and not as easily remembered.

Stage 2 sleep is light sleep with very little eye movement, and some body movement. Sleep-talking and sleep-walking usually occur during stage 2, if they occur at all. In stages 3 and 4 (deep sleep) there is an outpouring of growth hormone into the bloodstream. The growth hormone aids in using certain food materials for body growth, maintenance, and repair. Young children spend more of their sleep cycles in these stages than adults do. It would seem that they need sleep to grow. If you have a vigorous workout during the day, you may also spend more of your time in stages 3 and 4 than usual.

On the other hand, premature babies may spend up to 80 percent of their time in REM sleep. Just before birth, the brain is growing more rapidly than during any other time. So REM sleep may be associated with brain growth and mental activity. Senile people and the severely retarded spend little time in REM sleep.

Because the mind can be very active during sleep, sleep isn't always restful. You can toss and turn half the night. Dreams or nightmares can wake you up. And there are even some illnesses that flare up at night. Arthritis pain, asthma attacks, and pains from stomach ulcers often strike sleepers. One reason is probably that dreams full of excitement or worries have the same effects on the body as daytime experiences. (An empty stomach or too many blankets can also have these effects.) Dreams can increase heartbeat rate, blood pressure, and acid production in the stomach, as well as produce other effects. In fact, these responses may be stronger during sleep than during the day. The worries you put out of your mind in the daytime can ambush you in your dreams.

5-10 What's in a Dream?

Most dreams seem to be just disconnected, hazy thoughts. Each new dream makes you forget the last one. And most people quickly forget the final dream of the night when they get out of bed. Probably nothing of value has been lost or forgotten most of the time.

But you may occasionally have dreams that seem like reminders from the sleeping brain to the waking brain about things you've forgotten. For example, you might have worked on a bike or a piece of machinery during the day. That night, a piece you forgot to put back or forgot to check might come to mind in a dream. Or something or someone you didn't pay enough attention to while awake might occupy your mind during sleep.

Then there are the strange, creative dreams that seem like movies someone else wrote, but you are starring in. They seem to be important, but it is hard to figure out what they mean. This sort of dream has been described as "a personal letter to yourself."

If you learn to remember these dreams and how to interpret them, they can tell you a lot about yourself. Sometimes, however, it may be difficult or impossible to decide what a dream means, or if it even has any meaning at all. This section will give you some ideas that will help you try to interpret your dreams.

Obviously, you have to remember a dream before it can be interpreted. If you don't usually remember your dreams, try following these suggestions. As you are falling asleep, tell yourself several times, "I will remember a dream tonight," or "I will awaken from a dream tonight." Keep a pencil and paper or a tape recorder near your bed. When you wake up, do it gently. Don't sit bolt upright or jump out of bed. If you do, the dream will escape you. Instead, keep your eyes closed and mentally run through the dream you just had. Then write down as much of the dream as you can

If the gypsy dreamed the lion, what do you think the lion could represent?
Rousseau, Henri, *The Sleeping Gypsy,* 1897, oil on canvas, 51″ x 6′7″, collection,
The Museum of Modern Art, New York, gift of Mrs. Simon Guggenheim.

remember. Afterwards, you can begin to try to interpret it.

Dreams seem strange because they are created by a different way of thinking from the way we think while awake. The sleeping brain tends to think in symbols, not sentences. For example, you may dream of your mother as a witch one night and a queen the next. But all that appears in the dream is a queen or a witch. You add the interpretation. If you feel the world is putting a lot of pressure on you, you may dream of being under a steam roller. You might have to think about the symbol for a while before you connect it with aspects of your waking life.

The first thing to do when you try interpreting a dream of this sort is to keep in mind that it probably concerns how you feel about yourself and about other people. Dreams tell you how you really feel at the moment about your emotions and personal conflicts.

Take a person, an object, or an action in the dream. Who or what does it remind you of? Suppose you dreamed of flying. What do you think of flying? Does it stand for danger or adventure? Was your dream of flying exciting or fearful? Is there something you have been doing lately in your daily life that makes you "high" or makes you afraid you are getting away from down-to-earth matters? Let your mind wander around the idea of flying until it finds the interpretation that feels right. It usually will. If you treat the major figures and actions in a dream this way, you may come to understand it, at least partly.

Often people have upsetting dreams. They may do things in a dream that seem so horrible or stupid that they can hardly think about them, let alone do them, in waking life. Upon interpreting such dreams, if people are honest with themselves, they sometimes discover that they have certain feelings and longings that their waking self has forbidden them to think about. They may not be able to satisfy these feelings in real life, or even want to. But the part of the mind that dreams is refusing to deny that the feelings exist.

A peculiarity of the mind is that feelings that we deny become magnified and distorted. The more we deny their existence, the stronger they seem to become. One of the benefits of discovering through dream interpretation that you have "forbidden" feelings is that they usually shrink down to manageable size.

Sometimes dreams show us our problems in a clear way that helps us resolve them in waking life. Sometimes they even come with solutions to conflicts that we couldn't work out consciously, because the conscious, awake mind tries to ignore or deny frightening feelings and impulses. But at night, in its own way, the truth comes out.

Sometimes you gain some insight if you act out part of a dream or let the characters in it speak for themselves. Imagine that you dreamed of a street that had two houses on it. You tried interpreting the dream in the way just discussed, but the houses didn't seem to connect to anything or to any person in your life. The houses *might* stand for different ways you feel about yourself. Maybe one house is run-down and the other

is covered with fancy decorations, awnings, ironwork, and statues. Even though it may seem silly, put yourself in the place of the houses. Play the role of each one in whatever way it strikes you. For example:

Run-down house I'm uncared for. Everyone thinks I'm ugly.

Fancy house I'm handsome and kept up. I have lots of visitors.

Run-down house I'm really a good house. If people saw how solid and comfortable I am, I'd be loved, too.

Fancy house Actually, it's pretty expensive and takes a lot of time to keep looking so fancy and dressed up. . . .

You get the idea. Maybe one part of the dreamer feels tired of putting on airs while another part feels unjustly neglected. Try this method of getting at the significance of dreams, particularly if the same dream keeps recurring and seems strange or mysterious.

● **5-11 Investigating Your Dreams**

PROCEDURE

1. When you remember a dream in detail and don't feel it's too embarrassing to discuss, report it to your classmates. Tell them how you interpret it or ask for their help. They can't tell you what your dream means to you, but they may give you some ideas.

2. For practice, try interpreting the dream on the next page that a girl had several nights in a row. The girl lives in a city and has no contact with horses, except for sometimes seeing the mounted police patrolling a park near her apartment. She is an honor student and a sprinter on the school

track team. She is often too busy to spend much time with her friends and relatives, but she says she likes "being on the go all the time."

The Dream A herd of wild horses is running along a beach, kicking up sand and water. Some people in cars and on foot try to catch them. The horses seem to be running in slow motion, but no one can catch up with them. Even the horses lagging at the back of the herd are just out of reach. But then, suddenly, the horses discover that they've run into a corral. They keep running, but they run in place and get nowhere. When the people come up to close the gate of the corral, the horses begin leaping out over the wooden rails, and they all escape.

DISCUSSION

1. What might the girl's dream mean?

2. What questions would you ask the girl to help you interpret it?

5-12 Sleeping Problems

Insomnia (ihn SAHM nee uh), or having difficulty sleeping, takes several forms. Some people have a very hard time falling asleep, or they wake up much earlier than they want to. Others may not be able to sleep more than a few hours at a time without waking up. People who have insomnia sometimes feel that they don't sleep at all, but actually they drift in and out of sleep without realizing it. They probably get more sleep than they think they do.

One reason for insomnia is that everyone's internal "clock" is not "set" for the same time. Schools and businesses usually start early in the morning, although many people don't feel that they've really awakened until much later. If they had their choice, these people would sleep later and work a night shift. If you are a "night person," you may want to try arranging your schedule that way when you graduate from school. In any case, if you are on any one schedule for a long time, your internal clock will probably gradually reset itself to that schedule.

Sometimes insomnia is caused by illness. Pain or discomfort keep the insomniac from a good night's sleep. A bedroom too hot or too cold can also keep you awake. So can an uncomfortable bed. However, most of the time insomnia seems to be psychological in origin. You can be so excited by experiences you've had or that you expect to have that your mind flutters all night instead of resting. Many insomniacs are worried or depressed people whose troubles keep them awake. And the more tired they get because of the trouble they have sleeping, the more anxious they get. So they lie awake worrying about their sleeping problems as well as their original problems.

One solution to insomnia is to get out of bed and forget about trying to sleep. After you have broken the pattern of tossing restlessly, sleep may then come to you. Other methods are to read a dull book, have a warm glass of milk, listen to some soft, soothing music. An occasional night of poor sleep is common and no cause for concern. Constant insomnia is serious and should be discussed with a doctor.

Doctors sometimes prescribe sleeping pills for insomniacs, but not for long-term use. Sleeping pills are habit-forming and may leave a person feeling groggy in the morning. When combined with alcohol, sleeping pills can be very dangerous because they severely slow down the nervous system, sometimes causing unconsciousness and, occasionally, death. The sleeping pills sold over the counter in drugstores are not effective. Sleeping pills do not cure the cause of insomnia and should be avoided unless prescribed by a doctor.

People who sleep badly may take stimulant drugs in the morning. They do this in the hope of getting enough energy to get through the day. But these pills can also interfere with sleep. An unhealthy cycle can be set up of taking stimulants in the morning and sleeping pills at night.

5-13 Snoring

One of the most common reasons people have trouble sleeping sounds funny, unless it happens to you. It's being kept awake by another person's snoring. The sounds of gurgles, whistles, hisses, and rumbles can be very annoying. Snoring is common. Infants, old people, the healthy, the sick, and males and females of all races snore. Men seem to do it more than women, though. The noises result from congested or narrow breathing passages and vibrations of tissues around the back of the mouth and the opening of the throat. A person sleeping on his or her back is more likely to snore than someone sleeping on the side or on the stomach.

Surgical removal of enlarged tonsils, adenoids (AD uhn oydz), or nasal growths called polyps (PAHL ihps) may reduce snoring. Some medicines clear up a stuffy nose and reduce the amount of snoring. If someone else's snoring seriously interferes with your sleep, your remedy may have to be moving out of the room. A much less drastic measure would be to use earplugs.

Jot down a list of things that keep you from sleeping soundly, or that wake you up. How do you handle these problems? Do you consider yourself a "light sleeper" or a "sound sleeper"?

SELF CHECK

1. What are some of the effects of not getting enough sleep?

2. Describe REM sleep.

3. How do body functions change as a person progresses into the deepest stage of sleep?

4. How can dreams affect body functions?

5. Dreams consist of symbolic thoughts and feelings. How can knowing this help you interpret your own dreams?

6. What are some of the reasons people suffer from insomnia?

Chapter Summary

Although some animals can outperform people in specific ways, people have the greatest overall physical capabilities. Keeping fit means developing those capabilities to meet the physical and emotional demands of everyday life. People can choose the level of fitness they want to achieve. They can decide what kinds of physical activities they enjoy and can make up their own year-round fitness programs.

Physical activity as a part of everyday life is necessary for good health. Regular physical exertion strengthens bones, joints, and muscles. It improves the condition of the heart and blood vessels and increases the lungs' ability to take in oxygen and give off carbon dioxide. Maintaining desirable weight is easier when you combine regular physical activity and controlled diet. People under emotional tension find that physical activity lets them unwind.

Relaxation, rest, and sleep come naturally and easily to an active person. They are necessary for physical and emotional health. How much sleep to get is an individual matter. Lack of sleep affects people's behavior. It can make them irritable, accident-prone, and confused.

Sleep consists of cycles of four stages, each cycle going from lightest sleep to deepest sleep and back to lightest sleep. Each cycle takes about 90 minutes. The most vivid and detailed dreams occur during the first stage, in REM sleep. As sleep gets deeper vital body functions slow down. Anxieties and other tensions expressed in dreams can awaken sleepers or cause a flare-up of an existing illness.

Mental activity continues during sleep, and is often expressed in dreams. You can record and try to interpret your own dreams. Interpreting dreams means understanding them as symbols of your thoughts and feelings about yourself and other people. Dreams may represent wishes, fears, or, sometimes, solutions to problems you were trying to work out during the day.

Insomnia occurs when people either cannot fall asleep or wake up frequently during the night. It can result from illness, discomfort, excitement, worries, or noise. Occasional insomnia should not cause concern, but constant insomnia should be discussed with a doctor. Sleeping pills should be avoided unless prescribed by a doctor.

Chapter Self Check

1. How does keeping fit year-round contribute to enjoying life?

2. How would you decide on a level of fitness you'd like for yourself?

3. What factors should you consider when you choose physical activities?

4. What usually happens when an inactive person suddenly exercises vigorously?

5. What parts of the body benefit from regular activity? How?

6. What are the advantages of keeping fit through regular sports, games and other physical activities rather than through calisthenics?

7. How can keeping fit improve the way you look?

8. Why does weight control depend on both diet and regular activity?

9. What are some ways to protect yourself against serious injury during physical activity?

10. Why do coaches insist on warming-up exercises?

11. How can heat exhaustion or heat stroke be avoided?

12. About how many hours of sleep a night do you need?

13. What might make you need more sleep temporarily?

14. Why might you feel tired even after your usual number of hours of sleep?

15. What illnesses might become worse during sleep?

16. Some people believe that they "waste" about one-third of their lives sleeping. Do you agree or disagree?

17. How can interpreting your dreams teach you something about yourself?

18. Why is it difficult or impossible to interpret a dream of a stranger?

19. Why should sleeping pills be avoided unless prescribed by a doctor?

20. What causes snoring, and what can be done about it?

Read More About It

Benson, Herbert. *The Relaxation Response.* New York: William Morrow & Company, 1975. How the way we live affects our bodies and how people can relieve their tensions and prevent illnesses caused by stress. Discusses meditation techniques.

Faraday, Ann. *Dream Power.* New York: Coward, McCann & Geoghegan, Inc., 1972. Explains a number of techniques that are useful for dream interpretation.

Foulkes, David. *The Psychology of Sleep.* New York: Charles Scribner's Sons, 1966. A discussion of sleep research, the stages of sleep, and influences on dreams, including personality, environment, and daytime events.

Gregg, Walter H. *Physical Fitness Through Sports and Nutrition.* New York: Charles Scribner's Sons, 1975. How the body moves. Disciplining yourself and building self-confidence through a personal program of exercise and good nutrition.

Prudden, Bonnie. *Teenage Fitness.* New York: Harper & Row, 1965. How to ensure your own fitness one day at a time, with emphasis on making choices among enjoyable activities.

Royal Canadian Air Force. *Exercise Plans for Physical Fitness,* Revised Edition. New York: Simon & Schuster, Inc., 1962. An excellent method of attaining and maintaining fitness.

6
Eating

After completing the work in this chapter, you will be able to:

explain the differences between hunger and appetite.

identify five groups of nutrients in food and tell what their functions are.

explain how weight is related to Calorie intake.

tell what kinds of things you can learn about foods by reading package labels.

compare food values on the basis of unit prices.

Why Eat?

"I eat because I'm hungry."

But what does that answer mean? You want food when your stomach is empty. And when you see or smell a food you like, you probably want some. Most people eat for other reasons as well. Some eat when they are nervous or unhappy. Some automatically eat at certain times of the day, whether they are hungry or not.

Hunger is the body's physical need for food. Hunger results from changes in levels of certain chemicals in the body. The changes stimulate part of the brain, the hypothalamus, which senses the need for blood sugar by body cells. The hypothalamus turns on the feeling of hunger when the cells need sugar and turns it off when the cells have enough sugar. Muscle contractions of an empty stomach also produce feelings of hunger. And scientists have lately found that nerve impulses between the brain and the mouth and throat are also important in turning on feelings of hunger. No one knows how these factors combine.

Appetite is the psychological need to eat. Appetite and hunger can be discussed separately, even though they are as joined as mind and body. Our food preferences, eating habits, and past experiences affect our appetite. So do our moods. Appetite often wins over hunger in determining what people eat and when they eat.

Strong emotions and appetite work together, often with little or no relation to healthful eating. Some people lose their appetite when they are feeling down. Others overeat to try to make themselves feel better. Many people associate eating with feelings of companionship or social status. People who have little appetite for food sometimes have little appetite for life.

In extreme cases, people suffer from an illness called **anorexia nervosa** (an uh REHK see uh nur VOHS uh), in which people refuse to eat. People with this illness are extremely thin and nervous. They may have to receive hospital treatment to avoid starving themselves to death.

Eating habits are strong ones. Family customs and religious practices influence people's food preferences. Eating styles and diets vary according to nationality and ethnic background. But regardless of food preferences, everybody needs certain materials in food called **nutrients** (NOO tree uhnts). These are the components of food that the body needs to survive and stay healthy. The nutrient groups that human beings require are proteins, carbohydrates, fats, vitamins, and minerals.

Nutrients are provided by a great variety of foods and diets. Do you think you could rely entirely on your appetite to provide your body with nutrients? Probably not.

What Foods Do for Us

● **6-1 Investigating Your Eating Habits**

In this investigation, you are going to answer some questions that will help you understand what kind of eater you are. You may also get some ideas about how hunger and your appetite work together, and about the importance of food to you.

PROCEDURE

On a separate piece of paper list the numbers 1–8. Then read each of the following numbered questions. Next to the numbers on your paper, write the letter of the choice that best describes you, for each question. If you can't decide on a "best" choice, write the letters of all the choices that would accurately describe your eating habits.

1. What kinds of foods do you usually like to eat?
a. I eat most foods.
b. I pick at food.
c. I eat only my favorite foods.
d. I eat the same foods over and over.
e. I eat only a few foods.

2. In what form do most of your favorite foods come?
a. fresh
b. frozen
c. prepared at home
d. "natural" or "health" foods
e. prepared by a take-out service
f. snacks

3. What type of food do you like most?
a. fruits
b. vegetables
c. meats
d. seafood
e. milk, eggs, cheese
f. desserts or candy
g. cereals

4. What type of food do you like least?

a. fruits
b. vegetables
c. meats
d. seafood
e. milk, eggs, cheese
f. desserts or candy
g. cereals

5. What are you most likely to eat between meals?

a. fruit
b. potato chips
c. cookies or cake
d. raw vegetables
e. ice cream
f. nothing
g. other (describe)

6. When do you eat the most food?

a. on weekends
b. during vacations
c. on school days
d. on busy days
e. when upset
f. when hungry
g. when happy
h. when restless

7. When do you eat the most food during the day?

a. at breakfast
b. midmorning
c. at lunch
d. in the afternoon
e. at dinner
f. in the evening

8. In general, what kind of eater are you?

a. I usually rush through meals so I can do something else afterward.
b. I usually eat while watching television.
c. I usually talk a lot during meals and snacks.
d. I usually eat slowly.
e. When I'm with other people, I usually eat what they eat.
f. I usually eat regular meals every day.
g. I usually eat in order to do better in physical activities, such as games and sports.

DISCUSSION

1. Which would you say has the greatest effect on the kind of eater you are: appetite, hunger, or available food? Why?

2. What are some ways that your emotions affect the foods that you eat and when you eat?

After bad news, do you eat to feel better?

3. How do your family, friends, and other people affect what you eat and when you eat?

4. Why do you suppose food preferences differ so much among people?

5. What do you think "being a slave to one's appetite" means? Are you?

6. Can you trust your appetite to satisfy all your body's needs for food? Why or why not?

7. How important do you consider food to be? Why?

6-2 You Are What You Eat

Every cell in the body contains **proteins** (PROH teenz). Next to water, proteins are the most abundant substance in the body. They make up about 20 percent of body weight. Most of the body's protein is in muscles. Connective tissues, the walls of blood vessels, and the collagen threads that bind the mineral network of bones and teeth are also made of proteins.

Proteins are large, complex molecules built up of small units linked together in various patterns. The small units, or protein "building blocks," are **amino** (uh MEE noh) **acids.** Each amino acid contains oxygen, hydrogen, carbon, and nitrogen. Some have other chemicals, such as sulfur.

Digestive enzymes break down the proteins in food into their amino acids. The body's cells then must build the proteins they need from these building blocks. (The proteins in plants and animals we eat can't be used "as is" by people; the proteins have to be rebuilt.)

In order to grow and survive, people need 20 different amino acids. However, necessary amino acids are sometimes missing

Fattened for market, these cattle are a good source of protein, but contain a lot of fat.

from food. The body can make some missing amino acids from the others in food. Of the 20 amino acids that make up body proteins, the human body can make 12. These are called "non-essential" amino acids because we do not need to get them as is from food. The other 8 must come as is from food. These are therefore called "essential" amino acids. The essential amino acids must be provided in the diet.

The essential amino acids must be eaten in the right proportions. If there is not enough of one essential amino acid, the others cannot be used for building protein and tissue. The better the proportions of amino acids in a food, the more of its pro-

Fishing provides a good source of protein that is low in fat.

of amino acids. Combinations of food like grain and legumes provide what are called **complementary proteins,** which contain the right combination of amino acids. When you eat rice and beans or a peanut butter sandwich, you are eating complementary proteins. *Diet for a Small Planet,* listed in the "Read More About It" section at the end of this chapter, tells what foods provide complementary proteins.

Complementary proteins must be eaten at the same meal. The body does not store left-over amino acids from, say, breakfast toast, on the chance that you'll have pea soup for lunch. The amino acids that are not used are burned for energy.

Often people eat a small amount of high-quality protein with other foods to be sure they get enough protein. Combinations such as macaroni and cheese, fish and rice, and beef stew are good protein sources.

The daily need for protein varies. Body size, age, emotional stress, and physical condition are some factors that determine need for protein. Infants and young children generally have the greatest need for protein-rich diets. Not having enough protein, especially in early childhood, can cause stunted physical growth, mental retardation, and low resistance to infection and disease. People never outgrow their daily need. However, the need usually decreases as people grow older.

Minerals are inorganic substances (containing no carbon) that are also components of body tissue. The total mineral content of the body is only about five percent by weight, but without minerals the human body would not grow or work properly. For example, iron is a mineral in hemoglobin. And calcium and phosphorus are essential parts of bones and teeth.

Another inorganic substance that you might not think of as a nutrient is water. Without it none of the other chemicals in

tein the human body can use. That food contains high-quality protein. Eggs have the best proportions of amino acids for people. Fish, dairy products, and meat are also sources of high-quality protein.

Legumes (beans, peas, lentils) and nuts have plenty of some essential amino acids, but not much of others. Grains and seeds have the essential amino acids that legumes and nuts lack. So eating legumes and grains at the same meal gives a good combination

food would be of any use. The human body is about 55 percent water, most of it within the cells. Striated muscle tissue is about 80 percent water, but bone is less than 25 percent water. Blood and lymph are mostly water. Most of our water comes from the fluids we drink. But we also get water from many foods, particularly fruits and vegetables. People can live longer without food than without water. A loss of only 10 percent of the body's water can be fatal.

6-3 Where Do You Get All That Energy?

From food. But the energy in food had to come from somewhere too. Energy is never created or destroyed, only changed from one form to another. The energy in food comes from the sun. Plants take in energy (heat and light) from the sun. They use some of the energy and store the rest. When an animal eats a plant, it captures some of that stored energy. The animal uses some of it and stores the rest. When you eat a plant or animal, your body captures some of its stored energy. The body uses some and stores the rest, which allows you to keep going between meals, and even live for weeks without food if you have to.

The amount of energy in food is measured in **Calories.** One Calorie is the energy required to heat one kilogram (about a quart) of water one Celsius degree (about two Fahrenheit degrees). A Calorie is also called a kilocalorie. A **calorie,** spelled with a small c, is 1/1000 of a Calorie.

When you talk about the Calories in a hamburger or a pizza, you are talking about

If you don't have enough energy to get through the morning, try eating a good breakfast.

Pasta comes in many shapes and is fun to eat. Foods made from grain are a good source of carbohydrates and give you energy.

the amount of energy you can get from it. Fat has the most concentrated energy. Fat supplies about twice as many Calories as an equal amount of protein or carbohydrate. Vitamins, minerals, and water supply no Calories.

Starches and sugars are **carbohydrates** (kahr boh HY draytz), chemicals that contain only carbon, hydrogen, and oxygen. Grain-containing foods—including cereals, bread, cake, and pasta—and potatoes are rich in carbohydrates. So are candy and ice cream. In the digestive system, carbohydrates are broken down into simple sugars, such as glucose. After the body has used the amount of glucose it needs, some of the remaining glucose is stored in the liver as

glycogen. The muscles also store glycogen, as you learned in Chapter 3. Excess glucose is changed into fat and stored.

If a person does not eat enough carbohydrates, protein is used as fuel. The body may then not have enough protein available for tissue building. But eating too much carbohydrate, especially sugar, can cause fatness or tooth decay, or even contribute to diabetes. Also, a person who eats a lot of carbohydrates may not eat enough of the foods that supply protein, vitamins, and minerals.

Cellulose is a carbohydrate that the human body cannot digest. But we need cellulose as roughage to keep the intestines working well. A lack of cellulose can cause constipation. Some scientists think that diets low in roughage also make people prone to cancer of the colon. Cellulose is found in vegetables, fruits, and whole grains.

Fat is useful as a concentrated source of energy. It also serves other body needs. Fat under the skin helps keep body heat from escaping. And fat keeps the skin from becoming dry and flaky. Fat also carries some vitamins to all parts of the body. Butter, margarine, ice cream, salad dressings, tender steaks, animal fats, bacon, nuts, cheese, and cream are fatty foods. If you

are trying to lose weight, you should cut down the amount of these foods in your diet. Many North Americans get more than half of their Calories from fats, about twice as much as nutritionists suggest.

You have probably heard about saturated and unsaturated fats. Fat from warm-blooded animals is called **saturated fat**. It is solid at room temperature. Large quantities of saturated fat in the diet have been linked with diseases of the heart and blood vessels. Most vegetable and fish oils contain **unsaturated fats.** This kind of fat remains liquid at room temperature. The unsaturated fats

Spicy luncheon meats stacked high between crusty bread— a delicious sandwich, but high in saturated animal fat.

are believed to help reduce the amount of **cholesterol** (kuh LEHS tuh rawl) in the body. Cholesterol is a fatty substance produced by the body, as well as absorbed from food. Most doctors think that excess cholesterol in the blood forms harmful clumps deposited on the lining of artery walls. Eating fish instead of meat in some meals and cooking with vegetable oils rather than with animal fats usually reduces cholesterol levels in the body.

Do you wonder how many Calories you take in and how many you use every day? Appendix A lists the Calorie content of many popular foods. The Calories you use depend on your daily activities. People who burn up the Calories they take in are usually neither too fat nor too thin. Using the table below, try adding up the Calories you burn up in a day. Use Appendix A to figure out the foods that would supply those Calories.

The Calories you use also depend on your rate of metabolism (muh TAB uh lihz uhm). **Metabolism** refers to all the activities of body cells—breaking down foods, using energy, building tissue, and so on. Rate of metabolism varies from one person to another. The faster the rate of metabolism, the more Calories a person burns up.

AVERAGE CALORIE REQUIREMENTS OF ACTIVITIES

ACTIVITY	CALORIES/MINUTE
Sitting and reading	1.2
Working at a desk	2.2
Driving a car	2.4
Walking on level ground	3.6
Bowling	4.4
Swimming	5.0
Pushing a hand lawnmower	7.7
Chopping wood	8.0
Skiing	9.9
Playing handball	10.2

6-4 Regulating Body Functions

All of the vast number of body functions are regulated and coordinated with each other. Various nutrients are important in this process.

Vitamins and minerals control and direct some of the most important body functions. **Vitamins** do not build tissues or supply energy. But they help transform digested food into bones, muscles, skin, blood, nerves, and other tissues. Most vitamins must come from food because the body cannot manufacture them. Vitamin D is an exception. When the body is exposed to sunlight, vitamin D is produced in the skin.

Even mild vitamin deficiencies can cause many medical problems. Severe deficiencies can lead to blindness, crippling, or

If you are eating enough fruits and vegetables, you probably won't need vitamins from bottles.

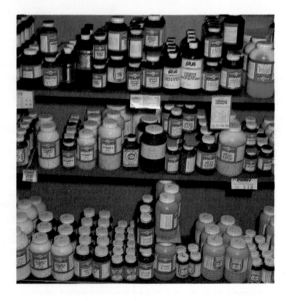

death. Information about vitamins is summarized in the table below.

On scanty evidence, some "authorities" and some manufacturers often publicize one vitamin or another as a cure-all. As a result, many people seem to have fallen in love with vitamins. They take vitamin pills to try to relieve pain, keep from looking older, have more energy, relieve baldness, and prevent heart attacks. Vitamins may relieve the symptoms of some illnesses. More likely, they act like a **placebo** (pluh SEE boh), a substance that has no proven effect but may be psychologically reassuring.

Taking large doses of vitamin pills over a long period of time, especially vitamins A, D, and K, can be hazardous. Most people who eat a variety of foods that are not processed or overcooked get all the vitamins they need in their diet. In special situations, doctors may prescribe vitamin pills.

Vitamin Needs

VITAMIN	SOURCES	FUNCTIONS	EFFECTS OF DEFICIENCY
A	liver, eggs, milk, cheese, green vegetables, carrots	aids growth of bones and soft tissues; helps eyes adapt to dim light; keeps skin and digestive organs healthy; aids in healing	*mild:* difficulty seeing at night; dry skin; increased likelihood of infection *severe:* serious eye diseases
B complex (a vitamin group)	liver, lean meat, dairy products, whole grains, legumes (much lost in cooking, especially at high temperatures and in water), nuts	aids in metabolism of proteins and carbohydrates; essential for functioning of cells (especially bone marrow), intestinal tract, nervous system	*mild:* skin and mouth ailments; anemia; general weakness; retarded growth; faulty digestion; ailments of nervous system *severe:* beriberi, pellagra, pernicious anemia
C	fresh fruits and vegetables, especially citrus fruits and tomatoes and leafy vegetables (destroyed by cooking)	maintains strength of blood vessels; important for metabolism of amino acids and development of teeth and connective tissue; large doses may prevent colds	*mild:* bruising easily; injuries heal slowly *severe:* scurvy (more needed when under stress)
D	enriched milk, eggs, fish-liver oil, made in the skin when exposed to sunlight	promotes growth and strength of bones and teeth; needed for efficient absorption of calcium from food	poor development of bones and teeth; rickets; softening of bones
E	vegetable oils, leafy vegetables, wheat germ, seeds	reduces use of oxygen by cells; may help recovery from some types of heart disease	anemia in infants; changes in make-up of blood
K	produced by bacteria in digestive system; green, leafy vegetables; liver	improves clotting ability of blood	bruising; hemorrhage

tain the body's disease resistance and to fight infections when they occur.

Minerals are another important group of nutrients that regulate body processes. Calcium, for example, besides helping to form bones and teeth, helps regulate heartbeat and is necessary for blood clotting. Iodine in the thyroid gland is part of a hormone that helps regulate rate of metabolism. Iron, a component of hemoglobin, has a vital role in carrying oxygen throughout the body. Facts about these and some other important minerals are summarized in the table on the next page. The body needs substantial amounts of at least 14 minerals. Traces of 40 or more are also necessary.

As with vitamins, many minerals go through periods of faddish popularity as cure-alls. But eating a varied diet that includes vegetables, meats, seafood, and dairy products should provide you with the minerals most scientists are fairly certain your body needs. Taking in extra minerals in pills or liquids may not be wise. An overdose of iron pills can be harmful. People with high blood pressure should restrict their sodium intake.

Like vitamins, water is an important body regulator. It helps control body temperature. Water dissolves materials and also bathes and lubricates body tissues. And within the cells, most chemical reactions take place in water.

Protein is a body-regulating substance also. It helps to maintain the proper movement of fluid into and out of the cells and to and from the bloodstream. Since proteins are too large to pass through cell membranes, some proteins—blood proteins—stay in the plasma. They prevent the accumulation of too much fluid in the body tissues. The body also needs proteins to form hormones, enzymes, and other important body chemicals. Protein is also needed to main-

SELF CHECK

1. What is the difference between hunger and appetite?

2. What are "essential" amino acids?

3. Name some foods that are rich in carbohydrates.

4. Describe the two main kinds of fats.

5. Name several vitamins, tell why the body needs them, and list some good food sources of them.

6. Name several minerals and describe their functions in the body.

Mineral Needs

MINERAL	SOURCES	FUNCTIONS	EFFECTS OF DEFICIENCY
calcium	milk, cheese, ice cream, leafy vegetables	helps form and maintain bones and teeth; helps regulate heartbeat, produce healthy muscular activity, maintain nerve tissue (children and adolescents need more than adults)	cramps; may be related to weak bones (absorption of calcium depends more on amount of vitamin D in diet than on amount of calcium)
fluoride	fish, meat, cheese, tea, fluoridated water	helps teeth resist decay; maintains strength and health of bones	tooth decay; softening of bones
iron	liver and other meats, eggs, whole-wheat bread, leafy vegetables, nuts, beans, prunes, dates, raisins, molasses	major part of hemoglobin; helps in process of replacing red blood cells (women need almost twice as much as men)	anemia, which causes general weakness
iodine	seafood, iodized salt, milk, vegetables	necessary for healthy functioning of thyroid gland	goiter (swelling of thyroid gland)
magnesium	whole grains, potatoes, vegetables, fruits, molasses	important for proper functioning of cells, enzymes, nerves, muscles	deficiency is rare but can cause cramps
phosphorus	milk and milk products, cereals, meat, fish	combines with calcium to form and maintain bones and teeth; a regulator of the heartbeat; works with B vitamins	may be related to weak bones
potassium	fruits, meat, milk	combines with other minerals to regulate cell metabolism; in balance with calcium and phosphorus, regulates heartbeat	general muscle weakness
sodium	table salt, bacon, ham, butter, monosodium glutamate, present in most prepared foods	helps regulate water content and cell metabolism; important for functioning of muscles and nerves	loss of sodium from profuse sweating may cause nausea and exhaustion
sulfur	protein, onions	part of proteins—needed for healthy skin, hair, nails, muscles, nerves	specific effects not known

Health Frontier

The World Food Crisis

The world's population is expected to double in the next 30 years. In many countries, food production has not kept up with the growth in population. Malnutrition is often most severe in cities, where unemployed people cannot afford nutritious food. The most serious kind of food shortage is an inadequate supply of protein. Millions of people all over the world are mentally and physically handicapped because they did not get enough protein when they were children.

The United States, Canada, and Australia grow so much grain that they export large amounts. But much of this food does not reach the people who need it most. And a few countries cannot feed the whole world forever. Farmers in the developing countries need to be able to grow more food. This does not mean changing from small family farms to large farms. Large, mechanized farms can produce more food for the amount of time people work on them. But a family with a small farm can grow more food per acre because they can give it more attention. Also, they need much less machinery and fuel.

Scientists are developing better varieties of food crops: plants that produce more grains, are resistant to insects and diseases, and are not knocked down by heavy rain. It is important also to help farmers get better tools and learn more efficient techniques. People are even starting to "farm" the ocean to grow fish and even seaweed as protein sources.

As people's economic positions improve, they tend to eat more meat. This means that in highly developed countries, grain that could feed people is fed to animals. To produce one pound (about 0.4 kilogram) of beef, a steer must eat 16 pounds (about seven kilograms) of grain and soy. So the more meat people eat, the more grain they are using. If everyone ate more grain and less meat, there would be more grain available as food to people in less advantaged countries.

Personal Eating Habits

6-5 **Weight Worries**

Ideal weight depends upon age, sex, body build, height, and amount of regular physical activity. Notions about ideal weight have varied from one society to another and from generation to generation. Sometimes fat has been "in," sometimes thin is "in." Insurance companies define ideal weight as that at which you are likely to live longest. If you are at your ideal weight you look, feel, and act your best.

Being overweight affects appearance and threatens health. Too much accumulated fat represents the beginning of health problems that can continue throughout life. Diseases of the heart and blood vessels, diabetes, high blood pressure, and kidney ailments are among the serious health problems associated with **obesity**—weight that exceeds the desirable amount by more than 15 or 20 percent.

Tension, worry, anxiety, and depression make some people overeat. Then, being too heavy makes them feel worse about themselves so they eat still more. Often, troubled people know why they overeat but cannot control themselves. Whatever the causes of being overweight, regular physical activity and a diet that meets body needs are the best ways of reducing. Crash diets, fad diets, and reducing medicines are shortcuts to proper weight that usually don't work or work only temporarily, and may be dangerous to your health.

Being underweight could be a temporary condition caused by rapid growth during youth. And of course some people are naturally thin or slender. If you have enough energy for what you enjoy doing and are not much more than about ten percent below an insurance company table of ideal weight for your height and age, you don't have a health problem. But fatigue, irritability, and weakness—combined with being underweight—indicate a health problem. People who suffer from those symptoms should get medical help.

Maintaining ideal weight depends partly on the rate of metabolism. Measuring this rate in a resting body is a test of **basal metabolism.** Basal metabolic rate is the minimum rate at which the body uses energy for essential life processes. The rate varies from one person to the next. Some people have abnormally high or low rates and may be underweight or overweight as a result. They can often be helped with medication. Maintaining ideal weight depends on what you eat, your activities, and your metabolism.

Some diet pills contain ingredients that swell up in the stomach and make a person feel full without eating. The danger is that the person won't eat the necessary daily nutrients.

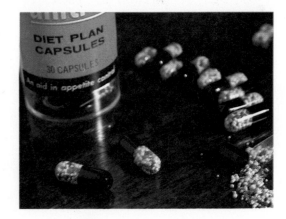

The Joy
of Eating

● 6-6 **Adventures in Gastronomy**

Gastronomy (gas TRAHN oh mee) is the art of "good eating." Are you ever bored with the foods you usually eat? Do you occasionally crave totally new foods, or do you prefer sticking to familiar ones? "Good eaters" choose their food for the pleasure of eating, as well as for nutritional value.

In this activity you are going to explore some of your reasons for trying or not trying certain foods.

PROCEDURE

1. Copy this table on a piece of paper.

FOODS I HAVE EATEN		FOODS I HAVE NOT EATEN
Like	*Dislike*	

Copy This Table on a Piece of Paper

2. Write in your table under "Like" or "Dislike" the names of the foods listed below that you have eaten. Under each food in your table briefly write what you like or don't like about each of these foods, such as color, smell, texture, or taste.

blood pudding	kidney pie
corn fritters	lentils
crickets	mussels
eel	rhubarb
fatback	raccoon stew
fried bananas	roasted soy beans
frogs' legs	succotash

grits	tapioca pudding
ham hocks	turtle soup
kale	yogurt

chili con carne (red peppers, meat, and usually beans)
chitlins (hog's intestines)
gefilte fish (fish balls made of fish, bread crumbs, eggs, and seasoning)
egg foo yung (a sort of omelet made with eggs, vegetables, and meat or fish)
tripe (cow's stomach lining)
venison (deer meat)

3. Write in your table under "Foods I Have Not Eaten" the names of the above listed foods that you have *not* eaten. Next to each, write the letter of the sentence below that most closely describes your reaction to the food.

a. I would like to try it.
b. I might like to try it.
c. I would probably not try it.
d. I would definitely not try it, under any conditions.

Under each food in this column briefly write the reasons for each of your reactions. For example, the color, smell, or texture you believe the food has might be a reason.

DISCUSSION

1. Did you and your classmates have similar reactions to many of the unfamiliar foods in the list? Which foods did most people have favorable ("a" and "b") reactions to? Unfavorable ("c" and "d") reactions to?

2. What were the most common reasons given for favorable reactions? For unfavorable reactions?

3. Do you think that some foods in the list might be more familiar to people your age in another part of the country?

Does the idea of eating cactus, seaweed, or squid interest you, revolt you, or simply remind you of a common dish at your house?

4. How does belonging to a different cultural, national, racial, or religious group affect a person's reactions to certain foods? Why do you think so?

5. People's eating habits can sometimes be compared with other aspects of their behavior. Do you notice any similarities between how much you enjoy eating and how much you are interested in other experiences? How do you think your eating habits reflect your personality?

SELF CHECK

1. What are some health hazards of being overweight?

2. What is the best plan for losing weight?

3. What are some reasons for trying out unusual foods?

Few people live this close to a farm. That's why most people depend on processed foods.

Selecting and Caring for Food

6-7 Processed and "Natural" Foods

Almost all the food in a supermarket has been **processed** to some extent. Very little food reaches your table without going through a factory where it is washed, trimmed, combined with other ingredients, cooked, frozen, packaged, canned, or processed in some other ways. Even something as simple as salt usually comes with chemicals added to prevent caking and provide iodine. Fresh fruits and vegetables are often sprayed to keep them from spoiling. As a result of modern food technology, we can buy a great variety of foods from many regions and countries, regardless of the season of the year. We can buy foods that don't spoil quickly and that are packaged in convenient amounts. And we can buy foods—even entire meals—that have been pre-cooked and only need to be heated up before eating.

All of this variety and convenience sometimes has a steep price. The high heat that may be used in canning or precooking foods destroys some vitamins. Some of the taste and texture of fresh foods are also lost in the factory. That problem is sometimes worsened when varieties of foods are grown not for taste but for ease of processing. For example, tough-skinned varieties of tomatoes have been developed for easy machine picking, but they have less flavor than regular tomatoes.

The biggest problem with modern food technology—the one you hear about so often—concerns chemical **additives.** The average American and Canadian consumes over five pounds (about two and one-half kilograms) of food additives each year. Additives are added to food to prevent spoilage and to improve color, flavor, nutrition, or other food characteristics. So, for example, dry breakfast cereals usually come labeled "BHA and BHT added to reduce spoilage." (BHA and BHT stand for the chemical names.) Oranges are dyed a uniform orange color. Cereals and milk usually come with vitamin additives. And hams

Chemicals make it possible to grow more food, but you end up eating some of the chemicals.

MAKES FOUR 6 FL. OZ. SERVINGS

INGREDIENTS: SPRAY DRIED VEGETABLE FAT, MODIFIED FOOD STARCH, DRIED CORN SYRUP, NATURAL FLAVORS, SALT, WHEY SOLIDS, MONOSODIUM GLUTAMATE (FLAVOR ENHANCER), DEHYDRATED CHICKEN, NONFAT MILK SOLIDS, VEGETABLE GUM, DEHYDRATED ONIONS, BUTTERMILK SOLIDS, DEHYDRATED PARSLEY, OLEORESIN TURMERIC, DISODIUM INOSINATE AND DISODIUM GUANYLATE (FLAVOR ENHANCERS).

These are the ingredients of a typical convenience food, instant chicken soup.

often have meat tenderizers as well as water injected into them. Even meats that are not injected or treated in a processing plant may contain high amounts of certain chemicals and hormones that were fed to the animals while they were alive. In all, over a thousand chemicals are added to our foods.

Additive manufacturers are supposed to test new additives and get government approval before using them. Many of the common additives have been in use for a long time and are generally regarded as safe. But every month, it seems, one of the common additives is found to cause cancer, birth defects, or other health problems in laboratory animals. After such a discovery a long debate often occurs between government officials and manufacturers as to what the test results mean for humans and what should be done. Some questionable additives are left on the market; some end up being banned. (Sodium nitrite, for example, is banned in many European countries. And the World Health Organization has stated that nitrites should not be added to baby foods. But 70 percent of the pork processed in the United States is treated with nitrites to prevent the growth of dangerous bacteria, as well as to make the meat reddish.) Many foods still on the market contain additives that have not been adequately tested or that have questionable safety.

The "natural foods" movement grew out of concern over the problems of highly processed food and also out of concern over how foods are grown. So-called natural or organic foods are supposedly grown without pesticides and "artificial fertilizers" and have no additives. Since "organic farming" (growing foods "naturally") is done without pesticides, it doesn't pollute the environment, and the crops do not contain poisons. The composts, manures, and other natural fertilizers also have more valuable minerals than the "artificial fertilizers" made from petroleum. People who favor foods grown in this way and sold without much processing say that the foods are more nutritious. They point out that whole-wheat flour, for example, has more vitamins than unenriched white flour, which has had these and other nutrients removed for better keeping.

"Natural foods," "artificial fertilizers," and "organic farmers" are phrases that have more emotional value than accuracy attached to them. But the issue of producing pure, healthy foods by one method or

Have you tried gardening? People garden for fun, to save money, or to limit the chemicals added to their food.

another is important. Unfortunately, the "organic farming" methods don't seem suited to large-scale agriculture—at least not yet. Nor are most food processors and consumers ready to turn away from highly processed convenience foods. "Natural foods" are usually much more expensive than others. They are harder to find, and in many cases they are not necessarily better. Farm land that has had pesticides in the past, for example, may still contain these poisons even though a new owner doesn't use them. And no government agencies check how organic foods are actually grown or processed.

What can you do to reduce your intake of possibly dangerous additives? One thing would be eat fewer convenience foods— those that are precooked and frozen, canned, or dried. There are more additives in convenience foods than in fresh foods. Fresh foods are usually better tasting, more nutritious, and less expensive. Another thing you can do is read food labels carefully. Whenever possible, you can buy additive-free versions of the food you are interested in.

Frequently, the foods that have the most additives have names that give them away. For example, something called "cream-style, celery-flavored soup" will usually have many more artificial ingredients than "cream of celery soup." "Non-dairy whipped toppings" and "coffee lighteners" have more additives than cream or milk do. "Enriched" foods usually have some nutrients added to ingredients because some of their original nutrients were processed out. "Imitation-flavored" and "artificially colored" foods and drinks may contain questionable additives. The point is not that all additives are bad—they aren't. But until there are only safe additives in food, it is sensible to avoid eating them as much as you reasonably can.

● 6-8 Investigating Food Shopping

In this investigation you are going to compare different forms of a particular food and decide the forms that are most nutritious and the best buy. Other people in the class will investigate other foods. The information you gather may be useful when you next shop for food.

When you buy food, there are many factors to take into account. The most convenient food may not taste best. More nutritious food is often more work to prepare. You have to decide what is most important to you.

You can compare nutrients in packaged foods by reading the labels. The ingredients are listed in order of quantity in the food. In "vegetable-beef soup," for example, the first ingredient may be water, and beef may be sixth or seventh. Chemical additives are included in the list of ingredients. Cheaper brands of similar foods will sometimes have less of the desirable ingredients than the more expensive brand has.

Many stores now provide unit pricing information. The unit price is the price per pound, or liter, or another convenient unit. Canned peaches, for example, may be available in several different sizes. The unit price label on the shelf tells the price per pound for each size can, so you can tell which size is cheapest per unit. Of course, you may not want to buy the cheapest— maybe the can is too big for your family, or maybe the brand does not taste as good as another. But the unit price information is there to help you make the decision.

MATERIALS

labels from empty food cans, containers, or packages (with all the printed information)

Which of these items seems to be the best buy?

unit pricing information (from food stores: printed, or copied from postings on shelves)

PROCEDURE

1. The class will be divided into seven groups, one for each of the following categories of food: fruits, vegetables, meat or fish, dairy products, desserts, baked goods, and cereals.

2. Each group will choose one food category to investigate. Choose a food that comes in several of these forms: fresh, frozen (plain or with other ingredients), canned or packaged, natural or organically grown, and snack food. You do not have to use all the forms. One person will investigate each form.

3. Get labels and unit pricing information for the particular food you are surveying.

Find out the price of your food. If it is available in different size containers, compare the unit prices of several different sizes.

4. From the label of the food, copy the following information:

a. the ingredients in the order in which they appear on the label
b. the nutritional information, including the amount of each nutrient
c. the percentage of each of the U.S. Recommended Daily Allowances

For information about the nutrients in fresh fruits, vegetables, and meat or fish, you might look in a book about nutrition. Several books are listed in the "Read More About It" section at the end of this chapter. This type of information is sometimes given in cookbooks, too. If you need help locating the information, you can consult the dietician or librarian in your school. If you do not know what some of the ingredients or nutrients are, look them up or ask someone about them.

5. Meet with the other members of your group who have investigated a different form of the same food. Make a table of the ingredients, nutrients, and unit prices. Choose one person from the group to report to the class.

DISCUSSION

1. Which of the food categories are generally nutritious (high in nutrients)? Which forms of those foods are most nutritious? Are the foods enriched or naturally nutritious?

2. Which of the food categories are generally not nutritious? Why would you eat foods in these categories?

3. Which food forms have the most chemical additives? For what purposes are most of them added?

4. Considering all the information collected by the class, which foods do you think are the best buys? Are the best buys the least expensive?

6-9 Protecting Food

After food is bought at the store or picked from the garden, it must be treated properly to keep it fresh. Most fruits and vegetables should be refrigerated or eaten within a few days. Unripe fruit can be left at room temperature until it ripens. Fruits and vegetables should be washed thoroughly before they are eaten. They may be contaminated by poisonous chemicals used to control insects or by human and other animal wastes that have seeped into the ground.

Meat, fish, egg products, and milk must be kept cold. The trip from store to home should be as quick as possible, especially in warm weather. Bacteria that destroy food live and multiply at room temperature. Bacteria, yeasts, and molds from the air thrive in warm liquids and moist foods. Even pasteurized milk will turn sour if it is left in a warm place for several hours. You cannot tell from the odor or taste whether sour milk will simply cause a digestive upset or will make you more seriously ill. The label on a container of pasteurized milk usually advises you to keep it cold and to use it within one week.

Many food suppliers put dates on packages of food that spoil easily. You will find dates on products such as meats, poultry, baked goods, and dairy items. The date usually tells you the last day on which the food may be sold. It may also be the last

Check dates to be sure that products will be fresh when you plan to use them.

day the food is safe to eat. Canned goods can also have dates on them, but the dates may be in code. You can ask what the code means.

Home canning of food, if done improperly, can lead to a dangerous disease called **botulism** (BAHCH oo lihz uhm). Even a tiny amount of infected food can kill a person. The bacterium that causes botulism grows in most foods, except those that are very acid, such as tomatoes. Commercially canned food has almost always been cooked under pressure to kill botulism-causing bacteria, but once in a while a batch is not heated enough. To be safe, it is wise to boil canned vegetables and meat before eating them. Botulism cannot be detected from the appearance or smell of food.

Other types of spoilage in food are more obvious. The contents of any can that bulges or gives off a gas when it is opened

should be thrown away. Don't taste it. Any food that has a strange odor or taste, or a moldy appearance, should be thrown away.

Meat and fish sometimes contain eggs of worms that can cause painful diseases. It is safest not to eat raw meat or fish unless you know it has been inspected. Pork should always be cooked until the inside of the meat reaches at least 137°F (about 58°C). At this temperature some of the meat is still pink.

Vitamins can be lost or destroyed if food is overcooked. Vegetables should be cooked in only a very small amount of water; the water can then be used again in cooking or in soup. Never add baking soda to vegetables; it keeps their colors bright but destroys vitamins. Fruits and vegetables keep their vitamins best when they are refrigerated or frozen. Food exposed to sunlight loses some of its vitamins.

Home canning has grown more popular in the last few years as food prices have risen.

● 6-10 What's to Eat?

Instead of asking someone else, "What's to eat?" imagine that you are going to plan and prepare a meal yourself. What would you serve your family or perhaps a few friends? What factors should you consider in determining the foods you would serve?

PROCEDURE

1. On the basis of what you consider important in eating, list the foods you would include in the main meal of the day for your family or a few friends.

2. Next to each food in your list, tell why you would choose it.

DISCUSSION

1. Which foods did you include for protein, carbohydrates, vitamins, and minerals?

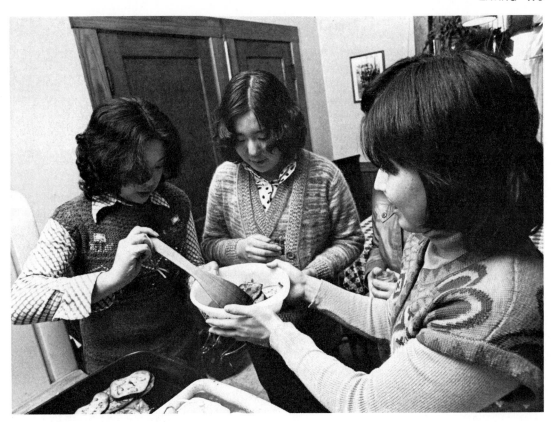

2. Were the foods you chose fresh or processed?

3. Did you consider the color, smell, and taste of food in planning an appealing meal?

4. Did you keep people's food preferences in mind? If so, how did this affect your choices?

5. Did you include an interesting dish that your family or friends may not have eaten before? What influenced your decision?

6. Are there any less expensive substitutes that you could have included in your meal, without sacrificing nutrition or appeal?

7. What are some alternatives for each food in your meal? Would the alternatives be as nutritious? Do you think some of the alternatives would make just as appealing a meal? Why or why not?

SELF CHECK

1. Why is some food processing necessary?

2. What are some of the reasons chemicals are added to food?

3. Is it always necessary to buy foods that contain additives?

4. What are some factors that make particular foods expensive?

5. How should fresh foods be protected?

6. How can botulism be avoided?

Chapter Summary

People eat because they are hungry. They eat specific types of food because they have an appetite. Hunger results from the stimulation of the nervous system by changes in the levels of certain chemicals in the body, by muscular contractions of an empty stomach, and nerve impulses between the brain and the mouth and throat. Appetite is influenced by emotional experiences, beginning in infancy and continuing throughout life, and by cultural, national, and racial background.

Proteins and minerals are necessary for growth. Proteins are built up of amino acids, which contain oxygen, hydrogen, carbon, and nitrogen. The body can make only 14 of the necessary 22 amino acids from other amino acids in food. The other 8 necessary amino acids must come as is from the daily diet. Meats supply these 8 essential amino acids. So do the right combinations of plant foods.

Minerals are needed for the growth and maintenance of bones and teeth and for the formation of hemoglobin. Water, like minerals, is a vital inorganic substance. It makes up about 55 percent of the body weight.

Calories are a measure of the energy in food. Fat has the most energy stored in concentrated form. Proteins and carbohydrates also supply energy. Vitamins, minerals, and water have no Calories. Carbohydrates supply the body's needs for sugar. Eating too much carbohydrate-rich and fat-rich food causes overweight.

Eating too little causes underweight, because the body then uses protein for fuel instead of for growth and maintenance.

Some fat is necessary to retain heat and to carry vitamins throughout the body. Unsaturated fats from vegetables and fish oils should be used instead of saturated (animal) fats whenever possible. Saturated fats have been linked with diseases of the heart and blood vessels.

Ideal weight is related to both diet and amount of regular physical activity. Many diseases of the heart and blood vessels, diabetes, and kidney ailments are associated with overweight. Some people overeat because of their emotional problems. Underweight also may be linked with feelings. An underweight person may be in good physical health, but weight loss without apparent reason indicates a health problem.

Vitamins and minerals regulate some important body functions. A balanced diet contains all the necessary vitamins and minerals. People with health problems may be advised by a doctor to take a vitamin or mineral supplement.

Consumers need to know about food processing as well as nutrients. Some additives are necessary to preserve food. Others may be harmful to health. Shoppers can find out about additives by reading labels carefully. One way to find out the true cost of food is to read the unit price labels on store shelves.

Chapter Self Check

1. How do the nervous system and chemicals in the blood affect hunger?

2. Describe some influences of emotions on appetite.

3. Why is appetite alone usually not a reliable guide to nutritious foods?

4. Why does the body need a supply of protein?

5. What percent of the body's weight is made up of protein?

6. Name some foods that are sources of high-quality protein.

7. Why must complementary proteins be eaten at the same meal?

8. What are some factors that determine people's daily need for protein?

9. What parts of the body are affected by minerals in the diet?

10. Define the Calorie.

11. Which nutrient provides the greatest amount of energy: fat, protein, or carbohydrate?

12. How many Calories are contained in one of your favorite meals?

13. Name some necessary nutrients that do not supply energy.

14. Why does everyone need some stored fat?

15. What are the health disadvantages of saturated fats?

16. What is the most effective way of maintaining ideal weight?

17. What is the relationship between metabolism and weight?

18. What vitamins may be lacking in people having the following health problems: (a) dry skin; (b) anemia; (c) slowly healing wounds; (d) scurvy; (e) rickets?

19. Explain why the following minerals are needed by the body: (a) calcium; (b) fluorine; (c) iron; (d) magnesium; (e) sodium.

20. How would your eating habits be affected if no foods were processed?

21. Does the government protect consumers against harmful additives?

22. What are "natural foods"?

23. How can you avoid food additives?

24. What precautions should be taken in home canning?

25. How do eating habits affect the world's food supply?

Read More About It

Ashley, Richard, and Duggal, Heidi. *Dictionary of Nutrition.* New York: St. Martin's Press, Inc., 1975. A concise, useful reference of basic nutritional information. Gives composition and nutrient values of over 400 foods and discusses factors such as food processing, preservatives, and pesticides.

Hériteau, Jacqueline. *Small Fruit and Vegetable Gardens.* New York: Popular Library, 1975. How to grow foods you like in a small yard or in a window box. Includes soil preparation and food preservation.

Jacobson, Michael, and Lersa, Catherine (editors). *Food for People, Not for Profit.* New York: Ballantine Books, 1975. Nutrition, food production, why food costs so much, and the importance of knowing how the food industry works.

Lappé, Frances Moore. *Diet for a Small Planet,* Revised Edition. New York: Ballantine Books, 1975. Reliance on more non-meat foods, both as a healthful way of eating and as a significant means of increasing the world's food supply. Includes a detailed explanation of complementary proteins.

Margolius, Sidney. *Health Foods: Facts and Fakes.* New York: Walker & Company, 1973. Natural and organic foods, nutrients, and additives. Discusses health fads and the protective responsibilities of governmental agencies.

Recommended Dietary Allowances, Eighth Edition. Washington, D.C.: National Academy of Sciences, 1974. A summary of nutritional recommendations and how they were established.

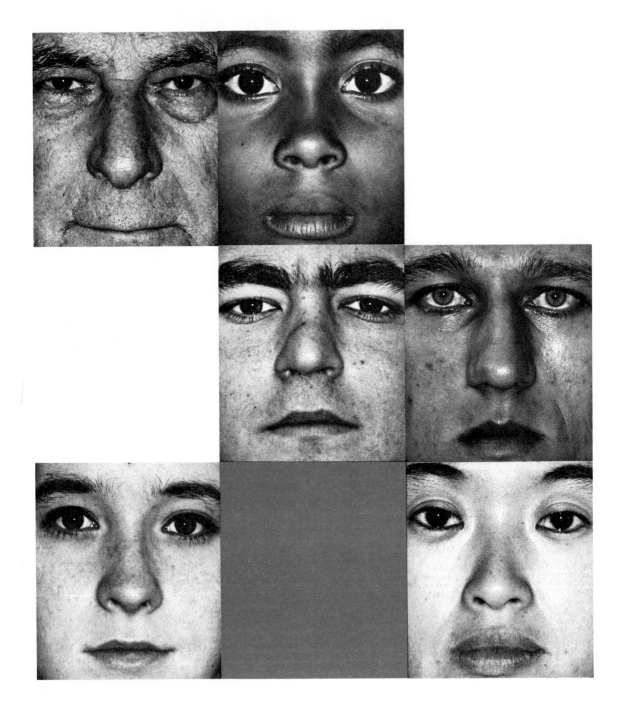

7
Looking the
Way You Want

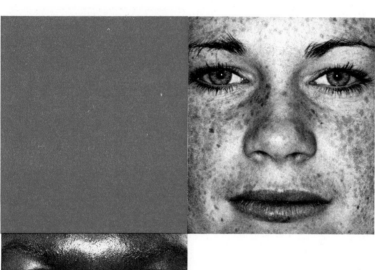

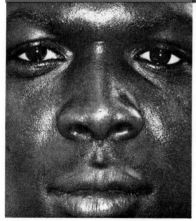

After completing the work in this chapter, you will be able to:

describe common skin problems and what can be done about them.

explain the precautions that should be taken when using cosmetics.

describe proper care of hair, nails, teeth, and gums.

explain several factors that affect appearance.

177

Impressions

"Hello."

"Could I speak to Linda Roth, please?"

"Yes, I'm Linda. . . . Who's this?"

"I'm Gary Wolfe. I'm new in school here and, uh, Phil Carver gave me your name and number and so I thought I'd just call and see if you wanted to go to Sara Roberts' party with me Saturday night."

Linda wonders what the owner of this uneasy voice coming over the telephone is like. How can she tell whether she wants to go out with him? She often tries to imagine what a person looks like on the basis of a voice. About half the time, she comes close. Sometimes, she finds she is wrong about everything—age, size, personality, and appearance.

Linda pauses before answering, thinking, *I probably have the Saturday night shift at work this weekend.* "I don't know if I'm busy Saturday night or not," she replies. "Or whether I want to go out with you." *He sounds so nervous. I wonder if he's the guy who was such a show-off at Lisa's party last week.*

"If you've got another date, just say so. Maybe we can get together another time," Gary says. But he is thinking how nice she looked when Phil pointed her out in the cafeteria. *Beautiful, long hair, skinny, smooth skin, and no makeup. Just my type.*

Before he hangs up, I'd love to find out what he looks like, she thinks. *I can always switch with someone and work Sunday morning instead of Saturday night. I wonder if he's Phil's handsome friend with the mustache.* Then she blurts out, "Do you have a mustache?"

"No, but I can grow one by Saturday night if you want me to."

She laughs. *He's not the tall blond. I hope he's not the one with the greasy hair or the one with bad acne.*

"Don't worry about what I look like, Linda. I'm perfect, six foot eight, three hundred pounds."

"You're funny, Gary."

"Thanks." They both laugh.

Linda pauses and says, "Okay, Gary. I'd like to go to the party with you. I'll switch and work Sunday morning instead of Saturday night. Thanks for inviting me."

She says yes because she is willing to take a chance on meeting someone new.

Taking Care of Your Skin

7-1 What Do You Look Like?

If someone you called for a date asked you to describe yourself, how would you begin? By describing your facial features? The clothes you're wearing? Your height and weight? Or your personality? Stop and think about your overall appearance. How do you picture yourself? What do you like about the way you look and what would you like to change?

We all have two mental pictures of ourselves: the way we think we look and the way we'd like to look. When there is a big difference between those pictures, people go on diets, change their hairstyles, buy new clothes, get expensive medical and dental treatments, and try other ways to change their appearance. We spend a lot of money and effort to look "sophisticated," or "natural," or to project some other image of ourselves. Just about everyone wants to make a certain impression, depending on the situation.

Health has a greater effect on appearance than external things, such as clothes, makeup, and hairstyle. Skin, hair, teeth, nails, eyes, and the way you move and act are all influenced by your physical and emotional health. That is why people can tell a lot about your health just by looking at you. Firm skin, for example, indicates a nutritious diet and regular exercise. This is true despite occasional skin blemishes. Your emotions show too. People can tell if you are happy, worried, or angry. If you don't take care of your health, you can only fake good looks.

Although the rest of this chapter emphasizes specific ways to take care of your appearance, keep this in mind: What you look like depends not only on your health and on how you feel, but also on who's doing the looking. Everyone has a different idea of what's attractive.

Some people's favorite pastime is people-watching. How much can you tell about people from their appearance?

7-2 When Is Your Appearance Important?

Some aspects of your appearance may be important to you most of the time. Others may only be important to you in certain situations. For example, are you concerned about how your hair looks at the beach? At a dance?

PROCEDURE

On a separate piece of paper, list these aspects of appearance, one to a line: height, weight, body build, posture, hair, clothes, facial expression, teeth, makeup (if you use any), and cleanliness. Imagine yourself in each of the situations listed below. Write the letter of each situation next to those aspects of your appearance that you would consider important in that situation. (So, if the appearance of your hair matters to you at a dance, your paper will have "*hair* A.") You may use any letter as many times as you want.

A. attending a dance
B. meeting someone your age for the first time
C. performing alone in front of a large audience of students and teachers
D. watching a school football game
E. going to a movie with a few friends
F. taking a shower after physical education class

G. going to a doctor's office
H. being with a friend of the opposite sex
I. being with a friend of the same sex
J. being interviewed for a job as a store clerk
K. meeting the parents of someone you like
L. working as a grocery-store clerk
M. playing soccer

In which two situations are the most aspects of your appearance important to you? Why do you think this is so?

7-3 Skin Imperfections

Rosa Medeiro always dresses so that most of her neck is covered. She usually wears a brightly colored scarf or a turtleneck. Most people think this is just Rosa's style. But her close friends know that she dresses this way to cover up a light-colored blotch on her neck. They hardly ever think about it, but Rosa does. It's only a small blemish, but she's afraid that if she didn't keep it covered, everyone would stare at her.

The white spot on Rosa's neck is **vitiligo** (viht uhl EYE goh), a condition in which certain areas of the skin don't have normal pigment. Doctors do not know what causes it, but they believe that, in many cases, people inherit the tendency to have vitiligo. This irregularity in skin coloration is not harmful to health. Vitiligo is a problem only if people are self-conscious about it. However, the light areas don't suntan and are easily burned.

Unlike vitiligo, **freckles** are spots of skin that have more than the usual amount of pigment. Most people who have freckles have them on their hands, arms, and face. Sunlight often causes freckles to become more numerous and larger. Like vitiligo, freckling is usually an inherited trait. It is

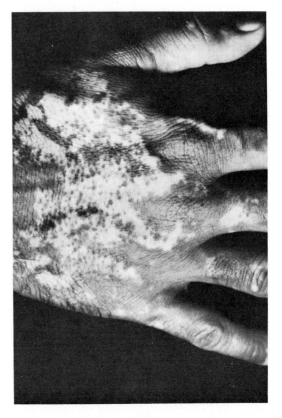

If you have patches of vitiligo, cover them or put on suntan lotion before going out for a day in the sun.

also neither the cause nor the result of illness. In most cases, freckles tend to fade as people grow older.

Other irregularities in skin coloration that are usually harmless but can cause embarrassment or annoyance are moles and birthmarks. **Moles** are small, pigmented spots. Sometimes the spots are raised or have hair growing from them. Some moles, particularly ones that receive constant irritation, may become cancerous. The cancer cells may grow into surrounding tissues or spread to other parts of the body through the bloodstream or lymphatic vessels. Don't scrape a mole or pull hairs from it. If a mole begins to grow rapidly, bleed, change color, or change in any other way, go to a doctor. The doctor can tell whether the mole may be harmful to your health. If necessary, it can be removed.

Birthmarks are abnormal networks of capillaries that are sometimes combined with rough, bumpy, or raised epidermis. Birthmarks often disappear in childhood without medical treatment. They rarely become cancerous and seldom become infected. You should not pick or rub birthmarks or other skin blemishes. If they cause too much embarrassment or become infected, a doctor can surgically remove them or treat them in other ways. Remember that nobody's skin is perfect. Don't worry if your skin has any of these imperfections. They are usually harmless and simply add to the differences between people.

7-4 Skin Problems

Some skin conditions, such as acne and blackheads, mostly affect just people your age. With the sudden increase in the production of sex hormones, the production of sebum also increases. Sebum is the oil produced by sebaceous glands in the skin. If the opening of a sebaceous gland becomes clogged or the sebum becomes thick, a pimple or blackhead forms. An **acne pimple** is an infection caused by bacteria in a sebaceous gland. A **blackhead** is a plug of oil and epidermal cells. The blackness results more from chemical changes in the sebum than from dirt. Infected blackheads and acne pimples often occur at the same time.

Many people your age have little trouble with these conditions. Others have a lot. This difference may result from differences in heredity, diet, and cleanliness, as well as hormone production. Emotional upsets and

not getting enough rest and exercise are believed to make acne problems worse.

Squeezing or scraping acne pimples and blackheads can spread infection and cause scars and pits. To remove a blackhead, first thoroughly wash the affected area with warm water and soap. Then press a clean, hot, wet towel or washcloth against the skin for a few minutes several times. In this way, the blackhead may soften enough so that it can easily be removed by gently pressing against the edge of the pore. If that doesn't work, do not try to force it out with your fingers or fingernails. Wait and repeat the procedure another time. If a pimple opens by itself, carefully wash around it with warm water and plain soap. Pat the skin dry and gently apply a small amount of alcohol to clean the skin around the sore.

Keeping the skin clean will usually effectively control acne. Use your own clean washcloth—never anyone else's—and wash twice a day with warm water and plain soap. Afterward rinse with cold water and gently pat the skin dry. If you have oily skin, try to wash your face, neck, chest, and back two or three times a day. The Federal Trade Commission of the United States has determined that *none* of the over-the-counter remedies currently sold to cure acne will do so.

Severe acne may need treatment by a **dermatologist** (dur muh TAHL uh jihst), a medical doctor who specializes in treating skin ailments. The dermatologist may prescribe medication that can hide the sores and help heal them. Sometimes the dermatologist may treat acne with ultraviolet light. A dermatologist can remove badly scarred epidermis with a high-speed brush. This is called "skin planing." It is minor surgery and should not be done by a beauty-shop operator or other non-medically trained person. After skin planing, new skin will replace the scarred or pitted epidermis.

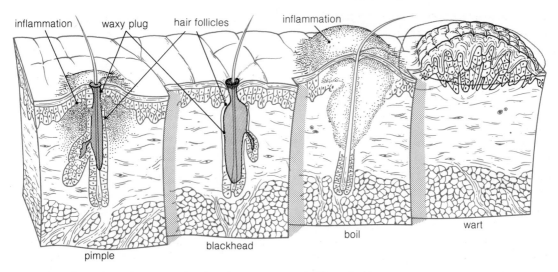

inflammation   waxy plug   hair follicles   inflammation

pimple

blackhead

boil

wart

A cross section of skin showing the structure of different skin problems and blemishes.

Although doctors disagree about the effect of diet on acne, high-fat foods, such as fried foods, chocolate, and ice cream, increase the activity of the sebaceous glands. Avoiding these foods helps most people control acne. Eat nutritious foods, including plenty of fruits and vegetables, and drink plenty of milk. Exercise regularly and get enough rest and relaxation. If you use cosmetics, use only non-oily ones. Apply them lightly and remove them thoroughly at night.

Basically, however, acne is incurable. The best you can do is keep it from getting worse. Having acne doesn't necessarily mean you are not washing well and eating right. Acne is just a part of growing up. It will probably go away by itself in a few years.

A **boil** is a hard, inflamed swelling caused by bacterial infection. Boils often appear when the body is susceptible to disease because of poor health or poor nutrition. A boil starts with bacteria entering an oil or sweat gland or a hair follicle. Only a doctor should treat a boil. Self-treatment may spread the infection. A boil can grow very large and become painful. An unusually severe form of a boil is called a **carbuncle** (KAHR buhng kuhl).

Warts are overgrowths of epidermal cells that may be darkened with melanin. Warts are caused by a virus, an organism much smaller than a bacterium. Warts rarely cause health problems, but since a wart has a large supply of capillaries, cutting or tearing it causes heavy bleeding. A wart that is large or often exposed to irritation, or one that persists for a long time, should be examined by a doctor. A doctor can remove it chemically or burn it off with an electric needle, a procedure called cauterization (kaw tuh rih ZAY shuhn). The wart-removal products available without a doctor's prescription are usually ineffective and may be harmful.

A **fever blister,** or **cold sore,** is also caused by a virus. Fever blisters are sores

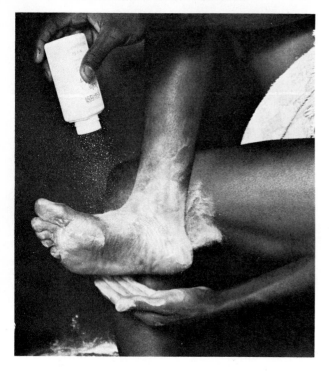

Cornstarch or a good foot powder can keep a fungus infection from taking hold.

If your feet tend to sweat, avoid footwear that is too warm for you.

on the face, especially on the lips or in and around the mouth. Fever blisters may occur at the same time as a cold or fever, or they may result from exposure to sun and wind. The blisters are uncomfortable, but they usually disappear in a week or two, leaving no scars. Occasionally moistening a fever blister with a small amount of an ointment containing camphor may relieve some of the discomfort. Frequent or persistent fever blisters or unusually severe fever blisters mean you should consult a doctor. They could be a symptom of some other disease that needs medical treatment.

Athlete's foot is a common, contagious skin disease caused by a microscopic fungus. The fungus grows rapidly on the warm, damp areas between the toes. Contaminated swimming pool walkways, locker rooms, and public showers are some places where people can pick up the infection. Athlete's foot is difficult to keep from spreading and hard to clear up. It's easier to prevent catching it in the first place. Avoid walking barefoot in public showers and dressing rooms. Instead, wear rubber sandals or wooden shoes whenever possible. Keeping the feet clean and dry also helps prevent and control the infection. A light dusting of the feet with cornstarch helps reduce perspiration. Talcum powder may contain asbestos fibers as an impurity. Since asbestos is a cancer-producing substance, it is safer to avoid talcum powder and to rely on cornstarch instead. Avoid closely knit nylon socks or stockings and tight plastic or rubber boots, since they prevent perspiration from evaporating from

The arrow points to the ringworm infection the owner caught from her kitten.

your feet and encourage the growth of athlete's foot. Instead, wear socks containing at least some cotton or wool, and leather shoes or boots.

Athlete's foot is often grouped with other highly contagious skin diseases called ringworm diseases. **Ringworm infections** result from a fungus, not from a worm. They are called ringworm only because the infections sometimes form ring-shaped patches on the skin. Ringworm fungi (FUHN jy) live on dead skin—that is, almost anywhere on the body—and in perspiration. They usually affect the armpits, scalp, and groin. Ringworm infections can cause severe itching and burning. Ringworm of the nails causes them to become thick and brittle.

Touching an infected pet, using a dirty comb or brush, and using someone else's towel or washcloth can spread ringworm diseases. As with other skin diseases, the best protection against ringworm diseases is to keep clean and wear clean clothes that don't make you sweat a lot. And use only your own comb and brush, and washcloth and towel. If you get a ringworm infection, see a doctor for medical treatment.

7-5 Sun Worshipers

Many light-skinned people think a suntan makes them more attractive, and the darker the tan the more attractive they feel. You may be surprised to learn that untanned skin used to be regarded as beautiful and as a sign of wealth and status. That was when most people worked outside, not in factories and office buildings. Those who did not labor outdoors remained untanned.

Although fashions change, the health aspects of tanning and skin care do not. A certain amount of sunlight—not much—is good for you. It can make you look healthier. It may reduce acne. And it changes a chemical in the cells of the dermis into vitamin D, a substance necessary for strong bones and teeth.

Too much exposure to sunlight can produce a painful sunburn, for both light-skinned and dark-skinned people. It can also age your skin and make you look old. People who spend a lot of time in the sun for many years get a wrinkled, tough, leathery look to their skin.

If you follow these rules, you will reduce your chances of getting a sunburn.

1. *Respect the power of the sun.* The rays of the noontime sun burn light skin quickly. During the first days of summer, start sunbathing early in the morning or late in the afternoon when the rays are less direct and less intense.

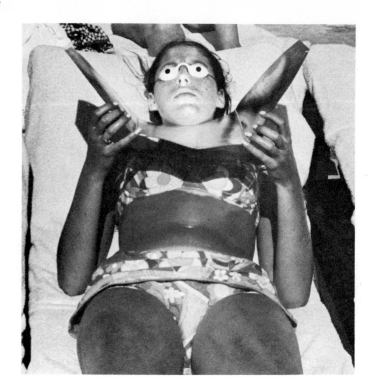

The pursuit of a perfect tan can lead to a perfectly awful sunburn.

2. *Watch for reflected sunlight.* The sun's rays are reflected by water, snow, and ice. Skiers can be burned as painfully as ocean bathers.

3. *Beware of hazy days.* The burning power of the sun is often greater on hazy days. Only complete cloud cover provides protection against sunburn.

4. *Know your own skin type.* Babies and children burn more quickly than adults. Fair skin burns more easily than dark skin.

5. *Time your exposure.* For almost everybody, 15 minutes a day is long enough for the first week of sunbathing. If this causes no problems, add 15 minutes a day each week. Get out of the sun after five or ten minutes if your skin is especially sensitive. Watch the thin-skinned portions of the body more carefully. You will feel a burn more quickly on the inner part of the forearms and behind the knees than on your back or chest. Remember that all of a burn does not show up immediately, and you do not always feel a burn right away.

6. *Use a suntan preparation.* Suntan lotions give some protection. Check the label to make sure the lotion contains PABA (para-amino-benzoic acid)—an effective sunscreen. Most suntan lotions wash off in water or perspiration and must be reapplied. Using a suntan lotion or cream does not eliminate the need for other precautions.

7. *Call a doctor if burning is severe.* Sunburn can cause sickness with chills and high fever. A doctor should examine anyone who is badly burned. Sunburn blisters require medical attention if they become infected.

Constant overexposure to the sun can also produce skin cancer. Almost all of the

Does the advertising octopus have many arms around you?

hundreds of thousands of cases of skin cancer reported in North America each year are thought to be related to the sun. Fortunately, most skin cancers can be removed with little trouble if caught in time.

Skin cancer has early warning signs:

1. A sore that does not heal.
2. Changes in the size or color of a wart or mole.
3. Formation of an unusually colored area on the skin.

These signs usually develop during the middle years of life and later, especially in the areas most exposed to the sun—the hands and face. Any of these warning signs calls for immediate medical attention. Though most skin cancers are not dangerous, some can spread to the rest of the body and be fatal.

7-6 Spray, Dab, Rub, and Roll On

Throughout history people have used chemicals to change their appearance. Today our society spends billions each year for well over 100,000 different health and beauty aids. These products include a tremendous variety of products advertised to make us smell good, look good, and to improve our skin and hair.

A **cosmetic** is a material that people rub, pour, sprinkle, or spray on their bodies to make themselves more attractive, or to change their appearance or smell. People buy cosmetics for many reasons. They may want to make their skin drier or moister. They may want to emphasize certain facial features, such as the shape of the eyes, the

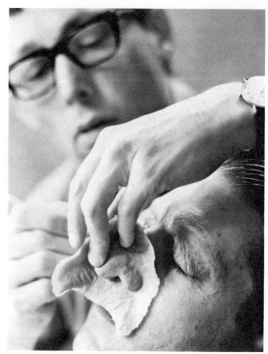

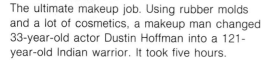
The ultimate makeup job. Using rubber molds and a lot of cosmetics, a makeup man changed 33-year-old actor Dustin Hoffman into a 121-year-old Indian warrior. It took five hours.

color of the lips, or the curve of the eyebrows. People often use cosmetics to try to conceal a real or imagined skin blemish. Some people use cosmetics to try to make themselves look older or younger. Light use of makeup to enhance a feature may work well for you. But depending on makeup to change something about your appearance can waste your time and money. No cosmetic can permanently change your appearance.

Manufacturing cosmetics is big business, and the cosmetic industry bombards us from all directions with advertisements. If you are sure that advertising claims haven't fooled you and that you really want to use certain cosmetics, buy them carefully. It's extremely important to read the safety precautions on labels and to follow the directions exactly, especially in using eye cosmetics.

Some people are especially sensitive to certain substances in cosmetics. After using a cosmetic, their skin may become red, dry, and itchy. Their eyes may itch and water, or their nasal passages may become stuffed up. This is an allergic reaction. Before using a cosmetic or hair preparation for the first time, do a patch test. Put a little of it on your arm or on the back of your hand or on just one small area of the scalp. Leave it for a few hours. If you notice any irritation, don't use the cosmetic. If an irritation develops after you have used a cosmetic, stop using it. If the condition seems serious, consult a doctor.

Canada and the United States have federal agencies that try to control the safety and labeling of cosmetics. But these agencies have limited powers to see that materials are pretested for safety or are quality controlled. And new cosmetics are mar-

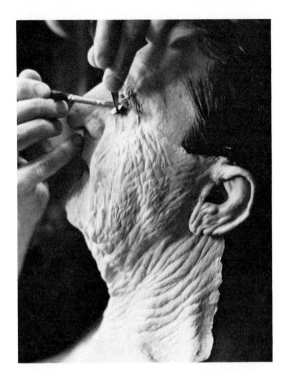

keted more quickly than they can be tested. The federal agencies will answer questions about the safety of various cosmetics or let you report bad effects from using a particular product. In the United States, write to Food and Drug Administration, Division of Colors and Cosmetic Technology, BF–430, 200 C Street, S.W., Washington, DC 20204. In Canada, write to Department of National Health and Welfare, Health Protection Branch, Brookeclaxton Building, Ottawa, Canada K1A 0K9.

If you want to use makeup, take another precaution in addition to following the directions. This is cleanliness. Heavy coatings of cream, lotion, or powder clog pores and prevent the release of sebum. Light-textured makeup is less likely to clog pores than heavier substances. Makeup should always be washed off carefully every night. Pull your hair back to cleanse the hairline area. A build-up of makeup under the hair

can cause a rash or other skin reaction. You can use a cleansing cream to remove makeup. Then remove the cream with soap and water.

Cold cream is a commonly used skin cleanser, but it leaves an oily film that should be removed with soap and water. Using a skin freshener with alcohol or another solvent removes not only the cold cream but some of the skin's natural oils as well. Cleansing lotions and creams should be used sparingly if you have oily skin.

You have probably seen and heard advertisements for skin creams with ingredients such as wheat-germ oil, lanolin, mineral oil, or various fruit oils. These skin creams have no unique powers. They do not go deep into the skin, nor do they nourish it. Use the least expensive cream or lotion that leaves your skin soft without irritating it.

Many products are advertised to control body odor. Body odor is the result of the actions of bacteria living on the skin. Perspiration under the arms, in the genital area, and on the hands, feet, and abdomen is odorless at first. Bacteria, however, cause perspiration to take on a pungent odor. Soaps kill or wash off some bacteria and keep perspiration odorless for a few hours. How soon afterwards odors develop and how strong they are depend on you, on the environment, and on what you're doing. Remember that some body odors are natural and not necessarily unpleasant to other people.

Two types of products are available to help you control odors. **Deodorants** are advertised to control odors but not perspiration. **Antiperspirants** are advertised to both control the flow of perspiration and mask odors. There is really very little difference between the two types. If any deodorant or antiperspirant irritates your skin, stop using it and try another brand. You may have to experiment with several until you find one that works for you without irritating your skin.

The so-called feminine deodorants do not control bacteria or perspiration and consist largely of perfumes and other chemicals. Many women find these products irritating to their skin. There is really no reason to use them. Regular bathing controls odors safely.

"Deodorant soaps" are advertised to kill bacteria and control body odor. However, some of these soaps may contain chemicals that are absorbed into the skin and can cause long-term internal damage.

SELF CHECK

1. What is the most important influence on appearance?

2. How can a mole become a health hazard?

3. How can you control acne?

4. What should someone who gets a boil do?

5. What are the early warning signals of skin cancer?

6. What precautions should be taken when using any cosmetic?

Hair, Nails, and Teeth

7-7 Shampooing and Shaving

You can cut it, dye it, curl it, straighten it, and bleach it. But the most important ways to keep your hair healthy and attractive are to keep it clean and take care of your overall health. Shampooing removes dirt, oil, and dead skin from the hair and scalp. Eating nutritious foods, getting enough exercise and rest, and generally taking care of your health will assure that the hair follicles in the scalp will receive a good supply of nutrient-rich blood.

How often your hair needs shampooing depends on several things. Its texture, cut, and how oily or dry it is are important. Lifestyle and environment are other factors that affect the kind of shampoo that is best for you and how often you need to shampoo. For example, someone who lives in the city and gets a lot of exercise probably has to shampoo often.

What were these hairdos meant to say about their owners?

Most shampoos contain synthetic detergents rather than soap. Some authorities claim that soap shampoos are better because they are less harsh on the hair than detergents. But when soap shampoos are used with hard water, they leave a dull and sometimes sticky film on the hair.

Additives in shampoos add to their cost. Some additives may be useful, but others simply make shampoos more expensive and no more effective. Most detergent shampoos have additives that make them less irritating to the scalp. Some shampoos also have ingredients, primarily proteins, that coat the hair. Some of these ingredients are useful. For example, they strengthen damaged hair and improve its texture. Despite the claims of advertisements, vitamins are not a useful additive in shampoos, according to most authorities.

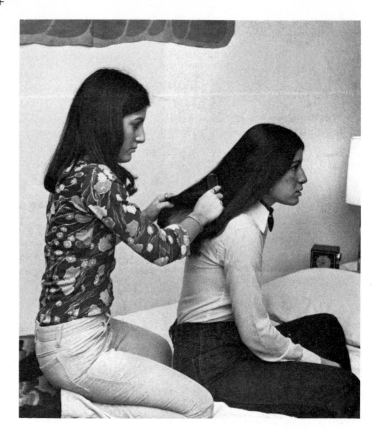

Light brushing can help your hair look clean and bright. But hundreds of hard strokes can hurt your scalp.

Before buying a shampoo, read the label to make sure it can take care of your needs. Take particular notice of any precautions on the label. As you probably know, endorsements by well-known people and "seals of approval" do not necessarily mean that the shampoo (or any other product) meets federal or state standards.

Regardless of the kind of shampoo you use, hair should be washed and dried gently and combed without tugging to get out the tangles. Most people think that the more shampoo they use the better. But a lot of suds is not as important as thoroughly brushing before and rinsing afterwards. People also often forget about washing their combs and brushes, but keeping your comb and brush clean helps keep your hair clean

longer. Incidentally, too much brushing, particularly with a brush that has stiff bristles, can damage the scalp and hair. So can too much "teasing" and hot air from electric hair driers.

Dandruff is not always easily controlled. Two different scalp conditions cause flaking. One is excessive dryness, causing bits of the dead skin to peel off the scalp. "Dry dandruff" results from the openings of the sebaceous glands becoming blocked, from using harsh shampoos, and from damaging the scalp with irritating hair products. The other scalp condition is more often the cause of dandruff and is harder to control than dry dandruff. It is caused by overactive sebaceous glands. This type of dandruff often involves severe itching. Other factors that cause or contribute to dandruff are poor general health, emotional upsets, and increased activity of bacteria and fungi that live on the scalp.

The two scalp conditions that cause dandruff require different treatments, either increasing or decreasing the amount of oil on the scalp. A medicated shampoo might help one type of dandruff but make the other type worse. Read carefully the information on several types and brands of dandruff shampoos before buying one. If excessive flaking persists and your scalp begins to itch or becomes inflamed, see a doctor.

Like your toothbrush and washcloth, your comb and brush should only be for your own use. Sharing them with other people or using someone else's can spread hair and scalp problems. **Lice,** which are small insects that live in animals' hair and feed on their blood, also spread from one person to another on combs and brushes. Lice reproduce rapidly, and their bites cause itching. Once a person has lice, scratching spreads them. People who have lice should get immediate medical treatment to protect themselves and others. A doctor or pharmacist can recommend an effective medication.

Hair dyes can cause skin irritation. Some researchers have found that chemicals in hair dyes cause cancer and birth defects in laboratory animals. Dyes should always be patch tested, even if the person has used the same dye before. Bleaches make the hair brittle. Hair that has been dyed or bleached should be protected from sun and wind. Rinses and tints, which can be washed out of the hair, are safer than dyes. Eyebrows and eyelashes should never be dyed. If dye or bleach gets into the eye, it can cause blindness. "Permanent waves" and products to straighten hair can also harm skin, eyes, and hair.

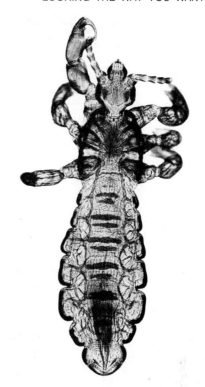

Besides causing scalp irritations with their bites, head lice may carry serious diseases.

Chemical hair removers, or **depilatories** (dih PIHL uh tawr eez), tend to destroy skin along with hair. In addition, certain chemicals in depilatories often cause allergic reactions and are harmful to the eyes. If you decide to use a depilatory, carefully read the precautions and directions, and follow them exactly. Be sure to test the depilatory on a small area of skin. Once you apply the depilatory it is important to complete the hair-removal process as quickly as you can to prevent excessive damage to your skin.

The only way to remove hair permanently is by **electrolysis** (ih lehk TRAHL uh sihs), the use of an electric needle to destroy the hair roots. This procedure should be done only by a trained and licensed person. Since

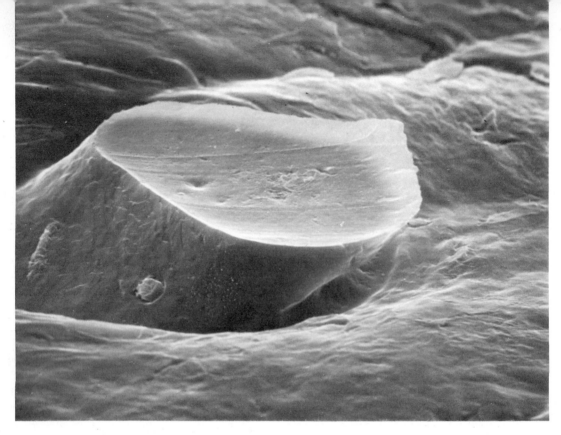

Thousands of times in a lifetime, hairs are cut down and make comebacks. This hair is shown seven hours after a shave.

electrolysis is expensive and time consuming, the process is practical for removing just small patches of unwanted hair.

Shaving is the most common way of controlling hair growth. Whether you use an electric shaver or a blade razor depends on the sensitivity of your skin and how close a shave you want. You can usually avoid nicks with an electric razor, but it is hard to shave as closely as with a blade razor. Pre- and after-shave products are sold for use with both shaving methods. They make shaving less uncomfortable and more effective, as well as relieve skin irritations.

Bleeding from a small cut due to shaving can be stopped by holding a piece of dry, absorbent paper against the skin for a few minutes. The paper then can be removed with cold water. A special device, called a styptic (STIHP tihk) pencil, will also stop bleeding effectively.

7-8 Nails

Cleanliness is important for the appearance and health of your nails as well as your hair. Other than keeping the nails clean, they need little more care than occasional trimming. Using a nailbrush and warm soapy water is a good way to remove dirt under the nails. A clean, blunt, wood instrument, called an orange stick, can also be used for that purpose.

When you trim your fingernails, use nail scissors or clippers and follow the curve of the ends of your fingers. If you shape or smooth your fingernails with a metal file or emery board, file in just one direction. Filing back and forth may leave rough edges that can cause nail splitting. To keep fingernails and hands in good condition, wear gloves when doing rough work or using harsh chemicals.

If you use nail cosmetics, read the labels for listed ingredients. Some nail products, especially those containing formaldehyde (fawr MAL duh hyd), have often caused serious reactions, including pain, bleeding, and even loosening and loss of nails. If the ingredients of a product are not listed, you are better off not buying it. After you buy a product, always try it out on just one nail. If you don't have any bad effects by the next day, it's probably all right to use. If you use nail polish, be sure not to paint over the cuticle, because the skin will stick to the growing nail and tear.

Sometimes a sliver of cuticle on the side of a nail may become loosened and form a **hangnail.** Carefully cut it off with nail or cuticle scissors. Trying to remove a hangnail by biting or tearing it may cause a very painful infection. Rubbing your nails with hand cream or lotion can help prevent dryness, which often causes hangnails. If you have a serious nail problem, rather than wasting time and money and possibly making the condition worse, go to a doctor or a **podiatrist** (puh DY uh trihst), a medical specialist who treats hand and foot ailments.

Another common cause of nail infection is an **ingrown toenail.** This is the growth of the corner of a toenail into the skin, resulting from wearing shoes that are too short or narrow and from improperly cutting toenails. Sometimes an ingrown toenail requires treatment by a doctor or podiatrist.

Toenails should be cut straight across and left long enough so that no flesh is in the front of the corners of the nails. Also use a nail brush or a clean orange stick to remove dirt around the edges and under toenails.

7-9 Smile

Our society values clean, regularly spaced teeth with an even bite, and healthy-looking gums. Our preference for natural-looking teeth is not shared worldwide. In some parts of the world, people proudly wear stainless-steel false teeth. And in other societies people file their teeth or stain them with dark dyes. In all societies, the appearance of the teeth and mouth is an important part of communication.

The part of the tooth showing outside the gum line is only about one-third of the whole tooth. This part is called the **crown.** It is covered and protected by **enamel,** the hardest material in the body. Most of the tooth underneath the enamel consists of a bonelike material, **dentin.** One or more **roots** securely anchor each tooth in a socket in the jawbone. Inside the roots are canals that have blood and lymphatic vessels and nerves extending into the **pulp** at the center of the tooth. The pulp is a soft, connective tissue.

Healthy gums consist of firm, pink tissue containing networks of blood and lymphatic vessels. The gums form a collar around each tooth. Food particles collect in a shallow groove between each tooth and the gum around it. In cleaning teeth, particular attention should be paid to removing food particles from these grooves by brushing and flossing.

Underneath the gums, a fibrous tissue called the **periodontal** (pehr ee oh DAHNT uhl) **membrane** helps to hold the teeth in

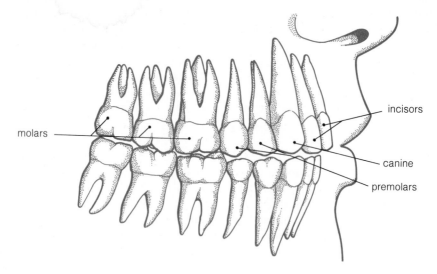

molars

incisors

canine

premolars

A set of permanent teeth with all the molars grown in. Which teeth act like scissors, and which act like grinders?

The internal structure of a tooth.

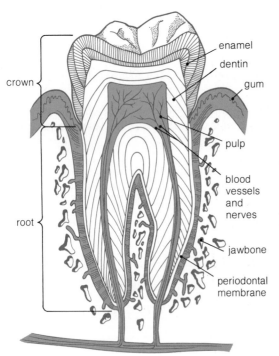

enamel

dentin

gum

crown

pulp

blood vessels and nerves

root

jawbone

periodontal membrane

place and cushions them against the pressure of biting and chewing.

People are born with buds for all their teeth, usually 20 primary or baby teeth and 32 permanent teeth. The first baby teeth usually grow through the gums and appear when a child is about six or eight months old. At about six years of age, a child's first permanent teeth—the "six-year molars" or first molars—begin to appear. These teeth grow in back of the primary teeth. The four six-year molars influence the shape of the jaw and the placement of the other permanent teeth as they grow through the gums. As permanent teeth start to replace primary teeth, the roots of the primary teeth are gradually absorbed into the jaw. Only the crowns are left when primary teeth fall out.

The second molars, or "twelve-year molars," usually appear between the ages of eleven and thirteen years. The last permanent teeth to appear are the third molars, or "wisdom teeth," which may not appear until people are in their twenties. Occasionally, one or more third molars do not form at all. Or they sometimes grow crooked and have to be surgically removed before they damage the adjoining teeth.

Certain nutrients are especially important for tooth development. The major minerals that make up teeth are calcium and phosphorus. Milk and milk products are the best sources of calcium. Citrus fruits and leafy green vegetables have some calcium too. Many foods contain phosphorus, particularly high-protein foods such as meat, poultry, fish, dried beans, and eggs. Whole-grain cereals and breads are also good sources of phosphorus. Vitamins A, C, and D are important in the development and maintenance of healthy teeth and gums. Vitamin C is particularly important in maintaining healthy periodontal tissue. Fluoride strengthens teeth and makes them more decay

resistant. Because of its beneficial effect on teeth, many communities add fluoride to drinking water. Some dentists apply fluoride solutions to the surfaces of the teeth. And some toothpastes contain it.

The texture of food also affects teeth and gums. Foods that require vigorous chewing—such as raw fruits and vegetables, hard-crusted bread, nuts, and meat—stimulate the nerves in the tooth sockets. The blood supply then increases, bringing more nutrients to the connective tissue that holds the teeth in the jaws. The exercise from chewing strengthens the teeth and gums as exercise strengthens other parts of the body. Eating soft, sticky food does not exercise the teeth and gums in the same way. In addition, this kind of food tends to cling to the teeth, particularly in the grooves at the

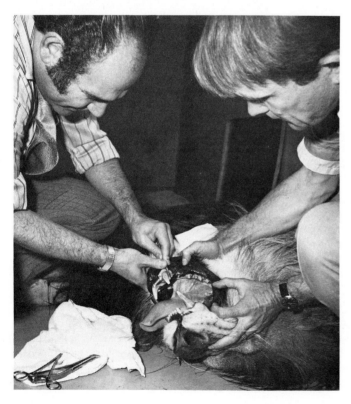

Captive lions need dental care. This one is getting his teeth cleaned.

Whether you brush up and down, side-ways, or use your own strokes, the important thing is to remove plaque and bits of food.

gum line. This contributes to cavities and gum disease.

Right after eating, certain bacteria that live in the mouth start to chemically change the remaining food particles, especially sugar and starches. Acid produced by the bacteria breaks down tooth enamel and can eventually form **cavities.** Once cavities form in the enamel, the decay eats into the dentin. If a dentist does not remove the decay and fill the cavity, the decay starts to damage the pulp. Then the tooth usually begins to ache because the pulp contains nerves. Bacteria may eventually cause painful, pus-filled sores called **abscesses** (AB sehs uhz) at the root end of an infected tooth. The infection may then enter the bloodstream and spread throughout the body.

Diseases of the tissue around the teeth are called **periodontal diseases.** Even though periodontal diseases are more com-mon in adults, everyone can get them. One of the most common causes of such disease is **tartar,** a hard mineral substance that builds up on teeth at the gum line. This crustlike covering gradually forms from a sticky mucus called **plaque** (PLAK) that contains bacteria, food particles, and dead tissue. Bacteria from both plaque and tartar can infect the gums and cause the loss of teeth. Smoking also can lead to gum prob-lems and discoloration of teeth.

An uneven bite is another cause of gum problems. People who have overcrowded or crooked teeth or whose front teeth protrude cannot chew food efficiently. An uneven bite can contribute to cavities and lead to tooth loss. **Orthodontia** (awr thuh DAHN shuh) can usually change teeth placement and the shape of the jaws by using slow, gentle pres-sure. People whose bones are still grow-ing—children and people your age—can benefit the most from wearing braces on

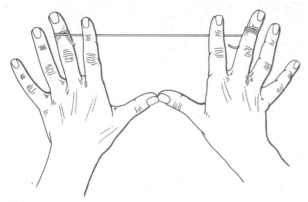

Suggestions for flossing: Begin with about 18 inches or 50 centimeters of floss.

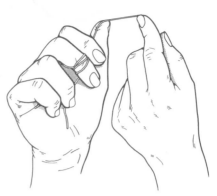

The thumbs and index fingers direct the floss between the teeth.

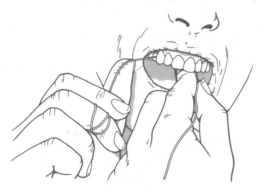

Gently move the floss up and down on the side of each tooth until the surfaces feel clean. Be careful not to push the floss too far into the gums.

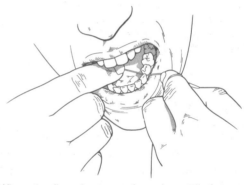

When the floss becomes frayed or soiled, turn from one middle finger to the other to bring up a fresh section.

their teeth. Orthodontia takes a long time, and it is expensive. But it is sometimes necessary to avoid future tooth and gum problems and to have attractive, even teeth.

7-10 **A Clean Mouth**

Regular dental checkups, at least twice a year, are important in maintaining healthy teeth and gums and preventing minor problems from becoming serious. During a checkup a dentist or a dental hygienist thoroughly cleans the teeth and removes the tartar that builds up around the gum line. If cavities are found by examination or an X ray, they are filled by the dentist. The general condition of the teeth and gums is also checked.

In addition to professional dental care, the best ways to keep your teeth and gums healthy are regular cleaning and choosing food wisely. Brushing the teeth removes food particles that decay-forming bacteria live on. The sooner you brush your teeth after eating, the better, particularly after eating sweet snacks and other high-carbohydrate foods. People often cannot brush right after eating, but thoroughly rinsing the teeth with water helps. Brushing the teeth and gums also stimulates the blood flow in the gums, and therefore helps them stay firm and healthy.

Dentists usually recommend a soft toothbrush, so that the bristles can be easily worked into the spaces between the teeth and between the teeth and gums. Baking soda and salt are effective cleansers to use with brushing. Commercial toothpastes or powders containing fluoride and other materials provide added protection against cavities. However, many toothpastes and powders, especially those advertised to whiten teeth, contain abrasives and other possibly harmful chemical additives. A dentist or a dental hygienist can recommend a good toothpaste or powder for cleaning teeth.

Part of cleaning the teeth and gums is the regular use of **dental floss,** a strong thread. Dental floss helps remove food particles and plaque from between the teeth where the toothbrush can't reach, and stimulates the gums. Be careful not to cut into the gums by putting too much pressure on the dental floss.

Some dentists recommend electric toothbrushes, because they massage the gums more thoroughly than toothbrushing by hand. Some dentists also suggest the use of devices that force a strong stream of water between the teeth. This jet of water helps remove food particles that even vigorous brushing can miss. It also stimulates the gums.

Unpleasant breath, or **halitosis** (hal uh TOH sihs), is an embarrassing condition resulting from a variety of causes. Smoking or eating certain foods such as onions causes temporary breath odor. Halitosis is a persistent condition, most commonly caused by an accumulation of food particles between the teeth, by cavities, or by gum disease. It can also result from throat and sinus infections or from diseases of internal organs. By regularly brushing and flossing the teeth—not just in the morning but also before going to bed and at midday if possible—most people can get rid of bad breath. If good oral hygiene doesn't work, a dentist or a doctor should find the cause so that it can be properly treated. Halitosis can be a sign of a serious disease. But it is usually caused by a problem that a medically trained person can easily detect and treat.

People cannot tell if they have halitosis just by the taste in the mouth. A person with a bad-tasting mouth may have no breath odor, while someone with no unpleasant taste may have bad breath.

Many people feel pressured by advertising to use mouthwashes, sprays, or candy mints for their breath. Many of these products are advertised as sore-throat remedies too. But despite what commercials and advertisements show, no commercial product effectively combats halitosis, prevents sore throats, or relieves the pain of a sore throat for very long. Strong and unpleasant-tasting toothpastes and mouthwashes are no more effective than sweet and mild-tasting ones. Mouthwashes that contain alcohol dry the mucous membranes. This irritates a sore throat or makes a person more susceptible to getting one. In addition, viruses, the cause of most sore-throat infections, are not killed by alcohol. As a result, self-treatment is totally ineffective. A serious viral infection of the throat requires medical treatment in order to prevent heart or kidney damage. If you are convinced that using a mouth rinse is beneficial, use water or a salt-water mixture, made with one-half of a teaspoon of salt in a glassful of water.

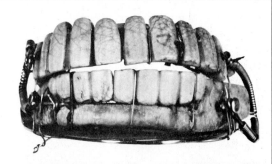

Health Frontier

Replacing Lost Teeth

A tooth is knocked out in a bicycle accident or in a basketball game. Does that mean a false tooth or denture will have to be installed? Not necessarily. Dentists are lately having more success in reimplanting teeth. Tooth transplants also are being performed.

Reimplantation means the replacement of a good tooth in its original socket. Dentists have known how to do this for quite a while, but usually the tooth becomes loose in one or two years. Dental research has established that if a tooth is reimplanted within 30 minutes after an accident, it might last as long as 10 years. But 30 minutes isn't much time. One experimental technique to make reimplantation last longer, even if more time has elapsed between an accident and arrival at the dentist's office, is to treat the tooth with fluoride before inserting it back into the jaw. Researchers have found that fluoride-treated reimplanted teeth stay in the mouth longer.

Transplantation involves the same problem as transplanting a kidney or other organ or tissue. The body fights the foreign substance. A transplanted tooth is rejected slowly. The average life expectancy for a transplanted tooth is about four years. On an experimental basis, the survival time has been increased to about seven years. The new technique is to remove all the soft periodontal tissue from the tooth, remove the pulp, and soak the tooth in a fluoride solution.

George Washington looks as though he had uncomfortable dentures.

Reimplantation and transplantation won't completely eliminate the need for dentures. But these techniques may someday become routine procedures in a dentist's office.

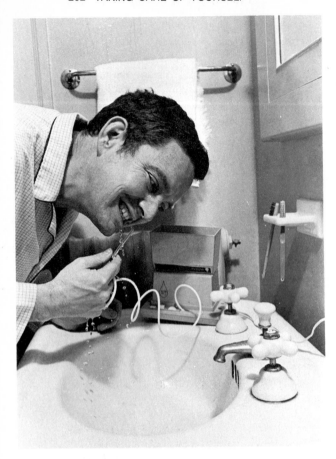

Devices that shoot a jet of water between the teeth are a help in removing bits of food.

● **7-11 Investigating How Well You Brush**

One method to help you improve your toothbrushing technique is to use a dental disclosing wafer or solution before brushing. These products contain a harmless dye that stains plaque bright red.

In this investigation, you are going to use a dye to show the plaque on your teeth, and then brush thoroughly to remove it. Working in pairs, you will observe the effect of toothbrushing in the morning on the accumulation of plaque during the day.

MATERIALS

disclosing wafer
  or solution
mirror
paper cup
toothbrush
toothpaste or powder
water

PROCEDURE

1. Brush your teeth as usual in the morning on the day you do the investigation.

2. Chew a disclosing wafer or rinse your mouth with a disclosing solution. Swish it between your teeth for about 30 seconds.

3. Rinse your mouth with water and look at your teeth in the mirror. Compare the amount of stain on your teeth with the appearance of your partner's teeth.

4. Using toothpaste or powder, brush your teeth until all the stain is removed.

DISCUSSION

1. Does brushing the teeth in the morning have much effect on the accumulation of plaque during the day?

2. Which of these factors do you think contribute most to good dental health: (a) the kind of toothbrush you use, (b) the kind of toothpaste you use, (c) the way you brush, or (d) the frequency of brushing? Why do you think so?

3. If people brush thoroughly and regularly, do you think they still should have their teeth professionally cleaned once or twice a year?

● **7-12 How Would You Like to Look?**

If you could look just the way you wanted to, what aspects of your appearance would you change? Would you like these to be permanent changes or only temporary?

PROCEDURE

On a separate piece of paper, copy the list of physical characteristics below. You would probably not want to change all of these characteristics about yourself, and some might not be appropriate. Next to those characteristics of yourself that you like the way they are, write "keep the same." Write "doesn't apply" next to any characteristic that doesn't fit with your style. Next to each characteristic you would like to change, tell how you would like to change it.

hair color	eye color
hair	body build
height	weight
complexion	fingernails
teeth	makeup
facial hair	

After you have written how you would like to change certain characteristics of your appearance, put an "X" next to those you have some control over. Put "XX" next to those you have complete control over.

DISCUSSION

1. What could you do to improve those aspects of your appearance that you have put X's next to?

2. Do most members of your class agree on the aspects of appearance that people have complete control over? If not, which aspects do you disagree on?

3. Why do you think so many people look for "miracle" cosmetics to make drastic changes in their appearance?

4. What effect do you think advertising has on people's discontents?

SELF CHECK

1. What are the most important influences on the appearance of hair?

2. What are the advantages and disadvantages of depilatories, electrolysis, and shaving?

3. How can ingrown toenails be prevented?

4. List three factors that are important in keeping teeth and gums healthy.

5. How can halitosis be prevented?

Chapter Summary

Although there are many ways you can change your appearance from the outside, your health affects your looks more than anything you do to your skin or hair. Skin, hair, nails, and teeth reflect state of health and the presence of disease.

Some skin problems, such as acne, primarily affect people your age. Most minor skin problems can be controlled by cleanliness, care in the use of cosmetics, nutritious diet, and regular exercise. Infections such as athlete's foot are easier to prevent than to cure. A small amount of exposure to sunlight is good for you, but too much can have serious effects, including skin cancer.

Buy and use cosmetics carefully. Read the labels, follow the directions, and test any cosmetic on a small area of skin to be sure it doesn't cause irritation. Most of the "special ingredients" that make cosmetics expensive are ineffective.

Healthy hair requires cleanliness and good overall health. Dandruff can be caused by scalp that is either too oily or too dry. Sharing a comb or brush may spread diseases and lice. Hair can be removed by shaving, depilatories, or electrolysis. Hangnails and ingrown toenails can become infected.

Cavities are the most common dental problem among people your age. Periodontal disease is often caused by a build-up of tartar on teeth at the gum line. A dentist or a dental hygienist can remove tartar before it starts to cause trouble. An uneven bite can be corrected by orthodontia. In addition to regular dental checkups, the best ways to keep teeth and gums in good condition are to clean them regularly and choose your diet wisely.

Chapter Self Check

1. What problems, if any, can be caused by vitiligo? By freckles?

2. When should a mole or a birthmark receive medical attention?

3. Describe some ways to control acne.

4. How can athlete's foot be prevented?

5. Why is a small amount of exposure to sunlight helpful?

6. What are the possible consequences of too much exposure to sunlight?

7. How can you test a cosmetic to find out if it causes irritation?

8. What causes body odor?

9. What factors affect how often hair should be washed?

10. What should be done about dandruff?

11. Name three methods of removing hair. What precautions should be taken with each method?

12. Describe proper care of the nails.

13. How does diet affect the health of the teeth?

14. What problems may develop if a cavity in a tooth is not filled?

15. What is plaque? Why should it be removed?

16. What are some benefits of orthodontia?

17. How can most people avoid halitosis?

Read More About It

Chase, Deborah. *The Medically Based No-Non-sense Beauty Book.* New York: Alfred A. Knopf, Inc., 1974. The structure of skin and hair and how cosmetics affect them. A what-to-do book about appearance, with a glossary of cosmetics and ingredients.

Donnan, Marcia. *Cosmetics from the Kitchen.* New York: Holt, Rinehart and Winston, 1973. Recipes for home-made beauty aids, cleansers, and other cosmetics, plus a guide to safe use of cosmetics.

Galton, Lawrence. *The Laboratory of the Body.* New York: Pyramid, 1972. Scientists from many fields study the mouth for a better understanding of the entire body.

Krochmal, Connie. *A Guide to Natural Cosmetics.* New York: Quadrangle, 1973. How plants and other natural materials can be used to make cosmetics. Illustrated.

Lubowe, Irwin I., and Huss, Barbara. *A Teenage Guide to Healthy Skin and Hair,* Revised Edition. New York: E. P. Dutton and Co., 1972. Many aspects of skin and hair care, including what to do about everyday problems. Topics include hair styling, coloring, and suntan.

Zebooker, Eli P. *Your Teeth, Your Dentist, and Your Health.* New York: Exposition Press, 1973. A brief, easy-to-read discussion about what to do to keep your teeth. The author, a dentist, emphasizes that in many cases tooth loss is unnecessary.

Unit 3 GETTING IN TOUCH WITH YOURSELF

8
Who Are You?

After completing the work in this chapter, you will be able to:

describe the factors that make each human being different from all others.

tell which differences between men and women are inborn and which are learned.

describe how groups affect an individual's personality and how individuals affect the groups they belong to.

discuss some of the ways family life influences an individual's personality.

list some kinds of human behavior explained by theories of the unconscious mind.

describe some of the characteristics of your personality.

I Am a Person Who . . .

Write your name at the top of a piece of paper. Then begin ten lines with the words *I am.* Complete each line so that it describes something about you. For example, "I am a junior in high school," or "I am a person who likes sports," or whatever else is important to you about yourself. (You don't have to show your paper to anyone else if you don't want to.)

Your ten lines tell a lot about your **personality,** or the behavior, attitudes, and feelings that make you an individual. It is unlikely that anyone else in the world would write down the same ten *I am* lines that you just did. Even though you and other people have many similarities, no other person is exactly like you. And you are not exactly like anyone else.

One reason for your uniqueness is that no one else has your particular combination of genes (unless you have an identical twin). Your personality is shaped in part by your genes. It is also shaped by your family life, your environment, and the groups you belong to. No one else has exactly the same mix of all those factors and influences that you do.

How many of your *I am* lines seem to depend on your environment or on particular experiences you have had? How many lines seem to depend on your inborn characteristics?

The Biological Inheritance

8-1 You Among the Animals

This chapter is organized something like a sequence in a movie, called a zoom shot. In the beginning, the camera is so far away that the main characters can't be seen. All you see are tiny creatures in a vast landscape. Then the camera slowly zooms in. The creatures become a crowd of people. The crowd turns into groups. A group divides into the main characters, their families, and friends. The main characters become bigger. And finally—in a close-up—the hero and heroine fill the screen. Because we know where they are, where they fit into the larger picture, we are better able to understand who they are and what they are up to than if we began by looking at them in isolation.

We have begun our "zoom-shot chapter" with the camera so far away that all you can see are living creatures in general.

All living things have many similarities as well as obvious differences. What do you have in common with other living things?

What important similarities do these friends have?

Think about the following list. Then write down on a piece of paper those characteristics that apply to (a) all or most animals and (b) humans only.

eat food	solve problems
find or build shelters	have social organizations
need love	die
need clothing	exercise
communicate	sleep
reproduce	show curiosity
like companionship	play

What characteristics (on the list or not) set people apart from other animals?

8-2 One Species, Many Differences

About two million species of plants and animals share the earth. A **species** (SPEE seez) is a group of living things with many of the same characteristics. Members of a species can reproduce with each other, but not with members of other species. As a member of the human species, *Homo sapiens* (HOH moh SAY pee ehnz), you have certain characteristics in common with all the other people on Earth. From your cells to your complex brain to the range of emotions you can feel, you show your humanity. The first four chapters of this book described many human traits. They are passed on from one generation to another through genes.

Within the human species you can see great variations—people with many different skin colors, hair textures, eyelid and lip shapes, and so on. These varying traits are also passed on by genes. Your own genetic inheritance includes traits that run in your family.

Some characteristics such as intelligence, height, and body build seem to be affected by a combination of many genes. Because

of this, it is not possible to predict what a child will be like as an adult just by knowing how the parents measure on these factors. In addition, traits such as intelligence and height are not fixed at birth. They are only partly dependent on genes. How they develop depends on an individual's experiences. People may make the most of their inherited abilities. Or they may be held back by malnutrition, poor education, lack of will power, or other circumstances.

SELF CHECK

1. What are some important traits that all animals have in common?

2. Name some human traits that vary among people.

3. What are some human traits that are fixed at birth?

4. What are some human traits that are influenced both by genes and by experience?

Individuals in Society

● **8-3 Masculinity and Femininity**

Within the human species, you belong to either the male or female sex. Many of the differences between the two sexes are obvious. Most of these obvious differences, such as body build and hair growth, are biological. They are determined by genes. But what about personality? Are certain personality traits feminine or masculine? Are people born with them?

PROCEDURE

Here are some common ideas about sex differences in personality. After you read this list, write down on a separate piece of paper the statements you think are true.

1. Girls are more sociable than boys.

2. Boys have greater self-esteem than girls.

3. Girls learn by emotional response and boys learn by rational analysis.

4. Boys are more ambitious than girls.

5. Girls tend to be easily influenced; boys tend to think for themselves.

6. Girls enjoy music, art, and literature more than boys do; boys like science more than girls do.

7. Boys are less interested in marrying and raising a family than girls are.

8. Girls pay more attention to their appearance than boys do.

9. Boys understand machinery better than girls do.

10. Girls talk more than boys.

Now go back over the list. For each statement you listed as true, write whether the trait mentioned seems to be innate (something a person is born with) or cultural (the result of the influence of society).

DISCUSSION

1. Compare your opinions with those of other people in your class. How many males and how many females think a particular statement is true?

2. Which traits did people describe as innate? As cultural?

3. How do you explain the class's results?

4. You might want to ask some older people in your home to do this activity. How do their results compare with those of your class? Can you explain any differences?

8-4 Avoiding Sex Stereotypes

It is likely that your survey in the last section produced a number of "true" responses. It is also likely that some people answered "innate" for a umber of the items listed. However, ar as scientific research can tell, not one of the statements describes an innate, biological difference between the sexes. Some males and some females may in fact behave as the listed statements claim. Many others do not. Today it is believed that much "characteristically" male and female behavior is due to upbringing and the expectations of society.

Many North American fathers (maybe most of them) still swing their sons in the air and teach them active sports as soon as they can. The same fathers play with their daughters differently. They hold them more securely, offer them dolls rather than dump trucks, and speak to them in a gentler way than to their sons. Many mothers also treat their sons and daughters differently. Both parents may expect their children to show

Do you feel sex stereotypes prevent you from doing things you would like to do?

different types of behavior and interests, depending on the child's sex. In many cases a child accepts these expectations as his or her own beliefs. In this way, many ideas about masculine and feminine behavior are formed in infancy and early childhood.

Males and females have many of the same opinions, interests, feelings, and abilities. A person does not have to act out sex stereotypes. If you strive to be an individual, you can resist them, or avoid them, or move away from a restrictive situation when you are able to. You can develop your own values and interests and make career choices based on your personal goals.

There are now many laws in the United States and Canada that ban sex discrimination in business and government. Only in a few special cases, such as when a theater needs an actor or an actress for a particular role, is it legal to refuse to hire someone on the basis of sex. Salaries, promotions, and other job benefits are required by law to be equal for males and females.

Many government agencies are at work to combat sex discrimination. If you believe that you are being discriminated against in employment or schooling because of your sex, try to locate help in your state or province. Or you can get in touch with the Equal Employment Opportunity Commission, 1800 G Street, N.W., Washington, DC 20506;

The diversity of customs—playing jazz at a funeral in New Orleans, celebrating the Chinese New Year with a dragon dance, and reading a holy scroll on the Jewish Sabbath.

or the Fair Employment Practices Branch, Canada Department of Labour, 340 Laurier Avenue, West, Ottawa, Ontario K1A 0M7.

8-5 How Groups Affect Personality

Have you ever gone to a wedding or a funeral or some other ceremony of an ethnic group or religion different from your own? You may have found the ceremony strange and hard to understand. Why do some groups have elaborate weddings, for example, while others practice fairly simple exchanges of vows? Why do some people bury their dead immediately while other groups of people have the body on view for several days?

You might like to study how the present-day ideas and actions of different ethnic, social, and religious groups have developed. Try listing the groups you belong to. Your "groups" could be your nation, religion, race, social club, or group of friends. Do you know much about their customs and

beliefs? The more you learn about them, the more you may understand about your own personality.

People don't always realize how much the beliefs, customs, and attitudes of their groups affect them. Right from birth, when we all depend completely on other people for survival, we are influenced by the way they think and behave.

The opposite is also true. That is, the members affect the personality of the group. The individuals in a group at any one time have a great deal to say about what the group is like. When the beliefs of individuals change, the group changes. Can you think of examples of ways particular groups you know of have changed? Have you ever changed the beliefs or behavior of a group?

Some people, unfortunately, think of group membership in rigid ways. They form stereotyped notions about group members. It isn't difficult to see this is unfair. People want to be regarded as individuals. No one wants to be treated as a category. Groups are never based on the complete similarity of all the members. How could they be?

● 8-6 A Personal Membership List

Make a table like the one below, on a separate piece of paper. Fill in as much information as you can about all the different groups you belong to.

NAME OF GROUP I BELONG TO	HOW I GOT TO BE A MEMBER (BORN, PLACED THERE, JOINED)	CHARACTERISTICS I HAVE IN COMMON WITH OTHER GROUP MEMBERS	WAYS I DIFFER FROM OTHER GROUP MEMBERS
	Copy This Table on a Piece of Paper		

There are different kinds of leadership in different situations. Sometimes the leader is chosen or hired. Sometimes one person just starts acting like a leader.

DISCUSSION

1. Discuss your table with your classmates. Have some groups been named by more than one member of the class? If so, did these people write any of the same common characteristics and differences?

2. Does being a member of a group reduce your uniqueness?

8-7 Leaders and Followers

In many discussions about groups, people seem to assume that a group leader gives orders and the other members—the followers—obey. It is also assumed that leaders have one set of characteristics in common and followers have another. Are these assumptions correct?

PROCEDURE

On a separate piece of paper, list the numbers 1–18. Next to the numbers, write whether you think the personality traits listed below are characteristic of (a) good leaders, (b) good followers, (c) both, or (d) neither. Be ready to explain all your (c) and (d) answers.

1. being able to follow directions
2. being able to give directions
3. having confidence in others
4. being able to work alone
5. knowing exactly what you want
6. getting along well with people
7. frequently "telling people off"
8. being able to speak well in front of a group
9. feeling jealous of your friends' achievements
10. being discouraged easily
11. getting over disappointments fairly easily
12. talking more and louder than anyone else
13. having a pleasant appearance
14. being honest and sincere
15. being willing to do more than your share
16. contributing ideas
17. accepting responsibility
18. wanting to be popular

DISCUSSION

1. Compare your answers with those of your classmates. Discuss the answers that differ.

2. Do you and your classmates have any stereotyped ideas and attitudes about leaders and followers?

3. Identify the characteristics of a leader and a follower that *you* possess.

4. How can a person be a leader in one situation and a follower in another?

5. Do leaders accomplish more than followers do?

6. Do followers influence what a group believes or how it behaves?

8-8 Families

The first group you find yourself in is your family. All the experts agree that family life is tremendously important in shaping children's personalities. But there is very little agreement on how children should be brought up or on how different family arrangements affect them.

What people make up your family? Mother, father, and children make up the traditional family in North America. This arrangement is called a **nuclear family.** Until recent times, the role of each person in such a family was well defined. The father defended the home and hunted, farmed, or worked to provide the family with food, shelter, and an income. The mother cared for the children, cooked, cleaned, and did a large number of other things that kept the family healthy and secure. Today this pattern of family organization is found in a large percentage of North American homes. However, some of the roles within the nuclear family are changing. For economic and other reasons, more and more women are seeking jobs outside the home. When this happens, some of their tasks may be taken over by the children or fathers.

Today, for a number of reasons, many families have just one parent in the home. This arrangement puts additional burdens on the single parent, who must attempt to

In this extended family in an Israeli kibbutz, there are lots of people of different ages to share experiences with.

be both mother and father to the children. In such circumstances, the older children in the family, a relative, or an outside agency may assume a key role in rearing the younger children.

In some communities, the **extended family** is popular. This involves close relatives, such as grandparents, living in the same building or in the same area as the family. In the extended family it is quite common for both parents to have full-time jobs, with other family members caring for the children and home.

Another style of family life is the **expanded family.** This involves several adults and children who may not be related living together. In North America several adults may share a large house that none could afford alone. Another reason people choose this kind of communal living is to share child-rearing responsibilities. In some cultures, such as those on certain Polynesian islands or Israeli kibbutzim, whole villages are large expanded families.

How many adults and children did you grow up with? Do you have any personality traits similar to theirs? Have you ever said something and then thought, "Hey, that's

As a child, were you mostly left alone to make your own rules, as this girl was? Or were you given responsibilities and rules to follow, like the boy on the opposite page?

just the way my mom sounds"? You may have the same experience 20 or 30 years from now. You have taken into your personality some of the traits you observed while you were growing up.

The opposite can also be true. You may be just the reverse of a parent or older brother or sister in some ways. For example, unusually neat and orderly parents can have children who are unusually disorganized with their possessions and in their actions. Some unaggressive or passive parents find that their children are often aggressive and at times even violent. It is usually easy—after the fact—to see how a particular behavior pattern in a child was encouraged by his or her parents' behavior. But all too often one can't predict the effects of particular child-rearing practices.

Of all the problems of child-rearing, the one that most parents have the most trouble

with is deciding how much freedom or discipline children should have. "Permissive" parenting emphasizes understanding the child's needs and reasoning with the child, rather than giving commands. Underlying this approach to parenting is the idea that children can develop best when they have freedom to try things for themselves. "Restrictive" parents emphasize discipline, respect for authority, and the property rights of others. This approach is based on the idea that children cannot know enough to decide for themselves. They must first learn "the rules." Love and affection are important ingredients in both types of parenting. Most parents are not wholly permissive or restrictive, but they usually lean one way or the other.

Permissive and restrictive attitudes seem to work like social fads. The pendulum swings back and forth between these two

sides, often with great rapidity. In 1938 for example, a widely read United States government publication recommended binding a stiff cuff on an infant's arm to prevent thumb-sucking. Thumb-sucking was considered "infantile" and had to be outgrown quickly. But in 1942, mothers were told not to interfere with the harmless pleasure of thumb-sucking. Today, parents have the choice of painting bad-tasting chemicals on a baby's thumbs, substituting "pacifiers" for thumbs, or leaving the infant alone. Each practice is widely used.

From thumb-sucking to restrictions on teenage dating, popular attitudes toward child-rearing change from year to year. It is nearly impossible to recommend a certain set of child-rearing practices as ideal, although many are clearly not desirable. Parents differ, children differ, and the effects of any practice on a particular child are unpredictable. It is also difficult and dangerous to carry out scientific experiments with children in matters that might affect their entire personalities. On the other hand, some scientists consider it dangerous to blunder along without scientific guidance.

Did your upbringing tend to be more permissive or more restrictive? How do you think that affected your personality? Would you want to raise your children the same way you were brought up or differently?

Can you remember when you began to question the ideas and authority of your parents or other adults in your family? Even very young children show their desire to be independent. People your age sometimes resent offers of help and advice from adults. Your feeling may be that you want to know that your parents are there when you need them. But you also want to decide for yourself when to go to them for advice or support. Their attitudes are likely to be different. They may not be ready to accept your independence.

SELF CHECK

1. Write down one idea about males and one about females that you once believed were accurate but now realize are stereotypes. Where did you get these stereotyped ideas from?

2. What are some advantages of knowing about the beliefs and customs of your own group?

3. Why is it impossible for anyone to avoid being affected by his or her group's attitudes and traditions?

4. What are some characteristics that all members of a group have?

How the Mind Works

8-9 **The Hidden Self**

The self that you see busy with friends, family, and school is not your entire self. It is only the public side of you. You are also aware of an inner self that consists of thoughts, opinions, emotions, and sensations. When you aren't talking to other people, you probably "hear" your mind talking to itself. It keeps busy most of the time—identifying sights, sounds, and other sensations. It analyzes situations and just rambles on from one thought to another. But busy as the conscious mind is, most psychologists and psychiatrists think that it is only the tip of an iceberg. They say that there is a larger, submerged part—the **unconscious.**

As far as scientists can tell, the unconscious isn't a specific, physical portion of the brain. It is an idea, or theory. In fact, various theories of the unconscious have been proposed to explain a lot of human behavior we cannot otherwise explain. Dreaming is one example. When we dream,

it usually seems as though our conscious mind were watching a movie produced and directed by someone else (our unconscious?).

Everyone remembers making slips of the tongue—saying one thing while consciously intending to say something else. These acts, like dreams, are said to be instances when unconscious feelings slip into consciousness. It seems that unconscious feelings can enter the conscious mind against our will.

How much of your early childhood can you remember? Perhaps a few events and feelings. Most of your experiences, you might think, have faded from your memory. But people sometimes remember in great detail events from their childhood. You may have had such an unexpected flash of memory yourself. It appears that nothing that ever happens to us is truly lost. It gets stored in our unconscious. Much of the unconscious seems to consist of these childhood experiences.

Wishes, impulses, and memories that the conscious mind doesn't want to think about

Do you ever get a vague feeling that there is another part of you hidden inside—an unconscious part of you?

may be intentionally forgotten. They then become part of the unconscious also. This is called **repression** (rih PREHSH uhn). What is too unpleasant to think about we repress from our conscious minds.

Among the strongest feelings that are repressed are those involving one or both parents. All children and parents have conflicts over discipline, eating, showing affection, toilet training, and other matters. If a child's anger, frustration, hatred, pain, and grief cannot be safely expressed, they are repressed. For example, a child wanting affection may cry long and painfully. If this happens often and neither parent comforts the child, the child may learn to tighten muscles to choke off the painful crying be-

fore it starts. In that way, the needs that led to crying are repressed.

An early pattern of behavior—in this instance, denying the need for love and refusing to cry—can become a basic part of a person's personality. He or she may tend to act in a similar way in all sorts of situations later on in life. This sort of unconscious behavior pattern, as well as specific memories, becomes part of the unconscious.

Psychologists, psychiatrists, and other scientists who study the mind have various ways of helping people to recover lost memories. Sometimes if people understand their repressed feelings, they stop acting in ways that served some purpose for them when they were young but are no longer

A part of you feels desires . . .

a part of you tries to solve
problems and satisfy desires
in a rational way . . .

helpful. But it can be very difficult to recollect painful memories of the past. And it is not easy to change one's usual way of behaving even when the reasons for it are understood.

A pioneer in developing a theory of the unconscious and its role in human behavior was Sigmund Freud (FROYD), who lived from 1856 to 1939. In Freud's theory, which he called **psychoanalytic** (sy koh an uh LIHT ihk) **theory,** there are three basic parts to the personality: id, ego, and superego.

The **id** consists of the basic biological needs for food, warmth, sleep, affection, and, as people mature, sex. The growing child learns that these inborn desires cannot always be fulfilled. Crying for food does

and a part of you feels ashamed or guilty for acting badly.

not always bring results, for example. And many objects such as sand can be put into the mouth without satisfying hunger. The **ego** develops as a part of the mind that leads a person to act on the basis of what has been learned about the world, not simply on the basis of what the person wants.

While the ego develops, the **superego** also develops. The superego consists of standards of behavior that the child learns from early experiences, particularly at home. According to Freud, the superego makes people afraid or ashamed of certain feelings and actions. The superego also consists of the ideals we try to live up to. (Conscience plus ideals make up the superego.)

In Freudian theory, the id and parts of the superego are unconscious. The ego is the familiar, conscious mind. At first the ego develops to help the organism deal with the environment. Later, the ego has the added task of balancing the demands of the id against the demands of the superego. Since the id, superego, and environment are often pulling in different directions, the ego often feels like a battleground.

Around the world, people enjoy putting on masks to change themselves into frightening things. Is this behavior an inborn trait? Is it evidence of a collective unconscious?

Like an adventurer bringing back word of a newly discovered continent, Freud opened up the unconscious for exploration. His model of mental development has often been criticized (although not always fairly), but he was the trail blazer.

There seems to be much more in our unconscious storehouse than the negative, repressed memories and behavior patterns that Freud emphasized. Indeed, there is evidence that we have within us a vast amount of neutral and positive memories, feelings, and guidelines for thinking and perceiving the world around us.

In theories developed by other people, the mind is like an onion, with various conscious layers. Some other models of the mind emphasize how growing up in different societies shapes the conscious and the unconscious. But one important theory claims that people in every society on Earth have a number of unconscious thought patterns in common. In this theory, there is a "collective unconscious," as well as everyone's individual version. Models of the mind are not in short supply! There is so much about human thought and behavior that still needs to be explained.

8-10 Expressing Your Individuality

You can't get an understanding of a living thing—whether it's a single cell or a person—by looking at it in isolation from its environment, all by itself. To tell what something really is, you have to see where it fits in.

Consider a single cell in a human body. It makes up part of a tissue, which makes up part of an organ, which makes up part of one or more organ systems, which make up a living person. To understand the nature of a single cell, you have to see how it fits into the overall pattern, what it contributes to other cells, and what it gets from them.

To get a better understanding of who you are, you also have to find out where you fit in, what you have in common with other people, and what sets you apart from other people. This chapter started out with the largest groups you belong to, and then narrowed down the focus. You have the same body construction as billions of other people. You have the sexual characteristics of about half the people in the world. You have acquired some of the ideas and customs of your groups, and you have been influenced by your family. You have a lot of the same interests and activities that your friends have. What makes you an individual, different from everybody else?

Part of the answer is that there is more than one "you." Don't you behave differently in different situations? Aren't you more likely to joke with some friends than with others, and to talk about a variety of things with a variety of people? You may be an aggressive person in a hockey game but a quiet one with your friends. To answer the question, "Who are you?" you really have to first ask, "When, where, and under what circumstances?"

You express your individuality in making choices for yourself. You choose your friends, decide the subjects in school that interest you or bore you, and select your free-time activities. If you decide to work for extra money, or must work to help your family, you'd like to have some choice as to what to do. It is important for people to feel that there are choices, that they have something to say about how they run their lives.

Your deepest feelings and ideas, the ones you may not talk about often, also identify you. Although everyone has basic human emotions, you have your own ways of expressing them. Healthy people take responsibility for how they express their feelings.

There are many ways to express your individuality—by being artistic, by celebrating your traditions, by choosing activities and jobs.

When they have conflicts with other people and tensions within themselves, they try to find ways of resolving or relieving these situations. Chapter 9 discusses helpful techniques for dealing with conflicts.

Human beings are flowing, changing creatures—constant in some ways from birth until death, but otherwise growing and different from day to day and year to year. And not all of the ways we change depend on outside influences. Even though our personalities are shaped by the past, we have the power to disown it, to walk away, to change ourselves.

● **8-11 Investigating Your Personality**

In this investigation you are going to describe how you might react to various situations and then analyze your reactions.

PROCEDURE

On a separate piece of paper, list the letters a–n. Then read the following descriptions of situations, one at a time. Next to the letters on your paper, write down your immediate

A long, dreary day or the pleasures of friendship? Personality, not the situation itself, makes the difference.

reactions to the situations listed here. You can be brief.

a. You meet a good friend you haven't seen in a long time. Your friend gives you a big hug.

b. You find yourself waiting for a bus with a person who once spread an untrue rumor about you.

c. Your father has just asked you to help clean out the cellar.

d. It's Friday night. Your family has gone out. You didn't make plans to see any friends. You're alone. How do you feel?

e. Your boss on a part-time job criticizes you for coming to work late.

f. You go to a party at which you see a couple of friends but you don't know the other people. Who do you spend your time with?

g. Your friend's car has broken down on a summer day. You and your friend are sitting in it, alongside the highway, very hot and uncomfortable. You have been waiting for a tow truck for a long time.

h. You really like watching a late-night TV program. But you haven't been feeling well lately and realize that you aren't getting enough sleep. One of your favorite stars is on the late show tonight.

i. You've just heard some good news and are very pleased.

j. You are baby-sitting, and the baby has gone to sleep. You can't leave the house, there's nothing on TV worth watching, and you are bored.

k. You've discovered that a member of your family is an alcoholic. In school, your best friend happens by, looks at your face, and asks what's wrong.

l. You come home from school tired and irritable. Your younger sister reminds you that you promised to help her with a model airplane.

m. You are with a group of friends discussing the candidates for class president. Your friends all dislike the person you favor.

n. For the second time you've tried to solve a problem, without success.

DISCUSSION

1. What do the descriptions of your reactions tell you about yourself? As you reread each of your descriptions, answer the question below that has the same letter.

Does what you wrote describe how you usually:
a. respond to affection?
b. treat people you don't like?
c. deal with unpleasant responsibilities?
d. feel when you are alone?
e. react to criticism?
f. respond to strangers?
g. react to physical discomfort?
h. take care of your health?
i. show your happiness?
j. deal with boredom?
k. discuss personal matters with your friends?
l. keep your promises?
m. stand up for what you believe?
n. deal with frustration?

2. Which of your descriptions also tell how you would have reacted five years ago?

3. Which of your descriptions also tell how you hope you will react five years from now?

4. Which of your descriptions tell how you think most people your age react to similar situations?

SELF CHECK

1. What is meant by the "unconscious"?

2. Think of any slip of the tongue you made or heard someone else make recently. What did you learn about the feelings or attitudes that may lie behind that mistake?

3. What do dreams and slips of the tongue have in common?

4. How can a repressed feeling affect a person's behavior?

5. What did Freud mean by the terms id, ego, and superego?

6. Describe some ways you express your individuality.

Chapter Summary

We have many characteristics in common with other living things as well as with other people. In spite of this, every human being is an individual both physically and emotionally.

Some human traits, such as sex, and eye and skin color, are inherited and fixed for life. Many other traits, though also inherited, are shaped by environment as they develop. Personality is deeply influenced by family life and by the attitudes, feelings, and behavior of the groups an individual is involved with throughout life. Every individual is a member of many different groups. Both the leaders and the followers in a group influence the group and each other.

Group influences are passed on to an individual first by the family. There are many kinds of family arrangements. All of them create the first and strongest impressions on an individual. Everyone carries family and group influences and attitudes within her or his personality.

Many of the feelings and conflicts of very early childhood seem to be forgotten, but they remain in the unconscious. They continue to influence thoughts and behavior and sometimes slip into consciousness unexpectedly, for example, in slips of the tongue and in dreams.

In spite of biological similarities and influences on individuals, every person has many ways of expressing individuality. These include the development of values and deep feelings, choices of friends, activities, and attitudes.

Slips of the tongue: Your unconscious is showing!

Chapter Self Check

1. What biological characteristic makes every person unique?

2. What non-biological factors shape an individual's personality?

3. Describe some characteristics that set humans apart from other living things.

4. Do you consider your genes or your environment and experience more important in the

following areas: (a) intelligence; (b) muscular development; (c) resistance to disease; (d) ability to show affection; (e) amount of energy; and (g) choice of hobbies?

5. Do you think there are any innate, psychological differences between males and females? If so, what are they? How could you prove that these differences are innate?

6. How many groups do you belong to? What are they?

7. Do you think there are aspects of your personality that have not been influenced by your family and groups? If so, which ones?

8. What causes a group's beliefs to change?

9. List some characteristics of (a) a good leader, and (b) a good follower.

10. Do you think parents should be guided by child-rearing theories (a) much of the time, (b) sometimes, or (c) not at all? Why do you think so?

11. What evidence is there of a "hidden self" in human beings?

12. What is repression?

13. What kinds of things are repressed?

14. According to Freud's theory, what are the three basic parts of the personality? Describe each briefly.

15. What aspects of your behavior and personality do you think best show your individuality?

16. How much freedom do you think you have to direct your own life and shape your own personality? Explain your answer.

Read More About It

Hall, Elizabeth. *Why We Do What We Do*. Boston: Houghton Mifflin Company, 1973. What psychology is and how people can use it to understand themselves.

Marine, Gene. *A Male Guide to Women's Liberation*. New York: Holt, Rinehart and Winston, Inc., 1972. An analysis of sex discrimination and how to deal with it, by a man sympathetic to the goals of Women's Liberation.

Morgan, Robin (ed.). *Sisterhood Is Powerful*. New York: Random House, Inc., 1970. Collected writings by and about women. How women have filled many roles historically and how their roles are changing.

Primitive Worlds: People Lost in Time. Washington, D.C.: Special Publications Division, National Geographic Society, 1973. How isolated groups of people still live in ancient ways. Descriptions of different types of families, customs, and traditions.

Rogers, Carl R. *On Becoming a Person*. Boston: Houghton Mifflin Company, 1961. A psychologist discusses personal growth, including the setting of goals, and relationships between individuals.

Wheelis, Allen. *How People Change*. New York: Harper & Row, Perennial Library, 1974. Internal and external obstacles to change and how people can overcome them.

9
Problem Solving

After completing the work in this chapter, you will be able to:

identify the differences between reality problems and inner conflicts.

describe some tactics that are useful for solving problems.

determine how well you deal with conflicts and make decisions.

explain how defense mechanisms are used.

distinguish between neurotic and psychotic behavior.

tell where people can go for help with difficulties that are overwhelming.

suggest ways of dealing with difficult people.

Roger Strikes Out

Roger Haplis woke up earlier than usual, but worried as usual. He twisted and turned in bed wondering if the day would go any better than the last few had. He didn't want to go to school. In fact, he didn't feel like doing anything. Yesterday he asked his father if he could buy a motorcycle that one of his classmates was selling. As usual, it seemed to him, his father hardly listened before saying no. He tried to explain how he would pay for all the costs himself, including insurance. But his father just walked away. They couldn't talk anything over anymore.

Roger had been sleeping poorly for over a month now. He hated to get up in the morning and would wait until everyone else had left the house. Then he would race to school without eating. He was late for school six times in a row.

But what did it matter? He was behind in all his classes anyway. He had missed three days because of a cold, and he couldn't bring himself to ask for help to catch up. He knew he wasn't a very good student. He could never organize answers to essay questions even when he understood the material. And he felt pretty sure his teachers didn't like him enough to take time to give him extra help.

At lunch Roger was feeling terrible. He had a splitting headache. One minute he could hardly keep awake. The next, he had a tremendous urge to pick up every plate on the table and smash it against the wall. He barely controlled himself.

All of a sudden, out of the corner of his eye, he noticed Mr. Popular and his crowd strolling in. He was overcome with rage. Before he knew what he was doing, he found himself striking out at his classmate and shouting, "If you don't pay me back that ten dollars, you'll be sorry."

When the commotion was over, Roger ended up with a suspension slip. How could he face his father with that—let alone get a motorcycle? What would become of his courses? What would happen if he flunked out of school? He thought, "No one can help me now."

Effective Behavior

9-1 Problems and Conflicts

Young children often think that when they get older—say old enough to go to high school—their lives will be easier to manage. High school students often think that when they graduate and go to work or college, that will be their time of freedom. And young adults may long for the time when they marry and "settle down," thinking that their big problems will be over then. Eventually, some people long for their retirement at age 65, or even for death. At every age, a lot of people see the problems and conflicts they have to deal with as unpleasant things to get through so that they can reach a conflict-free time and "really start living." But of course there is no such magical time. Problems and conflicts are a large part of life at any age.

Do you dream of a "heaven on earth" in your future, when conflict-free moments like this one last forever?

We always have to deal with the conflicting demands made by family, by school and work, by the people and technology around us, and by the ever-changing state of our bodies and feelings.

Some problems might be called "reality problems." If you owe money and don't have any, that's a reality problem. So is finding a job so you can earn some money.

If, however, you need a job but are afraid to ask for one—afraid of meeting strangers or afraid that you somehow don't measure up—then you have a personal conflict within yourself rather than a "reality problem." If you allow your worry or fear to continue, you will not solve your money problem. And your feelings of fear, worry, and helplessness may grow to the point that you start having trouble in other aspects of your life.

The story at the beginning of this chapter tells about a person who has many problems. Which of Roger's troubles are reality problems? Which troubles are due to Roger's conflicts within himself? Which are both?

Some people seem to have more difficulties than other people: ill health, poverty, bad luck, or having to deal with troublesome people much of the time. But other people seem to make life harder for themselves than it has to be. They seem unable to solve reality problems that some people take in stride.

One reason may be that they can't think clearly about their reality problems. Their inner conflicts keep getting in the way. Another reason may be that they just don't know how to handle specific problems— how to study for exams, for instance. A

There are three types of conflicts involving things you want and things you want to avoid.

third reason that some people seem overwhelmed by small, new problems in their lives is that some important old problem has gone unresolved. The longer you fail to resolve an old problem, the harder it gets to do so. You can get more worried, more confused, and less able to make daily decisions. Your original problem is still with you, and it has helped bring about some new ones.

Sometimes it seems as though there are only two possibilities in handling a problem—you can succeed or fail in dealing with it. If you fail, you still have the problem. It might even get worse. If you succeed, you have rid yourself of it and you have learned how to deal with similar situations in the future. You have grown.

A third possibility in handling a problem is less clear-cut than outright success or failure. It is **coping**, or managing a problem with some degree of effectiveness. Coping represents a wide range of possibilities. People who have many responsibilities and little time sometimes cope by letting some less important jobs go undone. A shy person may cope with social uneasiness at a party by talking to just one friend the entire time.

Coping can be much more than just getting by. It can be an effective form of behavior in cases where situations can't really be changed. Coping can, at times, be gratifying and can make it easier to deal with a problem when it comes up again.

One of the biggest obstacles to coping or dealing successfully with problems is general fear of them. This is the frame of mind that wants to push the calendar ahead to a problem-free time. This way of thinking considers problems as life's interruptions, not part of life's real substance. But there is

Does it take much pressure to make you feel bent out of shape and distorted?

another way to think about most problems that gets you started on their solution. People who seem to be successful, happy, and well adjusted look forward to new experiences and challenges. They recognize that life is more than a set of routines, and that problems are opportunities for growth. Problems and challenges can lead to new relationships. They can encourage you to organize your life in better ways. They can help you find out about your strengths and potentials. They often make you live more deeply and thoughtfully.

9-2 Problem-Solving Tactics

Perhaps the first thing that good problem solvers do is try to separate their reality problems from their inner conflicts. Many situations have aspects of both. But each aspect usually calls for a separate solution. In the activity that follows this section, you can get some practice at sorting out these aspects of problems.

Many problems have to be solved by trial and error. That is, you try something and see if it works. If it doesn't, you change your tactic. Here are some tactics that people have used to resolve a problem. You have probably used many of them yourself, even though you probably never thought about them as items in a list.

1. *Dissolve it.* Maybe what you've been looking at as a problem isn't one; maybe it's just the way things are. Or maybe it's someone else's problem, not yours.

2. *Solve it gradually.* If the goal is very far away or the obstacles are many, you may have to proceed one step at a time.

Thinking up problem-solving tactics usually makes you feel better and cope better when you are overwhelmed by problems.

3. *Solve it quickly.* If there are many obstacles between you and your goal, you might try achieving it in a single, bold leap.

4. *Ask an expert or a resource person.* Not for the solution to your problem (usually) but for the information you need to help you make your own decision—especially in areas of health and human relations.

5. *Do it yourself.* If someone else is supposed to be providing a service for you and isn't, you may have to stop waiting and do it yourself.

6. *Wait for inspiration.* Sleep on the problem or take a long walk. Stop worrying and let your head get some good unconscious work done on the problem. Prepare for this by calmly stating to yourself or writing down exactly what the problem is.

7. *Consider a change in tactics.* Do this when one of the above approaches fails. Maybe you're being too direct when a softer touch would work, or maybe the other way around. Make a fresh start.

What other problem-solving tactics could you add to the list? Can you describe some situations in which these ideas could be helpful?

9-3 Finding Better Ways

The following five cases tell about people with problems. In each case the individual is reacting to a specific problem but is not solving it very well. The reactions may even be bringing on further difficulties.

PROCEDURE

Using the list of tactics in the last section and any fresh ideas you have, describe some better ways to deal with these problems. Before you offer solutions, be sure that you have sorted out the reality aspects of the problems from the inner aspects.

Tom Sweet knows he is at least 40 pounds overweight. He is sure everyone at school is laughing at him behind his back because he's fat. He won't participate in school activities or hang around with friends. He is very lonely.

Barbara Rivera has put off writing a term paper because she could not decide on a topic that was both interesting and not too much work. The paper is due soon.

Evelyn Kar has just moved to a new town. She has made no attempt to make new friends. Anytime anyone tries to be friendly to her, she just says she doesn't need them and hates the school. "All I want is to go back where I lived before."

Frank Chen has noticed a classmate copying from his paper during an exam. He is afraid to say anything, but he is also so angry that he can't concentrate on his own test. He probably won't get as high a mark as he hoped for, and he is afraid the same thing will happen again.

Almost every day at dinner, Fred Crowley's parents argue bitterly. Fred wants things to be peaceful. He tries to help by pointing out when one of them is right or wrong about something. This makes his parents also argue with him.

DISCUSSION

1. What are the biggest obstacles for these people in solving their problems?

2. What part of each situation is a reality problem? An inner conflict?

3. Is it likely that any of these people would listen to your advice and try to follow it?

9-4 **How Well Are You Managing?**

How do you measure how well or how poorly you are dealing with problems and conflicts? You have already seen that effective approaches to problems are the ones that resolve or settle them. Behavior and attitudes that let problems build up are ineffective. But there is more to effective behavior than that. You can also measure how well you manage by how you feel about yourself and other people.

Are you able to be honest with yourself, both in your own mind and in your relations with others? It has been said, "To be completely honest with oneself is the very best effort a human being can make." Honest, healthy behavior leads to growth and new experiences. It feels good. Dishonest behavior, on the other hand, is restrictive. If you consistently avoid facing facts, or hide your real feelings from other people, you

reduce or destroy your ability to move toward personal goals. That sort of behavior makes you feel inadequate, unhappy, and out of control.

It is important to admit to yourself how you actually feel and not shut off your feelings. It is important to know when you are unhappy and why.

Many people feel ashamed or embarrassed to admit (even to themselves) when they are angry, or afraid, or feel some other emotion they regard as "bad." But fear and anger are as natural as love and pleasure. You can be angry with someone without letting anger ruin the relationship. A sudden outburst of anger is often not called for. But anger in some cases may be an effective way of coping. If you don't allow yourself to get angry at a person who has taken advantage of you, you won't be able to deal with the situation effectively. Fear, too, is sometimes necessary. It is a feeling that serves to warn us of danger. Are there any kinds of emotions that you usually deny you feel?

Are you able to cry? Are you able to show warmth and sympathy? Or do you hide your feelings, even from yourself?

If you wonder how effectively you manage your own feelings and behavior, think how you might answer questions like these:

1. *Are my actions helping me solve the problem at hand?* Working away without achieving a result is a waste of energy and reduces your ability to see the problem clearly.

2. *Am I over-reacting?* You may lose your temper easily, be unable to tolerate opinions different from your own, or feel overwhelmed by small difficulties. Ask yourself whether the situation really calls for your reaction. Perhaps an over-reaction is caused by some strong feelings that you have earlier denied.

3. *How do I feel about the way I usually handle problems?* You may compromise in an argument or agree to change your behavior and later feel uncomfortable about the way you made your decision. Were you honest with yourself? Did you act on the basis of your feelings and opinions? An honest disagreement can be a more effective way of behaving in the long run than a mere smoothing over of differences.

4. *Do I understand why I behave as I do?* All behavior serves a purpose, even if the purpose is not apparent. Ineffective ways of behaving may protect an individual from having to face unacceptable feelings and ideas. Prolonged ineffective behavior could

To avoid conflicts, people often put up with shallow relationships that don't satisfy them. It is usually better to express your needs—argue if you have to—and try to resolve conflicts.

require counseling. Everyone is sometimes puzzled by his or her actions. Attempting to understand your behavior can lead to growth.

5. *What do I want for myself and what am I doing about it?* Maybe you haven't started to think about career goals. But what about goals such as making enough money to buy a new bike or learning a new sport? Your interest in setting up your immediate and future goals and in working toward them is an important measure of how effectively you behave.

● 9-5 Investigating What's Important To You

Resolving one problem may create others. To grow in one relationship may mean having to end other relationships or change old patterns of behavior. When there are difficult alternatives to choose from, how do you make your decisions? What areas of your life are the most important when you are trying to think through a new course of action?

PROCEDURE

Pick out from the following list four general concerns that you have when you are trying to decide on a course of action. Then think of two other concerns you might have that aren't listed. Write down on a separate piece of paper the six concerns in the order of their importance to you.

Before I make a decision, I need to know:

whether my decision will harm others
whether my decision fits my personality
whether I might lose a friend because of
  my decision
how my decision will affect my future
the possible rewards for me
the possible risks for me
whether my decision fits the way I look
  at life
what my decision means to my whole life
the effect of my decision on my emotions

DISCUSSION

1. How many of the six concerns that you chose show that you are thinking about yourself?

2. How many show that you are thinking about other people?

3. Do any of the items that are important to you show that you are thinking about the long-term results of your decision?

4. Do any show that you are thinking about the immediate results of your decision?

5. Are the items that are important to you similar to those that others in your class feel are important?

6. How many items show that you are trying to improve yourself?

7. Do you use any items for a slightly dishonest reason?

SELF CHECK

1. Explain some differences between reality problems and inner conflicts.

2. Why do some people seem able to handle reality problems more effectively than other people?

3. Describe some problem-solving techniques.

4. What are some of the consequences of refusing to face facts?

5. Identify one or more causes of over-reacting.

6. Why can disagreeing with someone be more effective than pretending to agree?

Things can get so bad that you turn off the world. Children use defense mechanisms when they can't fight back very well.

Ineffective Behavior

9-6 Defense Mechanisms

No one meets all of life's problems head-on—not even all the small ones. When situations arouse emotions that are very upsetting, people may unconsciously use **defense mechanisms** to ward off the upset. Defense mechanisms keep a person from being overwhelmed by fear, anxiety, grief, loneliness, guilt, and other strong feelings. By using defense mechanisms, people manage to go on with their lives even though important problems may be unresolved.

Repression, which you read about in Chapter 8, is a defense mechanism. It is a way that the conscious mind pushes aside upsetting thoughts and feelings. Repression is a kind of forgetting. The other defense mechanisms all seem to involve some aspects of forgetfulness, too.

When people find "good" reasons to justify behavior that makes them uneasy, they are using a defense mechanism called **rationalization** (rash uhn uhl uh ZAY shuhn). The real reasons for the behavior have been repressed. If you fail at something important, and then tell yourself it really didn't matter, you are rationalizing. People can rationalize away all sorts of frustrations, feelings of insecurity, and guilt.

Projection consists of denying an unwanted personal trait by repressing it from consciousness and assigning it to someone else. Prejudiced people, for example, often see in groups that they dislike those characteristics of themselves that they find threatening. "Those people" are likely to be aggressive, conniving, stupid, and odd looking—which, of course, none of "our people" are!

Have you ever shouted at a younger brother or sister after a bad day at school? You may have been angry at a teacher, but it was safer to release, or displace, your anger at someone else. **Displacement** is a defense mechanism in which a person directs an emotion to a safe place. Punching a bag in the gym, for instance, is a safer way of getting rid of anger than punching a classmate.

Making up for dissatisfaction in one area by excelling in another is called **compensation.** It is not the same as having a strong interest in something in the first place. For example, without being aware of trying to compensate, a student with mediocre grades may work extra hard to excel in sports, or the other way around.

There are many other defense mechanisms. They have the same general functions as the ones just listed. Healthy, normal people use them sometimes. For example, repression may make it possible for a person to forget a tragedy or a disappointment and go on to new activities. But defense mechanisms can also be harmful. A person who rationalizes all the time can have trouble keeping sight of his or her feelings and goals. And grief that is felt and lived through can give you greater personal

Do you ever argue with a projection of yourself—for example with a side of you that feels stupid or hostile?

strength and sympathy for others than grief that is repressed.

Feelings and memories that people defend themselves against may often become magnified and distorted. They may become the subject matter of upsetting dreams. The more disturbing such feelings become, the more they seem to require defense mechanisms. So, instead of helping a person to cope, defense mechanisms in the long run can have just the opposite effect.

9-7 Failing to Cope

Ineffective ways of acting take time to develop. They usually arise in childhood. Some children grow up holding back or distorting their impulses and feelings. They continually use defense mechanisms to deal with themselves and other people. This behavior may have helped the child to deal with difficult home situations. But it doesn't help the adult trapped in the childhood behavioral pattern. This constant, ineffective behavior is sometimes called **neurotic** (noo RAHT ihk). Some typical neurotic behavior patterns are described later in this section.

Neurotic behavior involves unconscious conflicts and, usually, feelings of anxiety. **Anxiety** is a state of uneasiness or worry. It is different from fear because fear has a real object, something truly fearful. Anxiety tends to be general and have no clear object. It arises, some psychologists think, when a person gets into a situation that produces uncomfortably strong emotions or impulses to do something frightening. For example, a mild-mannered person who always denies angry feelings might feel very angry in a certain situation, angry enough to hit someone. Or a "tough guy" might have tender feelings he was afraid of. There are many similar examples you could imagine. To hold back the strong feelings, the neu-

People make themselves anxious without knowing how they do it or, usually, why.

rotic person unconsciously tightens chest muscles and inhibits deep breathing. This reduces the amount of oxygen available for "fueling" the unwanted impulse or feeling. When anyone, neurotic or not, runs short of oxygen this way, it produces anxiety (a word that originally meant a strangled or constricted feeling).

One way to get temporary relief from the feeling is to get more oxygen into the lungs. It doesn't help to try to inhale more deeply, since the chest muscles are tightly constricted. Instead, the person should concentrate on *exhaling* as completely as possible, going along with the tight chest muscles. A strong exhalation will automatically produce a deeper inhalation. Anxious feelings and muscle tightness are usually relieved to some extent after a few minutes of working on breathing this way.

Anxiety is often an unwanted side effect of dealing with unconscious conflicts by trying to deny them. The opposite sort of feeling—being overwhelmed by an outburst of anger or excitement when it seems uncalled for—is also typical of some neurotics. These feelings often seem to arise when a situation is not really threatening, when it is safe to blow off steam. In a situation that *is* threatening, the neurotic usually acts with too little passion and may feel anxiety.

People who grow up with neurotic behavior patterns feel anxious and upset much of the time. Their inner conflicts keep them from effectively managing their lives. They may want to enjoy life more than they do. And they usually cannot understand why they hold themselves back in some situations and over-react in others. In addition to experiencing troubled emotions, such individuals often suffer physical distress such as frequent headaches, muscle tensions, and diseases of the respiratory and digestive systems.

Some of the more common forms of neurotic behavior are anxiety neurosis, obsessive-compulsive neuroses, phobias, and hysteria. A person with an **anxiety neurosis** feels worried without knowing why. Attacks of anxiety may be mild or severe. In severe cases a person may feel that she or he is "going to pieces." Some people seem to fear that their true feelings will get out of control and get them into trouble. Other people become anxious when they think of doing something that is against their moral code.

Fear of a commonplace thing—that's a phobia. Some people even have phobic reactions to pictures of cats, snakes, spiders, and other things.

People who work later and harder than anyone else may be "work-aholics," a new name for a type of obsessive-compulsive.

An **obsessive-compulsive** person has certain thoughts (obsessions) crowding his or her mind much of the time, or feels the need to keep doing certain things over and over (compulsions). The compulsion may be fairly harmless, like washing one's hands dozens of times a day. Harmless, obsessive thoughts may keep the neurotic's conscious mind off anxiety-producing feelings. Compulsive acts may do the same thing, for example, by taking an inner feeling of uncleanliness and "projecting" it onto one's hands. An obsessive-compulsive person may be valuable to an employer if the person feels the need to work long hours until everything has been thoroughly done. But such people often worry so much over details that nothing substantial ever gets done. There never seems to be time for pleasure or relaxation for these people. Free time arouses anxiety in them, and they try to keep busy instead.

A **phobia** (FOH bee uh) is a strong fear, resulting from the focusing of anxious feelings on a special object or situation. A person may have a phobia about heights, open spaces, small spaces, tame animals, the dark, microorganisms, riding in an elevator—just about anything. Some phobias result when an anxiety over an internal conflict is directed toward a specific object that seems perfectly harmless to other people. The phobia enables the individual to avoid the anxiety-producing situation.

Hysteria (hih STEHR ee uh) is another common form of neurosis. It is characterized by physical symptoms that have no physical cause. Someone suffering from hysteria may suddenly be unable to see or hear or move a limb. Shortly after killing an enemy, a soldier in combat once found that his right arm was paralyzed. It is likely that the paralysis was a form of hysterical neurosis. The paralysis "punished" the arm that had committed the killing and assured the soldier that he could not do any more killing. Had he been able to express his troubled feelings at doing his soldierly duty, the attack of paralysis might not have occurred or might not have been so severe.

Everyone feels alone and isolated at times. It is a price we pay for being individuals. Some very troubled people can hardly ever make contact with others.

9-8 Losing Touch With Reality

Neuroses are constant emotional and behavioral difficulties that reduce a person's ability to cope. **Psychoses** (sy KOH seez) involve the entire personality so completely that people get out of touch with reality. Their emotions become distorted, behavior becomes irrational, and they often imagine things that aren't really there. Depending on the type of psychosis, a person may be able to cope at some times, then lose this ability completely and require hospitalization.

The most common psychoses are forms of **schizophrenia** (skiht suh FREE nee uh).

Schizophrenia is a kind of catchall term referring to withdrawal from contacts with other people. In simple schizophrenia the individual has largely withdrawn from the world. Such people have few or no outside interests and show little emotion. In another form of schizophrenia, individuals may be emotional, but they laugh and cry at the wrong times. Their thoughts are disorganized and illogical.

Another kind of psychotic disorder is **catatonic schizophrenia.** Persons afflicted with this difficulty may go for weeks or months sitting, lying, or standing in the same, rigid position just staring into space. **Paranoid** (PAR uh noyd) **schizophrenics** have deluded thoughts about themselves and the rest of the world. They may feel very important, even confusing themselves with famous people. But they are convinced that the rest of the world is secretly persecuting them.

Some cases of psychosis seem to have physical causes. Changes in the brain caused by injury, disease, drugs, or old age may set off psychotic behavior. There is also evidence that a tendency to become schizophrenic may sometimes be inherited. Other cases of psychosis seem to have environmental causes. Long-standing problems, such as a very frustrating childhood, may set off irrational behavior. Physical and environmental causes may both be involved in many or most cases.

Psychoses may develop slowly. Feelings and behavior may gradually change. Signs that a person is beginning to over-react in situations and is losing touch with reality are reasons for concern.

9-9 Antisocial Behavior

Some people appear to cope very well, but they do it at the expense of everyone around them. The term **sociopath** (SOH see oh path) applies to people who seem to have no conscience. They do as they please, take what they want, and feel no guilt about hurting other people in the process. They rarely form long-lasting affectionate relationships with other people. They seem to be relatively free of anxiety and of the need for human acceptance, love, and support.

Some sociopaths appear to be successful. They may achieve their goals without breaking laws and may be admired for their toughness. Some become criminals, concerned only about being caught and unconcerned about the property or lives of their victims.

People who have antisocial personalities seem to look at and use other people as objects. Many of them can be charming and appealing when they choose to be—for a purpose. They may apparently form a strong relationship with one or more other people, then break it suddenly when these people are no longer needed.

Sociopaths may use rationalization skillfully. Some may believe that their behavior is justified because it contributes to some social or political goal that they consider more important than the welfare of any individuals who are in their way.

Generally, sociopaths do not recognize that they have any emotional disturbance. Unlike neurotics, they do not feel uncomfortable about their behavior and do not seek or accept help. For this reason, they are among the most difficult patients for therapists to treat.

9-10 Where Can People Go for Help?

When something bothers you, do you find someone to talk to about it? Talking things over with a friend or a trusted adult is often helpful. Bringing your feelings out into the open and listening to someone else's ideas and suggestions are good ways to work out temporary difficulties.

More formal help is available for people whose attitudes and behavior interfere with how they function or for people who feel uncomfortable with themselves and with other people. School counselors may be trained social workers or psychologists. They are available to most high school students for help with personal and emotional difficulties. A counselor or a family doctor may be the person to consult first if something troubles you.

Hot Line telephone services operate in many communities. Some of them are available all day and all night. The people

Friends or family are usually the first people to go to for comfort, advice, and help.

answering Hot Line calls just listen when a person wants someone to talk to, or they suggest other sources of help.

Many communities have special Suicide Prevention Centers for people who feel so depressed, so unable to cope, or so angry at themselves or the world that they fear they may commit suicide. Center telephone numbers and addresses are listed in the telephone directory. Large hospitals also may offer 24-hour staffing of Suicide Prevention Centers. Many thousands of people do kill themselves every year. Among people in the age group of 15–19 years, suicide is the third leading cause of death.

If the person you go to for help cannot supply exactly the kind of help you need, he or she may refer you to someone else who has skill and experience in dealing with problems like yours. The referral may be to a social worker, a religious advisor with special training in counseling, a psychotherapist, or a mental health clinic.

Psychotherapy (sy koh THEHR uh pee) includes all forms of treatment for emotional and behavioral difficulties. There are many different kinds of psychotherapy, all with their supporters and opponents, claims of success, and reports of failure. Some therapists are psychiatrists. They are medical doctors who specialize in mental health care. Others are psychologists or social workers with special training.

Some forms of psychotherapy involve a one-to-one exchange between the client and the therapist. Patients are encouraged to speak freely about their feelings and behavior. The therapist can usually provide a more objective and understanding view of the problems than the client has. Some therapists rely primarily on discussion of problems, others on acting problems out. Still other therapists spend a lot of time working to reduce body tensions as well as psychological ones. Some therapists prescribe tranquilizers or other drugs temporarily to help troubled people continue with their daily lives.

Psychotherapy can be carried out in groups. Several people meet with the therapist at one time to talk about their problems. The participants can help each other in several ways. They can be sympathetic and encouraging. Often they can provide valuable insights and information, especially when a participant discovers that he or she is not the only one in the world that suffers from a particular problem. People who have trouble getting along with others may find group sessions more useful than private therapy.

A special form of group therapy is "family therapy." Although only one member of

"Encounter groups" are a form of group therapy. They have helped people overcome fear and hostility toward others.

the family may have asked for help, the therapist meets with the entire family. The goal is for family members to learn how they feel about each other and how each one's behavior affects the others.

For people who have severe mental health problems, hospitalization is often necessary. Community hospitals may have psychiatric departments. Both public and private psychiatric hospitals treat large numbers of patients. However, a growing trend today is to try to help the mentally disturbed on an outpatient basis. It is argued that people are almost always better off living in their homes and communities than they are in an impersonal, large institution. People can live at home and still get regular psychiatric treatment.

The available types of help vary in how successfully they help people. A special therapy might be right for some patients and ineffective for others. A therapist who is received whole-heartedly by some people may make others uncomfortable. Theories and techniques for helping people keep changing. Some theories disappear and new ones quickly take their place. For people who feel troubled, the most important step is the first one—to talk over the situation with a trusted person and ask for a referral. This first step is also the beginning of change. It reflects the realization that a difficulty exists and that it is possible to do something about it. Attitudes and behavior *can* be changed. It *is* possible to learn how to be happier and more effective.

Most troubled people who claim that they do not need help or say that nothing is wrong with them are not ready to change. Very often people seek help only when their problems become crises and they are feeling overwhelmed. The desire to change a pattern of behavior is the key to all improvement, and that beginning must ultimately come from within.

● 9-11 Dealing With Difficult People

We sometimes encounter people whose behavior seems exaggerated or inappropriate. They may be having trouble coping, and they may make it more difficult for us to cope. It doesn't matter whether they are neurotic, psychotic, or simply upset because of some difficulty in their lives. If we can't avoid these people, we may have to cope with them. We may even want to try to help them.

PROCEDURE

For each case below, decide what you think would be the appropriate course of action for you to take.

The supervisor at the store where you work making deliveries is often angry. She shouts at people a lot. One day she blames you for not having delivered five orders. You are certain that no one told you to deliver those orders. Should you:

a. shout back at her?
b. explain the situation politely, and offer to take the deliveries even though it's past quitting time?
c. just explain calmly that it's not your fault?
d. tell the store owner that the supervisor is picking on you?
e. do something else? Explain what.

Should you always try to reason things out with others? When do you need to try other tactics?

You are sitting on the bus studying for an exam. An old man sits down next to you and starts telling you his troubles. He keeps complaining and asking your opinion about his various misfortunes. He sounds bitter and lonely. Should you:

a. listen and answer his questions politely?
b. get up and move away?
c. say politely that you don't have time to talk?
d. express your opinions if they disagree with his?
e. suggest he might enjoy visiting with some older people at a social club in the neighborhood?
f. do something else? Explain what.

You are baby-sitting. At midnight, little Frances wakes up and screams because of a dream about monsters. Should you:

a. run in, turn the lights on, and say cheerfully that monsters don't exist?

b. tell Frances to forget the dream and let her watch TV with you?

c. ask Frances to tell you all about the dream, hoping she will go back to sleep?

d. tell Frances you will protect her from monsters?

e. do something else? Explain what.

You are assigned to work on a report for the next month with Edith Marvell. You discover that Edith insists on finding out *all* the details about each part of the subject before going on. At this rate, you will never finish your report. Edith accuses you of having sloppy work habits and won't listen to your ideas. Should you:

a. tell the teacher you want a different partner?

b. ignore Edith and do the report yourself, the way you want?

c. try to talk with Edith and reach a compromise?

d. do something else? Explain what.

You and Kevin Mason have been spending a lot of time together. You enjoy many of the same things. But you notice that Kevin has begun getting very upset whenever you want to be by yourself or go somewhere with other people. Lately he has even threatened to stop being your friend unless you promise to spend your whole vacation doing things with him. Should you:

a. promise to spend all your vacation time with him?

b. refuse to?

c. explain that you like him and other people as well?

d. do something else? Explain what.

DISCUSSION

1. For each case, give reasons why you would respond in the way you have chosen.

2. For each case, which would be the *worst* thing to do?

3. What is the likelihood that you could get these five people to stop acting in upsetting ways?

4. What if Frances, in the third case, were a high school friend telling you that creatures from a UFO were after her? Is there any difference between dealing with children's irrational fears and those of adults?

SELF CHECK

1. What are some beneficial uses of defense mechanisms? What are the dangers of overusing them?

2. What is the most significant difference between a neurosis and a psychosis?

3. What are the characteristics of a sociopath? How does such a person differ from a neurotic?

4. When may a troubled person need more help than just talking things over with a friend?

Chapter Summary

Everybody has to deal with reality problems in the environment, such as those involving family, school, work, and other people. Individuals who have inner conflicts find it harder to deal with reality problems. If their inner conflicts are extreme, they may fail in almost every attempt to manage their lives.

A person's success in dealing with problems is a measure of growth. Between succeeding and failing lies coping, or managing difficult situations more or less satisfactorily. Identifying and resolving inner conflicts make it possible to cope with reality problems more effectively more of the time.

A useful way of measuring the effectiveness of behavior is how it makes a person feel. Being honest about inner feelings and relationships with other people makes it possible to grow and to enjoy new experiences. Refusal to face facts about feelings and reality makes people unhappy and ineffective. They may not know why they feel miserable and ineffective.

Defense mechanisms are a common coping device. But over-reliance on defense mechanisms and inability to resolve inner conflicts are signs of neurosis. Neurotic people often have feelings of anxiety. Neurosis can also produce physical symptoms, such as headaches, muscle tensions, and certain diseases.

A neurosis makes it difficult to cope. A psychosis is so severe that a person loses touch with reality. Psychotic individuals may withdraw from other people, show no feeling at all or inappropriate extremes of feeling, or have completely mistaken ideas about themselves and other people. A sociopathic person behaves in a hostile way toward society.

A troubled person may seek help from a friend. A school counselor or family doctor may refer people to a social worker, psychologist, psychiatrist, or religious advisor for counseling or psychotherapy. The goals of psychotherapy are to help people understand inner conflicts and to change their behavior.

Chapter Self Check

1. Why do some people have trouble telling the difference between reality problems and inner conflicts?

2. Give an example of how an inner conflict interferes with solving a reality problem.

3. Explain the statement, "Problems are opportunities for growth."

4. What are some reasons it may be difficult to be honest with oneself?

5. What can happen when a reality problem makes it difficult or hazardous to express true feelings?

6. What would be your advice to someone who is often puzzled by his or her behavior?

7. How can an individual know if he or she is overusing defense mechanisms?

8. Explain how some forms of ineffective adult behavior may be related to difficult childhood situations.

9. What is the difference between anxiety and fear?

10. Describe some ways neurosis interferes with enjoying life.

11. Give one or more examples of obsessive-compulsive behavior.

12. What are some physical symptoms of neurosis?

13. Describe two types of schizophrenia.

14. What is the common factor in the many forms of schizophrenia?

15. What physical factors may be involved in some cases of schizophrenia?

16. Give some examples of behavior that may identify a sociopathic person.

17. Give examples of the kinds of behavior that might make you think a friend needs help.

18. What advantages do you see in one-to-one therapy? In group therapy?

19. How would your knowledge of a troublesome person's problems affect your way of coping with him or her?

Read More About It

Greenberg, Joanne (Hannah Green). *I Never Promised You a Rose Garden*. New York: Signet (New American Library), 1973. At age sixteen, a girl needs care in a mental hospital. This is an account of her three years there and her slow recovery.

Hall, Elizabeth. *Why We Do What We Do*. Boston: Houghton Mifflin Company, 1973. What psychology is and how people can use it to understand themselves.

Kovel, Joel. *A Complete Guide to Therapy*. New York: Pantheon Books, 1976. A guide to the various kinds of therapies, their advantages and disadvantages, and risks to people with special problems, written by a psychiatrist.

Psychology Today: An Introduction. Del Mar California: CRM Books, 1972. A detailed survey of learning, human development, personality, and other areas of psychology.

Schreiber, Flora Rheta. *Sybil*. New York: Warner Books, 1973. Sixteen personalities in one schizophrenic woman, written with the cooperation of both the patient and her doctor, who helps her develop a single personality.

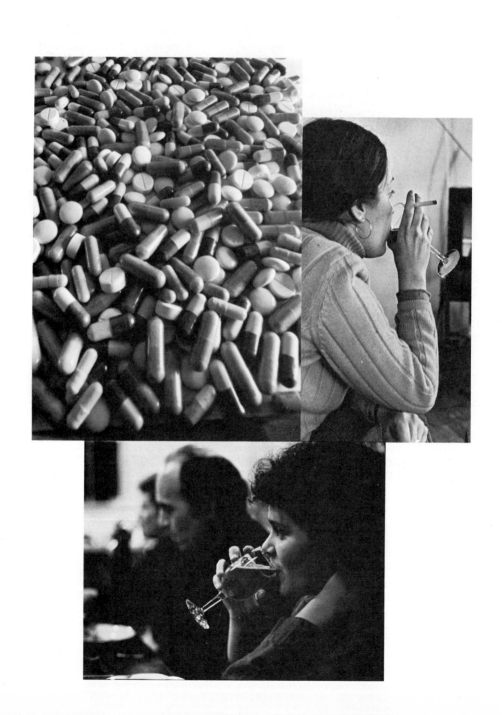

10
Deciding
About Drugs

After completing the work in this chapter, you will be able to:

identify reasons that you approve of for using drugs.

define drug abuse.

describe the three types of psychoactive drugs and some of their effects.

describe effects of smoking tobacco, drinking alcohol, and using other legal drugs.

identify ways people can get help with drug problems.

describe activities that help you relieve tension, use up extra energy, and find excitement, without using drugs.

Who Is a Drug User?

John decided to stay home. He usually went out with his friends, but one of them had been caught with some marijuana two days earlier. John was afraid that the police would be keeping a close eye on the group. Anyway, his parents were having friends over that he liked.

When the guests arrived, John welcomed them while his parents were making last-minute preparations. After they had all moved outside to the deck, somebody mentioned John's friend, Roy, the one who had been arrested. A discussion began about kids using drugs. The adults were very criti-cal of people who smoked marijuana and took other illegal drugs. John didn't say anything. He didn't want a big argument to start.

About three drinks later, Mrs. Brown told John's mother that she had been feeling nervous and upset quite a lot recently.

"What have you been taking for it?" asked John's mother.

"Nothing," Mrs. Brown replied. "When I really get anxious I just have a couple of drinks and that helps me get to sleep."

"Oh," said John's mother. "I was feeling at loose ends myself a few weeks ago. But not anymore. My doctor gave me a prescription for Valium. Let me tell you—the pills really helped! I have a few left. Would you like to try one?"

"Well, I don't know. . . ."

"They couldn't hurt, could they? The doctor said to take one any time I got tense or anxious. Once in a while I've felt bad enough to take two of them, and it didn't do any harm. Let me give you one."

"Okay, I'll try one. I guess they couldn't hurt me either."

Mrs. Brown washed the Valium down with her last swallow of Scotch and water. About an hour later she was yawning and fighting to stay awake. Mrs. Irving served them all some strong coffee. The conversation had come to a standstill, and Mr. Brown decided that it was time to leave.

After the Browns left, John felt confused. He wondered:

Were the Browns drug abusers?

Were his parents drug abusers?

Why were they all critical of kids who smoke marijuana? How was that different from the alcohol or prescription drugs they were using to feel better?

Was it a good idea for his mother to have given her prescription medicine to someone else?

Desired Effects and Risks

● 10-1 What Drug Uses Do You Approve Of?

Many substances come under the heading of "drugs." In this chapter the **drugs** to be discussed include anything people put into their bodies to change the way they feel, perceive things, or behave. A drug may be used occasionally or habitually. It may be legal or illegal. It may have specific medical uses or it may not. It may be very mild in its effects or very severe.

Procedure

Select from the following list those reasons for using drugs that you approve of for yourself. Do you approve of the same ones for other people?

to relax
to get energy
out of curiosity
to be sociable
to get to sleep
to get relief from problems
to relieve a headache
to improve sports performance
to help stay awake
to improve creativity
to gain weight
to lose weight
for thrills
to reduce muscle pain
to relieve a stomachache
to reduce inhibitions
for pleasant sensations
in a religious ceremony

Discussion

1. Do your answers differ from those of your classmates? Are there any general reasons for the different opinions?

2. Are there any circumstances that might make an unacceptable reason acceptable?

3. Are there any circumstances that might make an acceptable reason unacceptable?

Remember that you and your classmates are discussing your opinions. Opinions may differ. Even if there is general agreement, the minority opinion isn't necessarily wrong.

10-2 Mood-Altering Drugs

Mood-altering substances known as **psychoactive** (sy koh AK tihv) **drugs** affect the central nervous system. They influence the user's body, behavior, and personality. There are three general types of psychoactive drugs. The **depressants** slow down body and mind activities. The **stimulants** speed up these activities. The **hallucinogens** (huh LOO suh nuh juhnz), or psychedelics (sy kuh DEHL iks), change sensory perceptions and may lead to hallucinations. The Drug Chart on pages 264–265 gives detailed information about many of these drugs.

A few of the words used in the Drug Chart may be unfamiliar to you. *Delirium tremens* (dih LIHR ee uhm TREE muhnz) refers to mental confusion with anxiety, hallucinations, and tremors. *Depression* is a feeling of helplessness and hopelessness. It is not the same as sadness. A sad person feels warm, alive, and unhappy but not dull and unresponsive, as a depressed person feels. *Euphoric* (yoo FAWR ihk) is feeling very happy and blissful. *Impotence* occurs when a male is unable to respond sexually. *Stupor* is mental confusion, or being in a daze. *Addiction, habituation,* and *tolerance* are explained in Section 10-3.

One theory of how psychoactive drugs work is that they affect nerve synapses. Synapses are the tiny gaps between the separate neurons in a nerve pathway. Different drugs are believed to speed up or slow down the nerve impulses traveling across synapses. It is not understood precisely how drugs do that, and why changes at synapses lead to mood changes.

Depressant drugs are used for relaxation, relief from pain, reduction of anxiety, and aid in sleeping. They do not usually cause depression. The words are confusing. Stimulants are used to increase alertness, create a feeling of excitement, and give relief from worry. They may be used medically to reduce appetite, relieve fatigue, and treat anxiety and depression.

The effects of hallucinogens are especially unpredictable. Some people report very pleasant experiences of glowing colors, dazzling sounds, and the like. They may experience the world in strange and wondrous ways. Other people have lost their contact with reality and panicked, becoming temporarily psychotic from use of the same substance.

The way a drug affects a person depends on many different things. These include size, weight, and physical condition, and attitude and feelings at the time of taking the drug. The "Desired Effects" column in the Drug Chart gives some idea of how complex—and even conflicting—the psychological effects of mood-altering drugs can be. Individuals vary widely in how they are affected by particular drugs. Alcohol, for example, makes some people sleepy and others aggressive or happy. People can use alcohol to help them get to either state. That is another characteristic of mood-altering drugs. The user can often achieve a desired mood with the "help" of the drug. Other influences on the effect of a drug are whether the drug is mixed with other drugs, the purity of the drug itself, the amount taken, and how often it is taken. Even the social setting influences how a drug affects someone.

The effects of a drug are not necessarily limited to the user. If a pregnant woman takes a drug, it may pass from her bloodstream into the bloodstream of her unborn baby and harm it.

The effects of taking "street drugs" are never certain, even for experienced users. Let the buyer beware. Unlike legal drugs, street drugs are not regulated by any governmental agency whose job is to protect consumers. Street drugs are not inspected.

Narcotics sold in the street are, in fact, never pure. Dealers always "cut" what they sell. This means they stretch their supply by mixing in other substances. Sometimes the substitution will be a harmless, cheap substance such as sugar. But there is no way of telling. It could just as well be a poison such as arsenic. The Addiction Research Foundation of Ontario and other agencies often buy street drugs and analyze their contents. They have found, for example, no mescaline at all but instead some dangerous chemicals in dozens of doses of "mescaline" offered for sale all around a large Canadian city.

The unreliability of street-drug purchases can have dangerous and even fatal consequences. Some deaths have been described by officials as due to supposed overdoses of heroin. In view of the high price of this substance, it is extremely unlikely that anyone would sell too concentrated a product to a customer. It is more likely that the "heroin" was, in fact, something else and that the victim died from poisoning or from an allergic reaction.

One of the many factors to consider before deciding to use a drug is its legal status. As you undoubtedly know, heroin is an illegal drug. It is illegal to buy it, sell it, or use it. Most of the drugs in the Drug Chart are illegal unless prescribed by a doctor. And

Drug taking is an old human activity. Persian nobles of the fifteenth century smoked hashish.

many, such as heroin, cocaine, and marijuana, cannot by law even be prescribed by a doctor.

The laws controlling drugs vary from place to place. Federal laws apply to the manufacture of certain drugs, but local laws may govern their sale and use. For example, alcohol may be legally sold in one town but not in a neighboring town. The legal drinking age varies from 18 to 21 in different states. The penalties for using marijuana vary from small fines to long jail sentences depending on the state. The penalties for using drugs illegally depend also on the quantities involved, and whether one is selling or buying for personal use. Enforcement of drug laws also varies according to local customs.

You might be interested in finding out exactly what the state and local laws are regarding drug use in your community.

Psychoactive Drug Chart

DRUG TYPE	EXAMPLES	MEDICAL USES	DESIRED EFFECTS	RISKS Short-term	RISKS Long-term	DEPENDENCE
DEPRESSANTS						
beverage alcohol	beer wine liquor some medicines	used in some medicines that are taken by mouth	to relax, to escape from problems or inhibitions, to become euphoric	depression, decreased alertness, drowsiness, slurred speech, poor coordination, hangover; aggressive feelings, stupor, nausea, unconsciousness, and death, all with increased amounts	obesity, impotence, psychosis, ulcers, malnutrition, liver and brain damage; delirium tremens when withdrawn; death from alcohol-related illnesses	tolerance, habituation, addiction
barbiturates and similar-acting chemicals	Nembutal phenobarbital Seconal methaqualone (Sopor, Quaalude)	to treat insomnia, tension, and epileptic seizures	to relax, to become euphoric	decreased alertness, drowsiness, poor coordination, slurred speech, hangover, stupor; sleep or death with increased amounts	confusion, irritability, severe withdrawal symptoms	tolerance, habituation, addiction
inhalants (substances that you breathe in)	aerosols airplane glue ether "laughing gas" (nitrous oxide)	ether, nitrous oxide, and other gases used as anesthetics	to relax, to become euphoric	poor coordination, stupor; unconsciousness or death with increased amounts; some inhalants may damage linings of nose, mouth, throat, and lungs	hallucinations; damage to liver, kidneys, bone marrow, and brain	tolerance, habituation
narcotics and similar-acting chemicals	codeine	to treat coughing; to relieve pain	to relax, to escape from problems and tensions, to become euphoric	decreased alertness, hallucinations, stupor, unconsciousness, death with increased amounts	tiredness, constipation, temporary sterility and impotence	tolerance, habituation, addiction
	Demerol	to relieve pain				
	heroin	none in the U.S. or Canada				
	methadone	to prevent heroin withdrawal symptoms				
	morphine	to relieve pain				
	opium	to relieve pain				
	paregoric	to treat diarrhea				
	Percodan	to relieve pain				

	Examples	Medical uses	Reasons for use	Short-term effects	Long-term effects	Dependence
minor tranquilizers	Librium, Miltown/Equanil, Valium	to treat tension, anxiety, insomnia, muscle spasms	to relax; to relieve tension, anxiety, muscle spasms, sleeplessness	drowsiness, blurred vision, dizziness, reduced alertness	over-stimulation, sleep disturbance, changes in heartbeat and blood pressure	tolerance, habituation, addiction
HALLUCINOGENS						
cannabis	hashish, marijuana	experimental uses only, nothing established	to relax, to become euphoric, to change perceptions	confusion, panic, stupor	respiratory problems, cancer risks (if smoked)	habituation
other substances	DMT, LSD, mescaline, STP, peyote	experiments in psychology and psychiatry	to change perceptions	confusion, anxiety, panic, hallucinations, psychosis, tremors	delusions, psychosis	habituation
	PCP ("Angel Dust")	animal tranquilizer	to change perceptions	disorientation, rage, terror, depression	paranoid and violent behavior	
STIMULANTS						
amphetamines and similar-acting chemicals	Benzedrine, Dexedrine, Methedrine, Preludin, Ritalin	to treat obesity, depression, narcolepsy (sudden and uncontrollable need to sleep)	to increase alertness and energy, to become euphoric, to stay awake	over-stimulation, restlessness, irritability, insomnia, stomach difficulties, convulsions	insomnia, undesired weight loss, delusions, hallucinations, psychosis	tolerance, habituation, addiction
antidepressants	Elavil, Tofranil, Norpramin	to treat depression	to relieve depression, to increase energy, to relieve sleep disturbance	dry mouth, blurred vision, constipation, delayed urination, lowered blood pressure	increased risk of short-term symptoms	habituation
caffeine	chocolate, coffee, cola, No-Doz, tea	for oversedation, headache, drowsiness	to increase energy and alertness	restlessness, insomnia, upset stomach	restlessness, insomnia, upset stomach	tolerance, habituation, addiction
cocaine	cocaine	topical anesthetic	to feel self-confidence, power; to feel happy, euphoric	over-stimulation, erratic behavior, insomnia, irritability, hallucinations, psychosis	when sniffed: damage to linings of nose and blood vessels; psychosis	tolerance, habituation
nicotine	cigarettes, cigars, pipe tobacco	none	to relax, to increase alertness, for oral stimulation	headache, loss of appetite, nausea, coughing due to smoke	difficulty in breathing, heart and lung disease, cancer of mouth and throat due to smoke	tolerance, habituation, addiction

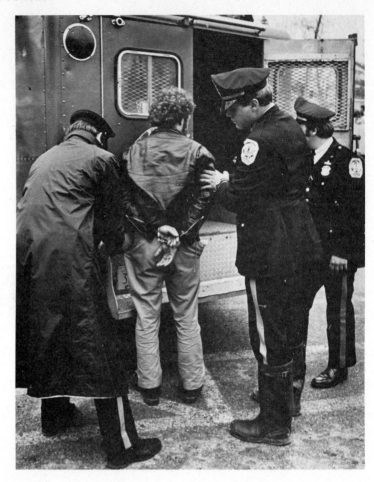

An addict may have to worry about a lot of things, including his drug supply, money, health, and the law.

10-3 Habituation, Addiction, and Tolerance

Using psychoactive drugs is very likely to be habit forming. People use a drug for the first time for a variety of reasons. These can probably all be grouped either under the heading "to get relief," "to get pleasure," or "to belong to the group." Users can become dependent on a drug to get these experiences. It is then distressing to do without the drug. This psychological dependence is **habituation** (huh bihch oo AY shuhn).

Some drugs alter more than moods. They change the way the body works. After taking one of these drugs for a while, a person begins to need it physically. If it is taken away (withdrawn) there will probably be great physical discomfort or pain. Someone who needs a drug in this way has a physical dependence or an **addiction.** The effects of drugs on infrequent users and on addicts can be quite different. Most of an addict's "pleasure" from a dose is simply relief from oncoming withdrawal symptoms.

With many drugs, people have to increase the amount taken each time, or take the

An addict is a prisoner of time. At regular intervals the effect of the drug wears off, and she needs more.

drug more often, in order to get the same effect. When this happens, a person has a **tolerance** for the drug. Tolerance varies from one person to another. You can have a tolerance for both drugs of addiction and drugs of habituation.

The differences between addiction and habituation are not always clear. Scientists still do not know enough about the effects of drugs to always be able to tell the difference between physical dependence and psychological dependence.

You can see in the last column of the Drug Chart that the use of any psychoactive drug can lead to psychological dependence, habituation. The substances that have addictive physical effects are alcohol, barbiturates, narcotics, minor tranquilizers, amphetamines, caffeine, and nicotine.

You have probably heard about cases of drug-related deaths involving barbiturates. In the case of barbiturates, an intentional overdose is clearly possible; a person simply takes too many pills. In accidental barbiturate "overdose" cases, the usual cause of death is taking a barbiturate along with something else such as alcohol. It does not take a large dose of a barbiturate to be dangerous—even fatal—if it is taken in combination with alcohol. Other combinations of drugs or overdoses of single drugs are also extremely dangerous.

SELF CHECK

1. What is a drug?

2. What are the three types of psychoactive drugs? Describe their effects.

3. Which group of psychoactive drugs has the least predictable effects?

4. What are the hazards of using "street drugs"?

5. What are habituation, addiction, and tolerance to drugs?

We've come a long way.

Our lung cancer rates
are catching up with men's.

Warning: The Surgeon General Has Determined
That Cigarette Smoking Is Dangerous to Your Health

Dangerous Legal Drugs

10-4 How Smoking Affects Health

People have smoked, chewed, or inhaled tobacco for centuries. Soon after Columbus and other early explorers brought tobacco to Europe, it was recognized as causing dependence. Smoking was forbidden by many European countries and churches. A Turkish sultan made smoking punishable by death. But none of this stopped the growing public use of tobacco. Recent discoveries that many diseases are associated with smoking have persuaded many people to quit, but the total number of smokers is still very high. People are still taking up smoking in great numbers.

The Surgeon General Has Determined That Cigarette Smoking Is Dangerous to

Your Health. This warning is required on ads and packs of cigarettes sold in the United States, and refers to many health dangers associated with smoking. Cigarette smokers have 70 percent more heart disease than nonsmokers. There is a great deal of evidence that smoking is the major cause of lung cancer in both men and women. Smoking is the major cause of chronic bronchitis and emphysema. In emphysema the walls of the tiny air sacs in the lungs break down, destroying much of the surface for absorption of oxygen. The victims can't get enough oxygen into the bloodstream, and they become "respiratory cripples." Some of them remain in bed for the rest of their lives.

There are many other health hazards for smokers, as well. For example, carbon monoxide, the poisonous waste product of combustion reactions, is present in harmful amounts in cigarette smoke. Carbon monoxide may decrease physical performance and increase heartbeat rate. Nicotine, the stimulant found in tobacco smoke, also increases heartbeat rate and may increase blood pressure.

Nonsmokers also suffer physical harm from the presence of smoke. Tobacco smoke is an air pollutant. The excess smoke that drifts off from a burning cigarette and the smoke that is exhaled make nonsmokers' hearts beat faster. Their blood pressure goes up, and the level of carbon monoxide in their blood increases. Lung illness is twice as common in young children whose parents smoke as in children of nonsmokers. People who have a chronic lung disease, such as asthma, may be especially affected by smoke in the air.

The risks of addiction or habituation have not been nearly so widely publicized as the other health effects of smoking. Once people start smoking they often cannot stop, even if they want to. Another reason people

Smokers hurt their friends without meaning to. Everyone inhales smoke when smokers light up.

continue to smoke is that the habits involved in smoking—lighting up and manipulating the cigarette, cigar, or pipe—are an important part of the pleasure people find in smoking. Another reason may be that the pleasure of putting something in the mouth, established in infancy, is important throughout life. Still another factor may be that some people associate cigars with wealth or power, pipes with being an intellectual, and cigarettes with being sophisticated or tough.

A study supported by the United States Public Health Service found these withdrawal symptoms among people who stopped smoking: nervousness, anxiety, headaches, loss of energy, constipation or diarrhea, insomnia, dizziness, sweating, cramps, and tremors. These symptoms are only temporary. Within a few weeks people who quit smoking usually feel healthier than when they were smoking. In addition, they usually find that the food they eat tastes better.

● ## 10-5 When Do Smokers Smoke?

Whether you smoke cigarettes or not, you have observed many people who do. Which of the following situations seem to be signals for smokers to light up?

while drinking coffee	while waiting for something to happen
after a meal	
while studying	while walking along the street
while reading	
while relaxing	while shopping
while exercising	during meetings
when upset	when hungry
after getting up in the morning	while trying to stay awake
while snacking	when feeling socially awkward
while working	
after not smoking for a while	when there's nothing else going on

DISCUSSION

1. What other signals can you add to the list?

2. What role do such signals play if a smoker attempts to stop?

3. Why do you think some of these signals almost always cause the smoker to light up?

4. What are some needs that smoking satisfies apart from merely satisfying the smoking habit?

5. How do nonsmokers satisfy these needs?

10-6 Alcohol and Health

Alcohol is widely used and widely abused. It is mixed in some medicines. Numerous religious rites include alcoholic beverages. But some religions condemn any use of it at all. Depending on the amount and the circumstances, it can depress or stimulate a drinker. It can be used moderately with no apparent harmful effects or in excess with damage to the brain and other vital organs. It was outlawed in the United States from 1919 until 1933, but people obtained it illegally and drank it anyway. It is second only to nicotine in the number of people dependent on it or addicted to it. And as the central attraction of many parties, alcohol is one of the most popular drugs. In our society, social drinking is generally approved of. Solitary drinking raises eyebrows.

The alcohol in all alcoholic beverages is ethyl alcohol, a substance produced from sugars by the process of fermentation. The strength of an alcoholic beverage is the percentage of alcohol it contains. Beer is much weaker than whiskey because the alcohol in beer is much more diluted. Whiskey contains eight to ten times the amount of alcohol that beer has, but people usually drink greater volumes of beer than whiskey. A large glass of beer has about the same amount of alcohol that a shot of whiskey has. The amount of alcohol a drinker consumes at one time depends on the amount

People have been encouraged to drink for many reasons besides wanting alcohol. Ads fool a lot of people into drinking to act glamorous.

of the beverage that is drunk and on how strong it is.

Alcohol gets to the brain quickly through the bloodstream. In the brain, one of its first effects is first speeding up and then slowing down the activities of the cerebrum. Although it generally takes more alcohol to make big people drunk than small people, a couple of drinks are usually enough to interfere with the parts of the brain that govern judgment, self-control, and voluntary body activities. Many people think of this as a stimulating effect, because a drinker may become more talkative or aggressive, or may act like the "life of the party." But alcohol slows down brain activity and is accurately listed as a depressant in the Drug Chart. The next stage of impaired activity shows up as poor muscle control, slurred speech, reduced sensory perception, lack of coordination, and sooner or later, inability to stand up and walk. With further drinking, people lose consciousness or "pass out."

Excessive drinking irritates the lining of the stomach. It can cause ulcers if continued over a long period of time. Heavy drinking also causes liver damage. This may be due in part to the fact that heavy drinkers often do not eat well. Recent research has shown also that brain damage and mental disorders can result from constant abuse of alcohol. The heart is also damaged by heavy drinking. Cancers, particularly of the throat, esophagus, larynx, and stomach, seem to be a greater risk for people who are heavy drinkers *and* heavy smokers. In

At some point—often hard to tell at the time—relaxation can turn into drunkenness and end in passing out.

The "drunkometer" or "breathalyzer" may be used after a car accident to find out if the driver was drunk.

France, where large quantities of wine are drunk, it is estimated that at least 50 percent of the hospital beds are filled by people with alcohol-related diseases.

Many people can enjoy an occasional drink for the taste, the sociability of the occasion, or the relaxing effect. Others seem to drink for more indirect and complex reasons. These include drinking to be a part of the group, to cover up feelings of inadequacy, to find temporary escape from fear or worry, and to attempt to calm down. Some people may drink because of self-hatred and a wish for self-destruction. You will find it interesting to go back to Section 10-5 and do the activity again for drinking instead of for smoking, to find out the situations that seem to stimulate drinking.

It is sometimes thought that people who drink excessively do so just because they have a problem with alcohol. However, drinking excessively is usually another form of the generally excessive behavior of most alcoholics. Their behavior problems need to be resolved as well as their drinking problems before they can be permanently rid of a dependence on alcohol. Unfortunately, although further damage can be prevented, the damage to the body already caused by excessive drinking cannot be undone.

10-7 Prescription and Over-the-Counter Drugs

Many products advertised to relieve pain, promote relaxation and sleep, or keep the user alert are sold in drugstores and supermarkets without a doctor's prescription. They are said to bring "fast pain relief," "restful sleep," "freedom from distress," and so on. But the United States Food and Drug Administration in a recent study reported that over half of the over-the-counter drugs have no proven effectiveness. And many have harmful side effects.

The companies that produce the drugs spend a great deal of money on advertising. The drug industry in the United States spends over $400 million a year on network TV advertising alone. For one brand-name headache remedy, the advertising cost to the customer is 41 cents out of each dollar the customer pays. As with deodorants and cosmetics, the industry strives to create demand for its products by telling the public it needs them.

Do you need a drug to help you get to sleep? To stay awake? To get rid of a headache? To calm you down? Most people can get over mild, temporary distress without drugs. If the drugs were less readily available and less widely advertised, fewer would be used. They would probably not be missed.

Unlike most drugs sold over the counter to make people "feel better," aspirin is one that works. It is a proven pain killer and muscle relaxant. It reduces fever and tissue inflammation. People tend to take too many aspirins and aspirin products, however. Aspirin can cause an upset stomach in many people, even taken in small doses. When taken in larger doses, it can cause stomach bleeding. Buffered aspirin and other aspirin products are only slightly more gentle to the stomach than plain aspirin.

Expensive advertising has helped make over-the-counter drugs popular. Their popularity also comes from their convenience and their low cost compared to medical visits. But cheaper is not always better. The practice of treating one's own symptoms can lead to overlooking serious health problems. This is the case for mental as well as physical problems. Constant pain, anxiety, and insomnia, for example, can be signs of serious problems requiring medical treatment. Self-treatment should be limited to short periods of time and never continued for weeks or months at a time without visiting a doctor.

Drugs that change one's state of mind can, of course, be obtained with a medical doctor's prescription. Like illegal drugs, any of the psychoactive drugs that are prescribed can lead to dependence and even addiction. Some people do not use drugs as prescribed. They may take more of a drug than instructed, because of a belief that if a little is good, more is better. Or they may not take the drug according to the prescribed schedule. They may want a bigger "high" or to be more tranquilized. These practices are dangerous. They can cause serious, permanent health damage and even death. The purity and dosage of legal prescription drugs have usually been carefully controlled during manufacture. But this does not guarantee that the drugs will be prescribed or used properly.

Many of the mood-altering drugs sold by prescription have harmful side effects, or unwanted effects. These can range from dizziness and blurred vision to feelings of depression. The doctor in most cases does not mention side effects to the patient, and neither does the pharmacist who fills the prescription. Warnings are usually given on the manufacturer's package, but not on the box or bottle the customer receives from the pharmacist. People often suffer severe side effects from prescription drugs without realizing what's hitting them. In addition, many drugs prescribed to treat a physical problem may have unwanted side effects of mood alteration. A patient should ask the doctor what the expected effect of any prescribed drug is and whether any side effects may also occur.

Self Check

1. Describe at least three harmful physical effects of smoking.

2. Is there any health danger to being around smokers if you aren't smoking?

3. How does drinking an alcoholic beverage affect the drinker's self-control?

4. What are some serious health effects of excessive drinking?

5. How can a drug prescribed by a doctor be abused?

Pills by the billions. The ads say happiness is just a swallow away.

How much is too much? Do you know?

Handling Drug Problems

10-8 What Is
Drug Abuse?

Who should take mood-altering drugs? Under what circumstances? These are not simple questions. You have read about some of the reasons people use drugs. You have also read about some harmful aspects of drug use. Which of the following items would you label *drug abuse*? Write your answers on a separate piece of paper.

1. having a glass of champagne at a New Year's Eve party

2. having four drinks at a New Year's Eve party
3. having seven drinks at a New Year's Eve party
4. having a beer at a picnic
5. smoking a cigarette with coffee every evening
6. smoking in order to kill appetite and lose weight
7. chain smoking
8. taking a tranquilizer before a job interview
9. taking a tranquilizer every morning before work

10. using caffeine pills during exam week
11. taking two aspirins for a headache
12. having a predinner drink for a headache
13. drinking wine at a party where you don't know anyone
14. drinking wine at a party with your best friends
15. smoking marijuana to help you get closer to someone
16. trying LSD to try to give you a memorable experience
17. any others you can think of

DISCUSSION

1. How would you define drug abuse?

2. Do any of your answers depend on the circumstances involved?

3. Do you think drug users should be legally restrained from abusing drugs or jailed if caught doing so?

The phone book may be a good place to start.

10-9 Where Can One Go for Help?

What happens when people realize that they have lost control over their drug use? Suppose they have become addicted to a drug that is damaging their health. Or they have a drug habit they can't afford to maintain. Or they realize they are using a drug as a way of escaping from reality. These problems can develop from both legal and illegal drugs: cigarettes, alcohol, heroin, or even coffee. Where can people get help?

In cases of severe addiction, hospitalization may be necessary. (Of course, cases of drug overdose or poisoning by impure street drugs need immediate hospital care also.) In some states, a person addicted to certain drugs may be required to undergo treatment in an institution. However, in the vast majority of cases, people who need help with a drug problem seek out that help voluntarily. In school, a counselor, social worker, teacher, or school nurse may be able to advise drug users or refer them to another source of help. Other sources of help may be a doctor, or a religious counselor.

The telephone directory is a good place to start looking for assistance. Here are some of the usual listings in the yellow pages:

Alcoholism Information and Treatment Centers
Drug Addiction Information and Treatment Centers
Drug Abuse Information and Treatment Centers

Smokers Information and Treatment Centers
Smoking Withdrawal
Social Service Organizations

Among these listings are local, county, and state agencies, nonprofit organizations, and hospital and medical centers that have outpatient facilities for dealing with drug problems.

Some drug users become habituated to drugs because of severe personal or social pressures in their lives. When they decide to try to change their habits, they may be more successful in resident communities where they can get help. At these places drug addicts or drug-dependent people spend months or years in a drug-free setting. The centers are organized to encourage people to abstain from using drugs. The social pressures that may have contributed to the development of a drug habit may not be present in these voluntary rehabilitation centers.

There are also places to go specifically for help with alcohol problems. The best known of these is Alcoholics Anonymous, a worldwide organization. It has branches in small towns as well as in large cities. It may be listed in the telephone directory simply as AA. It accepts teenagers as members.

In the AA program, members help each other. The first step for problem drinkers who come to AA is to recognize their problem, to admit that they are powerless with respect to alcohol and that their lives have become unmanageable. After this, the organization has techniques that work for helping alcoholics regain control over themselves. The AA program has helped thousands of people.

Another organization that has many branches is Al-Anon, with its companion Alateen. These groups help families and young people whose relatives are alcoholic.

Some lucky smokers are able to stop all at once just by deciding to stop or taper off. Smokers who need outside help in order to stop can find it in a number of forms. Private and group therapy are available at hospitals and public agencies and from private practitioners. Many techniques are used to get smokers to become nonsmokers. A smoker should look into various alternatives before signing up for an expensive program that could be run by unqualified people.

Any long-established habit, whether or not it involves drugs, is hard to change. Don't be discouraged if you have trouble breaking a habit. In fact, you ought to anticipate that you'll have trouble. Then you may be able to look at your initial distress or nervousness as something you expected to happen and also something you expect you will soon get over.

● 10-10 Investigating Other Ways to Change Your Mood

Sometimes you need to relax or calm down. Other times you need to burn up extra energy. At still other times you want something stimulating or exciting to happen. There are many things you can do to change your state of mind without using drugs.

PROCEDURE

Make a table like the one in the next column on a separate piece of paper.

TO RELIEVE TENSION	TO USE UP EXTRA ENERGY	TO FIND EXCITEMENT

Copy This Table on a Piece of Paper

Choose from the following list items that help you do any of the things described in the table, and write the items in your table. If some items belong in more than one column put them there. Then add to each column all additional items you can think of from among the things *you* like to do.

There are lots of ways to get into a mood or out of one, to find excitement or peace, to get high and have visions.

take a bicycle ride
fantasize
dance
sing
repair something
do a puzzle
play a musical in-
  strument
look up something
  you want to
  know more about
draw pictures

read a magazine,
  newspaper, or
  book
lift weights
watch television
help someone at
  school
do exercises
pray
telephone a friend
clean up a room
meditate

take care of plants
  or a garden
help out at a play-
  ground
read an adventure
  story
read about some-
  one who is like
  yourself
window-shop
build a model of
  something

take and develop
  photographs
practice a sport
jog
sit or lie down in a
  quiet place and
  think
go to a new place
browse in the li-
  brary
teach a friend to
  do something

go for a walk

work with a stamp
collection

write a letter to
someone

do a chore around
the house

go to a movie

help in a political
campaign

join an activity at
school or at a
community cen-
ter

DISCUSSION

1. Are some items in more than one column in your table?

2. Which column in your table has the most items? The fewest?

3. Would you like to have more ideas to draw from in the future? Share your ideas with your classmates and find out what other people like to do.

SELF CHECK

1. What is drug abuse?

2. What are some sources of help for people who have drug problems?

3. Name at least three physical and three mental activities that are useful for relaxing or relieving tension or anxiety.

Chapter Summary

Any substance that people put into their bodies to affect the way they feel, perceive things, or behave is considered to be a drug. Mood-altering or psychoactive drugs affect the body, behavior, and personality. Depressants, stimulants, and hallucinogens are the three types of psychoactive drugs. The effects of psychoactive drugs depend on attitude and feelings, desired effects, body size and weight, and physical condition. Some psychoactive drugs can be sold legally only with a medical doctor's prescription. Others are illegal under state, provincial, and federal laws. Legal drugs may be abused just as illegal drugs can be.

Most drugs are habit-forming to some degree. Users may become psychologically dependent (habituated) or physically dependent (addicted). With many drugs, users develop a tolerance. That is, they have to use more of the drug to get the same effect.

The steady use or abuse of tobacco and alcohol has serious health effects. Cigarette smokers are more likely to suffer from heart disease, lung cancer, bronchitis, and emphysema than nonsmokers. Alcohol reaches the brain quickly and reduces self-control, judgment, and voluntary control over body movements. Excessive use of alcohol damages the liver, the lining of the stomach, and eventually, the brain. Cancer of the throat, esophagus, larynx, and stomach have been associated with heavy drinking.

Drug addiction, overdosing, or poisoning must be treated medically, usually in a hospital. Drug users may need help in controlling or breaking their habit. People can seek help voluntarily from a variety of treatment centers, government agencies, hospital outpatient clinics, private organizations, or therapists working individually or with groups.

There are many choices of activities for relief from tension, release of extra energy, or excitement. Drugs are not needed to achieve these goals.

Chapter Self Check

1. What are some of the reasons people use drugs? Which of those uses are drug abuse?

2. What are psychoactive drugs?

3. What are some of the reported effects of hallucinogens?

4. What factors influence the way mood-altering drugs affect a user?

5. What may be the real cause of a so-called drug overdose?

6. What are the state and local laws controlling the use of alcohol in your community?

7. What is the difference between drug habituation and drug addiction?

8. What are some of the risks of being exposed to cigarette smoke without actually smoking?

9. What substance in tobacco is a stimulant?

10. What are some of the experiences of people who stop smoking?

11. Is whiskey more likely to make people drunk than beer?

12. If alcohol is a depressant, why does it seem to stimulate some drinkers?

13. Describe the stages of getting drunk.

14. What are some of the reasons people drink alcohol?

15. What are some common feelings and situations that people try to handle by using over-the-counter drugs?

16. What is the most serious danger of treating your own symptoms with drugs bought over the counter or old prescription drugs?

17. What drug problems may bring about hospitalization?

18. What are some of the organizations or people in your community that offer help to people with drug problems?

19. What organizations help alcoholics and help people who have alcoholics in their families?

20. Describe some things you can do to alter your mood or change your state of mind without taking drugs.

Read More About It

Brecher, Edward M., and Consumer Reports Editors. *Licit and Illicit Drugs.* Boston: Little, Brown and Company, 1972. Discusses the recent history of drug use and laws, as well as research into the effects of drugs.

Horman, Richard E., and Fox, Allan M. (editors). *Drug Awareness.* New York: Avon Books, 1970. Drugs and students, drug dependence, marijuana, hallucinogens, and other drug-related topics.

Zinberg, Norman E., and Robertson, John A. *Drugs and the Public.* New York: Simon & Schuster, Inc., 1972. Discusses changing public attitudes toward users of illegal drugs, the problems of drug laws, and some ways of controlling drug use.

11
Infectious Diseases

After completing the work in this chapter, you will be able to:

discuss the causes of infectious diseases.

compare the common respiratory diseases.

discuss syphilis and gonorrhea.

describe diseases spread by soil, food, water, and animals.

describe how the body protects itself against pathogens.

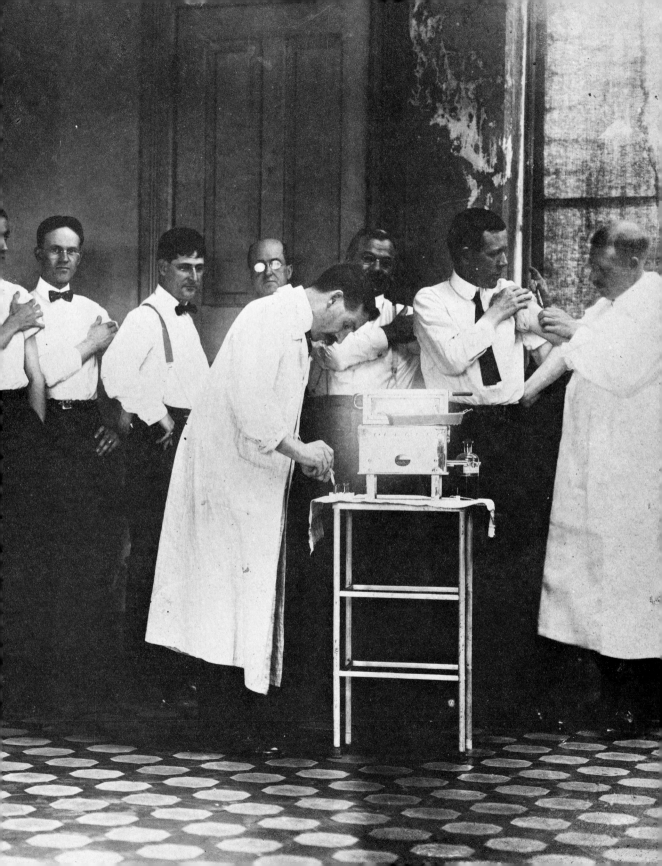

The Changing Threats to Life

If you had been born in the early nineteenth century, half of your sisters, brothers, and friends might have died when they were children. Diseases such as scarlet fever and whooping cough killed so many infants and children that only half of the babies born in the United States before 1850 reached their fifth birthday. Today, these killer diseases can be prevented or controlled. One deadly disease, smallpox, has been conquered.

Life expectancy is nearly double that of a century ago. Females born in the United States and Canada this year have a life expectancy of more than 75 years. Males have a life expectancy of about 68 years.

Statistics such as these do not mean that all disease has been conquered. The illnesses that people worry about today, such as heart disease and cancer, occur mostly among the middle-aged and elderly. More people live to be old, so there are more diseases of aging in the population.

Disease has not disappeared. But diseases change with the times, the environment, and the advances of medical science. Many serious infectious diseases, the kind you will read about in this chapter, can be prevented. When infectious diseases do occur, they usually can be controlled with medicine. You are much more likely to enjoy good health now and in adulthood than your parents or grandparents were.

The Spread of Disease

11-1 Causes of Disease

Disease is the condition of not functioning normally. Disease is also sometimes defined as the failure of an organism to adapt to its environment. A disease may affect one organ or the entire body. Some diseases are severe but last only a short time. Others last a long time. Everyone dies of either a disease or an accident.

Many different factors can cause disease. One major cause of sickness is infection by microorganisms, microbes for short. **Mi-crobes** (MY krohbz) are living things so small that they can be seen only through a microscope.

Some microbes help us stay healthy, but others make us sick. Microbes that can cause disease are called **pathogens** (PATH uh juhnz). Diseases caused by pathogens are called **infectious diseases.**

If an infectious disease can spread among people or between people and other animals, it is called a **contagious disease.** Many so-called childhood diseases (adults can get them too) such as mumps, chicken pox, and measles are both infectious and contagious.

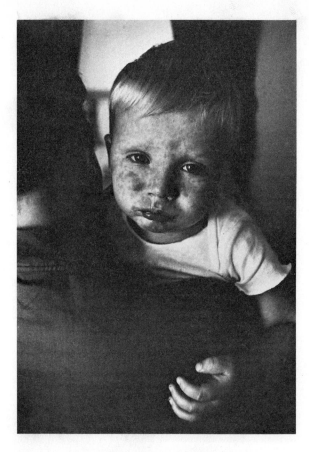

Measles is a childhood disease that can make a youngster miserable or appear in older people who escaped it when they were young.

The ability to prevent and control infectious diseases has added about 20 years to the life expectancy of North Americans in about the past 75 years. In this chapter, you will read about some of the infectious diseases and how the body defends itself against them.

Malfunctions of any body system are another major cause of disease. Some sicknesses, such as allergies and arthritis, result from a disturbance in a body system. A malfunction of an endocrine gland can trigger illness. Diseases of the heart and circulatory system are the number one cause of death in the United States and Canada. Disorders of the nervous system can cause many different illnesses. You will study diseases caused by malfunctions of body systems and inherited defects in Chapter 12.

Environmental factors trigger some diseases and make others worse. Air, water, and soil pollution by chemicals and pathogens contributes to many illnesses. Pollution also can shorten the lives of people who already are sick. Of the many theories about cancer, the most recent is that environmental factors are responsible in as many as 85 percent of all cases. Cancer is the second leading cause of death in the United States and Canada. Environmental causes and influences on disease are described in Chapter 13.

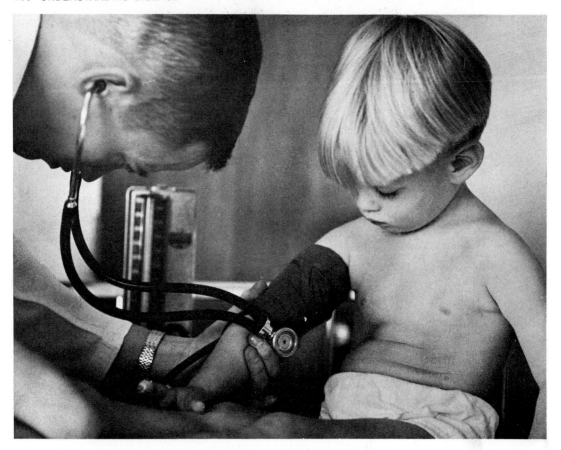

This child is having his blood pressure measured. Abnormal blood pressure may be a sign of a serious illness.

You have already studied the need for proper nutrition in preventing disease (Chapter 6). Injuries, another major cause of disease, are the topic of Chapter 14.

Different people respond differently to anything that causes disease. Influenza, for example, makes some people only slightly ill and sends others to the hospital, while many people are exposed to it and don't get sick at all.

People differ in the strength and effectiveness of their built-in defense system.

General physical condition also affects ability to fight off disease. Nutrition, amount of rest, and the environment all affect whether we stay well or get sick. A person's emotional state is another factor that may make him or her prone to certain illnesses. Working conditions and the quality of life also affect health and resistance to disease.

You can't judge by a friend's experience how your health will be affected by being near a person who has a cold, by eating contaminated food, or by using medications

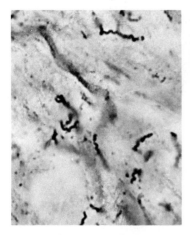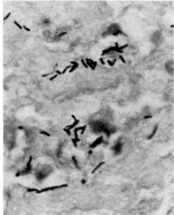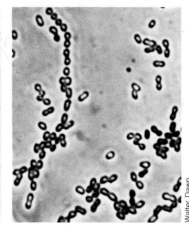

From left to right: the bacteria that cause syphilis, tuberculosis, and one of the various forms of pneumonia.

or other drugs. You have to know your own body and notice changes in it. A change may be a sign, or symptom, of disease.

11-2 Pathogens

We spend our lives in a world of invisible creatures. They occur in an almost infinite variety of sizes, shapes, and functions. Some of the millions of microbes around, on, and inside us are helpful. Certain microbes live in the intestines and destroy pathogens. Vitamin K is produced by bacteria in the intestines. Outside the body, other microbes make bread rise and produce cheese, wine, and beer.

The main types of pathogens are bacteria, viruses, rickettsiae, fungi, and protozoa. Pathogens can enter the body through the nose, mouth, or any other natural opening. They can also enter through a break in the skin. Some pathogens create a local infection, such as a boil. Others travel through the bloodstream and cause an infection throughout the body, or in a particular organ or body system. The major infectious diseases listed in this section are described later in the chapter.

Bacteria are single-celled organisms that reproduce by dividing. They vary in size and shape. Several thousand could fit into the period at the end of a sentence, and several million can live in a drop of water. When they invade a human body, some bacteria can damage or destroy cells. They do not live within cells. Some bacteria produce poisons, called **toxins.**

Viruses are much smaller than bacteria. They can be seen only with the most powerful electron microscopes. They are perhaps the simplest form of life. In a laboratory dish they act like nonliving crystals. They can reproduce only in living tissue. When they invade living cells, viruses control cell activities and change the cell protein into more viruses.

Measles, chicken pox, colds, and mumps are among the most common viral diseases. Influenza, infectious mononucleosis, rabies, smallpox, yellow fever, and polio are also caused by viruses.

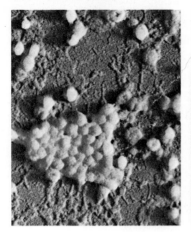 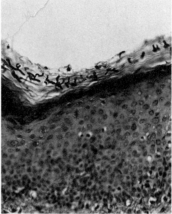 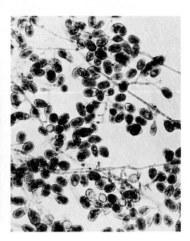

From left to right: influenza viruses, athlete's foot fungi (the short, dark rods), and the fungi that cause ringworm infections.

Rickettsiae (rih KEHT sih ee) are smaller than bacteria but larger than viruses. Like viruses, they grow only inside a living cell. Diseases caused by rickettsiae are spread by insects and ticks. These include diseases that have killed or sickened millions of people. Plague and typhus are among the rickettsial diseases.

Fungi are classified as plants, but they are not green and do not convert sunlight into food and energy. Mushrooms and yeast are fungi. Some fungi are pathogens. Fungi cause ringworm of the scalp, athlete's foot, and certain lung and ear diseases. Most fungi reproduce by forming spores, tiny seeds that set up a new growth. Fungal diseases tend to spread over a large area of the body unless they are controlled. They are also highly contagious.

Protozoa (proh tuh ZOH uh) are single-celled animals or plants. They are larger than bacteria but still cannot be seen without a microscope. Malaria and one kind of dysentery are caused by certain protozoa.

● 11-3 Epidemic

An **epidemic** is a disease spreading rapidly and affecting many people. A quarter of the people in Europe died in an epidemic in the fourteenth century. There are frequent epidemics of flu throughout the world. The epidemic of venereal disease becomes more widespread every year.

DAY	NUMBER OF PEOPLE WITH A COLD
0	1
1	2
2	4
3	8
4	
5	**Copy This Table**
6	
7	**on a Piece**
8	
9	**of Paper**
10	

A disease can spread very fast. Suppose you have a cold and give it to one other person each day. That person gives it to one more person each day, and so on. On a separate piece of paper, make a table like the one on page 288 showing how many people have caught the cold every day for ten days. The first three days are filled in for you.

DISCUSSION

1. How many people have caught the cold in ten days?

2. How long would it take for the cold to spread throughout your school? Your community?

SELF CHECK

1. Are all microbes pathogens? Explain your answer.

2. What is a major reason explaining why people can expect to live longer now than they did a century ago?

3. What are two differences between bacteria and viruses?

Some Infectious Diseases

11-4 The Common Cold

Some of the most common infectious diseases are also contagious. If someone who has a cold, influenza, measles, mumps, chicken pox, or tuberculosis goes to school, the disease is spread by direct contact or by sneezing or coughing.

The most common contagious disease is the cold. Practically everybody has occasional colds. They usually are only annoying, but they can lead to more serious respiratory diseases. A cold lasts one or two weeks, and no matter what anyone tells you, there is no cure.

Colds are transmitted by close contact, chiefly through coughing or sneezing. A cold virus also can be transmitted by contaminated eating utensils or towels. Colds are most contagious when they are just starting. If you have a cold, you can help yourself and other people by staying in bed and resting. Drink plenty of fluids, also.

Cold medicines do not cure a cold. They may even do more harm than good. **Antihistamines** (an tih HIHS tuh meenz) are medications that are effective against allergies. Their main effect in colds is to relieve sneezing; watery, itchy eyes; and an itchy, runny nose, making the patient more comfortable. But the drying effect can make a cough worse. Antihistamines may also cause drowsiness. **Decongestants** (dee kuhn JEHS tuhnts) dry the nose and promote sinus drainage and easier breathing. But they may increase blood pressure and heartbeat rate, so they can be dangerous for people who have high blood pressure or heart trouble. Aspirin relieves aches and reduces fever, which makes the patient more

Omikron

A sneeze can send enormous numbers of pathogens into the air.

comfortable. However, reducing fever may make the patient's recovery more difficult.

Nasal sprays relieve congestion at first. But when the effect wears off, the congestion is worse than before. In addition, if you use more spray to relieve the increased congestion, the congestion may become chronic. One cold remedy that is helpful is increasing the humidity in your room by using a vaporizer or a humidifier. Increased humidity thins the mucus and makes breathing easier. It is best not to put any medication in the water.

Colds can be caused by at least 100 different kinds of virus. These viruses are most at home in the cells lining the nose. When cold viruses get inside the nose, they go inside the cells and use the materials in the cells to form new viruses. The new viruses leave the first cells and enter other cells.

The body has two chemical weapons against cold viruses. When a cell is invaded, the cell produces a substance called **interferon** (ihn tuhr FIHR ahn), which interferes with the reproduction of the viruses in the cell. Interferon acts against all kinds of cold viruses. It works better at higher body temperatures. Aspirin, which reduces fever, may make interferon less effective.

Also in response to invasion by pathogens, the body produces substances called **antibodies,** which are carried by the blood. Antibodies cannot enter cells, but they can attack and destroy viruses as they move

There are easier ways to avoid catching a contagious disease!

from one cell to another. Each kind of antibody is effective against only one kind of virus. If your body is invaded by another kind of virus, you will need to make a different antibody. (You will learn more about antibodies in Section 11-9.)

The cells that are invaded also produce a clear fluid that washes some of the viruses away. You notice this as a runny nose. Sneezes and coughs shoot out droplets containing viruses, which may infect another person. As your body fights off the virus and you start to feel better, the fluid from your nose becomes thicker, full of the remains of cells that were killed by the virus.

If a cold virus enters your nose, you will not necessarily become sick. If you have

recently had a cold caused by the same kind of virus, there may still be enough of the antibody in your bloodstream to kill the virus. If the cells in your nose can produce interferon fast enough, the virus cannot get a good start. You are more likely to get a cold if you are tired or have not been eating properly.

The common cold is not a serious disease because the body is well equipped to fight the virus. However, the battle uses a lot of energy and can make a person more susceptible to other diseases, such as pneumonia. This is why it is important to rest, drink plenty of fluids, and eat well. If a fever lasts more than two or three days or goes above 101°F (38°C) and persists, call a

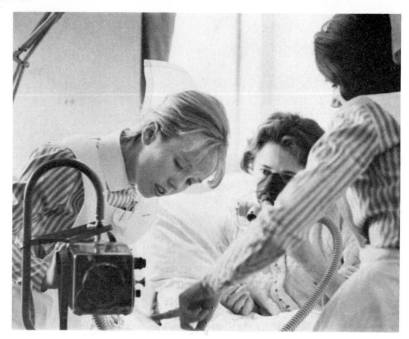

Respiratory and other diseases can keep people from getting enough oxygen to their cells. This woman is receiving extra oxygen through the tube attached to her face.

doctor. Other danger signals are persistent headache; earache; aching in the back, neck, or other muscles and joints; difficulty in breathing; severe cough; sore throat; and blood-stained sputum. **Sputum** (SPYOO tuhm) is material that is coughed up.

11-5 Other Respiratory Diseases

Influenza (flu) may resemble a cold but it can be much more serious. Worldwide epidemics of some strains of flu have killed millions of people. People who have flu are often surprised that they feel weak for a long time afterward. Vaccines (flu shots) are available for protection against some influenza viruses. But the viruses change from one year to the next. A different vaccine must be made each year. Public-health agencies advise people through newspapers, magazines, and television concerning the strains of flu that are likely to occur during the coming winter and whether a vaccine is available.

Flu can make people more susceptible to other diseases. Organisms that have been living harmlessly in the patient's respiratory system may break into cells that are damaged by the influenza virus. The patient may then come down with pneumonia or bronchitis. Influenza is most dangerous to people who are elderly or who have diseases of the heart or respiratory system.

The word **pneumonia** (noo MOHN yuh) refers to several infectious lung diseases. Pneumonia can be caused by either bacteria or viruses. It may strike suddenly or develop gradually. Symptoms include a cough; sharp, severe chest pains; bloody or rusty sputum; and a high fever that may start with a severe chill. The cells lining the air sacs in the affected parts of the lungs are so swollen by inflammation that air cannot get in or out. The patient has to work hard to get enough oxygen from the unaffected parts of the lungs. Pulse and breathing rates may double.

When a doctor taps a pneumonia patient's chest, it will sound solid instead of hollow. This is part of the diagnosis (dy uhg NOH sihs), or identification, of the disease. A chest X ray is taken to confirm the diagnosis and to see how far the disease has spread. Pneumonia is treated with medicines such as penicillin. Bacterial pneumonia used to be a leading cause of death. Now, because of modern medicines, it is rarely fatal if treated early.

A **strep throat** is an infection caused by a type of bacteria called **streptococcus** (strehp tuh KAHK uhs). These bacteria often live harmlessly in people's throats, but can cause disease when resistance is low. The common type of streptococcus can break down red blood cells. Symptoms of strep throat are usually more severe than those of an ordinary sore throat. There is headache, high fever, difficulty in swallowing, and swollen lymph nodes in the neck. There may be a rash. Medicines such as penicillin are effective against streptococcus. A strep throat should be treated promptly and thoroughly to prevent serious complications such as rheumatic fever and kidney disease.

Rheumatic (roo MAT ihk) **fever** is also caused by the streptococcus bacterium. It usually attacks children and adolescents. It begins with a sore throat, fever, abdominal pain, and headache. The symptoms may not be severe, and they usually disappear even without treatment. But if the infection is not treated, the bacteria make a toxin that can damage the heart by attacking the inner lining and the heart valves. By the time the patient becomes an adult, the heart cannot pump as well as it should. If the damage is discovered, heart surgery can correct or replace the damaged valves. But obviously

it is much better to diagnose and treat rheumatic fever before such damage occurs.

Infectious mononucleosis (mahn oh noo klee OH sihs), or mono, still baffles doctors. It is caused by a virus and is considered contagious. (It is sometimes called "the kissing disease.") But members of the same family or roommates do not usually get it at the same time. People are most likely to get mono if they are run down from overwork, lack of sleep, or poor nutrition.

People who have mono usually complain that they feel generally awful. They have a fever, sore throat, swollen lymph nodes, headaches, chills, and extreme fatigue. Mono can be diagnosed by a blood test because it causes characteristic changes in the white blood cells. Mononucleosis is usually mild. In rare cases it results in liver damage. Doctors advise mono patients to get at least two or three weeks of bed rest, drink a lot of fluids, and sometimes, take aspirin. Students worry about mono because they fear they may have to stay in bed for many weeks. Usually they do not. And fortunately, a person who has had mono will probably never get it again.

The bacteria responsible for **tuberculosis** (too bur kyuh LOH sihs), or TB, almost always attack the lungs, but they can also infect the bones, kidneys, lymph nodes, skin, larynx, joints, intestines, or other tissues and organs. TB develops slowly and takes a long time to cure. It is not a leading cause of death, as it was before the development of effective drugs and public health measures. But it still is a serious disease. Undiagnosed and untreated cases threaten the infected people and the people around them. Lung tuberculosis usually is spread through the sputum of an infected person. The TB bacteria can live in dried sputum for months and may be picked up anywhere.

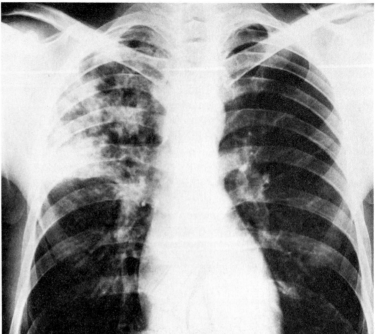

A moderately advanced case of TB, as shown by the solid white area on the person's right lung and the wispy white areas on both lungs. The large white mass in the center of the lower part of the X ray is called a "heart shadow."

Walter Dawn

Most people's bodies can resist infection from tuberculosis bacteria. Their bodies are able to trap the bacteria and seal them up with scar tissue. They may not know they have TB until the scar tissue shows up in an X ray. They should take good care of themselves and get checkups regularly.

People who have lower resistance, because of poor nutrition, age, or the existence of some other disease, may not be able to fight off the bacteria. The bacteria invade and destroy the lung tissue by a process that used to be known as "consumption." Sometimes a blood vessel is damaged, and the patient coughs up blood. This may also spread the bacteria throughout the body.

A skin test can show whether you have ever had TB bacteria in your body. People who have a positive test should get a chest X ray. If the disease is diagnosed, it can be treated and controlled. Anyone who feels tired for a long time, has chest pains, recurring fever, coughing spells, and bloody streaks in the sputum should be checked immediately.

11-6 Venereal Diseases

Venereal (vuh NIHR ee uhl) **diseases** (VD) are spread by sexual contact. They are almost never spread any other way, because the microbes that cause them cannot live long outside a human body. To infect a person, the microbes must be deposited on a warm, moist surface, such as the linings of the genitals or mouth, or on a break in the skin.

The most common venereal diseases are gonorrhea and syphilis. They are both caused by bacteria. **Syphilis** (SIHF uh lihs) is the more serious of the two. The bacteria may lie quietly in the body for ten days to three months. The first symptom may be a sore, or **chancre** (SHANG kuhr), usually at the place where the bacteria entered the body. The chancre is full of bacteria, which can easily be spread to other people. However, not everyone infected with syphilis develops a chancre. A woman may develop a chancre inside her body and not notice it. The chancre heals by itself, but the disease has not gone away. About nine weeks later, a rash may cover the entire body. Sores

may appear in the mouth and throat. Fever, headache, pain in the bones and joints, and a generally miserable feeling occur. Syphilis is highly contagious at this point. These symptoms, too, will disappear. If the disease is untreated, new symptoms appear in five to ten years. The bacteria may invade any part of the body, including the brain. A person with brain syphilis may suffer from mental illness or paralysis. Infection of the brain or heart may be fatal. Heart tissue infected with syphilis is shown on page 287.

Most cities have free public clinics, some of them in mobile vans, that are set up to test people for venereal diseases.

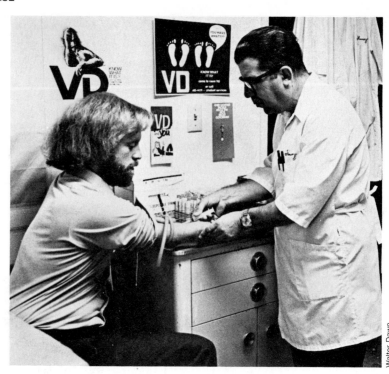

A syphilis test requires taking a blood sample.

Walter Dawn

Syphilis can be diagnosed and treated at any time. A doctor may notice subtle symptoms such as swollen lymph nodes around the groin. If a chancre develops, pus from it can be analyzed for bacteria. Usually one to three weeks after the chancre forms, the bacteria enter the bloodstream. After this, syphilis can be detected by a blood test. If a person thinks he or she has been exposed to syphilis, but a blood test is negative, another blood test should be taken a few weeks later, just to be sure.

Syphilis is treated with penicillin, or another drug if the patient is allergic to penicillin. The penicillin may be given as one large dose or several smaller ones. The treatment is considered complete when at least two blood tests are negative. The early stages of syphilis can be completely cured. If the bacteria have infected the heart or brain, the damage cannot be reversed, but further damage can be prevented.

Gonorrhea (gahn uh REE uh) is the most common bacterial infectious disease in North America. It produces its first symptoms five to seven days after contact. The infected person may notice a whitish material discharged from the genital-urinary tract, or a burning sensation when he or she urinates. Some men and most women do not develop immediate symptoms. But they can still give the disease to others, and it spreads inside their own bodies. Untreated gonorrhea can result in crippling, sterility, arthritis, or blindness. If the heart valves are involved, the disease can be fatal.

Gonorrhea can be detected by examining the discharged material under a microscope and finding gonorrhea bacteria. The test is reliable for men but less reliable for women.

Therefore a culture of the discharged material may be done. Some of the material is put in a substance in which bacteria, if any, can multiply. After a few days the bacteria can be detected easily. Because gonorrhea is so common and most women do not develop symptoms, many doctors recommend that a sexually active woman get a gonorrhea test with her regular physical examination. Gonorrhea can be cured by penicillin and other medications.

There are other, less common venereal diseases. Most of them can be treated. Anyone who notices a discharged substance, sores, or other symptoms around the genital area should get medical help.

If a pregnant woman has VD, her baby may be affected. Syphilis bacteria can infect the unborn baby, who may be born dead, deformed, or diseased. Gonorrhea bacteria can infect a baby's eyes during birth. This was once a major cause of blindness. Now the law requires that all newborn babies' eyes be treated with medicine to cure the disease if it is present.

A person who has had a venereal disease and been cured can catch the same disease again. A person can also have several different forms of VD at the same time. At present there are no vaccines to prevent people from getting any venereal disease.

Many of the symptoms of venereal diseases can also be caused by other diseases. However, anyone with symptoms should get medical help so the disease, whatever it may be, can be cured.

The symptoms of VD may not seem serious, and they may seem to go away after a while, but the diseases are very dangerous unless they are treated. Anyone who notices symptoms or thinks he or she may have been exposed to VD should go to a doctor or a free public health venereal disease clinic. Many cities have a VD Hot Line that people can call for information on diagnosis and treatment. The number is listed in the telephone directory. Doctors and clinics will respect patients' privacy. People who have VD should tell their sexual partners so they can get a test. To avoid infecting others, a person who has VD must not have any sexual activity until the disease is cured.

11-7 Diseases From Soil, Water, and Food

Pathogens in soil, food, and water are responsible for many serious disesases. Among them are typhoid fever, hookworm, dysentery, cholera, hepatitis, and tetanus. Except for dysentery and hepatitis, these diseases are now not common in North America.

The bacteria that cause **tetanus** live in soil and dust. They can enter the body through a break in the skin. The bacteria produce a powerful toxin that affects the central nervous system. Once the disease is established, there is no reliable treatment. The patient may die from inability to control breathing, or from exhaustion caused by convulsions and muscle spasms. Tetanus is often called "lockjaw" because the first sign is a stiff, rigid neck and jaw.

Tetanus is not as common as it used to be because people can be protected by immunization. (Immunization prevents people from getting a disease. It is discussed later in this chapter.) Doctors advise parents to have their babies immunized. A booster is needed every four to six years to stay protected. Since many people do not get regular shots, any deep or uneven wound that may be dirty should be cleaned by a doctor. A booster shot probably will be given at the same time.

Dysentery (DIHS uhn tehr ee) is an infection of the lower intestinal tract. It can be caused by bacteria, protozoa, or viruses.

When a lot of people drink or bathe in polluted water, epidemics are likely to occur. These people are bathing as part of a religious ceremony in the Ganges River in India, a country that has frequent epidemics.

The symptoms include diarrhea and cramps. Dysentery is spread by poor sanitation. People often get dysentery by drinking water that carries pathogens from the feces of disease carriers, or by eating fruit that has not been washed well. Simply washing your hands with contaminated water and then touching your mouth can cause dysentery.

Typhoid (TY foyd) **fever,** or simply typhoid, is also carried by food and water. It has been reduced to a minor health problem because of increased public health emphasis on the clean preparation of food and on adequate sanitation and a pure water supply. However, during such disasters as a flood or an earthquake, when sewage treatment facilities break down, people should get shots against typhoid. Typhoid shots also are recommended for travelers to certain foreign countries. Typhoid symptoms are fever, headache, loss of appetite, a rash, and sometimes severe diarrhea. Effective drugs are available. Untreated typhoid is often fatal.

Infectious hepatitis (hehp uh TY tihs) is most common in young adults but can occur at any age. The hepatitis virus affects several organs, especially the liver. Hepatitis most often begins with tiredness, loss of appetite, upset stomach, and pain in the abdomen. Fever may occur at first, but it goes away. The liver may enlarge and feel tender. The most obvious sign of infectious hepatitis is **jaundice** (JAWN dihs), a yellowing of the whites of the eyes and often of the skin as well. If this yellowing occurs, the urine will be much darker than usual and the feces very light in color.

Children often recover from infectious hepatitis in a week. An adult may need six to eight weeks. There is no medicine to cure hepatitis. Doctors prescribe bed rest and a high-protein, high-Calorie diet. These measures help protect the patient against the development of a chronic, prolonged form of the disease and from permanent liver damage.

Infectious hepatitis is usually spread when people live close together, as in schools, dormitories, summer camps, or military barracks. Eating shellfish from polluted water also can cause hepatitis. Sometimes public health officials have to forbid shellfish fishing or ban the sale of shellfish caught in polluted areas.

Serum hepatitis, another form of the disease, is transmitted either through a blood transfusion from an infected person or by an unsterile hypodermic needle. Drug users can get serum hepatitis when they use infected needles. People who get their ears

Foods can spoil quickly in the hot sun and cause food poisoning.

pierced can get serum hepatitis if the equipment is not adequately sterilized between customers.

No vaccine is yet available for protection against hepatitis, although an experimental vaccine has been developed. The only way to prevent hepatitis is to develop good personal hygiene habits. Always wash your hands after using the toilet and guard against contaminated foods and fluids.

A number of other diseases can be caused by contaminated food or drink. Bacteria in spoiled food can cause **food poisoning.** Foods most likely to produce this illness are pastries, eggs, and egg products such as custards, cream fillings, and mayonnaise. Meats also spoil easily. Picnics sometimes end with cases of food poisoning because some of the foods were not kept cold. Canned food can also contain bacteria. Throw away any can of food that bulges or gives off a gas when it is opened. Any food that has a strange odor or a moldy appearance should be thrown away. Do not taste it.

Botulism is a rare but extremely dangerous disease. The bacteria that cause botulism grow only where there is little oxygen. They are present in soil but can also grow in non-acid preserved foods, especially canned vegetables. They never grow in fresh food. The bacteria produce a toxin so powerful that just a taste of contaminated food can kill a person. They form spores that can survive boiling. To kill the spores, the canner must heat the food under pressure to reach very high temperatures. Commercial canneries usually heat the food hot enough, but people canning food at home often do not. So home-canned food is the most common cause of botulism. Fortunately the toxin itself can be destroyed by boiling. Botulism can be prevented by boiling all canned food before it is eaten. The toxin cannot be detected by smelling or looking at the food.

Parasitic worms live part of their life cycle within other animals. Parasitic worms travel from one person to another by way of food and water contaminated by feces. Worm infection can be painful and dangerous. Worms may be the size of a pinhead or very long, such as the tapeworm. **Trichinosis** (trihk uh NOH sihs) is caused by a small roundworm in infected pork. Thorough cooking gives protection. There is no specific medicine to cure trichinosis, so prevention is important. For other worms, such as tapeworms and pinworms, certain drugs are very effective.

11-8 Diseases Spread by Animals

Insects and ticks spread many infectious diseases. Some of them, such as typhus and plague, have changed the course of human history. The bubonic plague wiped out a large fraction of the population in Europe in the Middle Ages. Armies have frequently been beaten by typhus and other diseases before taking on their human enemies in battle.

Typhus (TY fuhs) is a group of infectious diseases caused by rickettsiae. The organisms are usually transmitted from infected mice and rats to people by lice, fleas, ticks, and mites. Typhus symptoms include headache, weakness, coughing, nausea, and chest pain. High fever, chills, vomiting, and a red rash follow. Typhus is a disease of overcrowding, poor sanitation, cold, hunger, and general physical weakness. It is sometimes called "war fever," "camp fever," or "jail fever."

Rocky Mountain spotted fever, or tick fever, is related to typhus. Despite its name, it is found in most parts of the Western Hemisphere. It is transmitted from rodents to people by ticks. Ticks attach themselves to the skin and feed on blood. Rocky Mountain spotted fever can be fatal, but it can be treated. If you are going in the woods or anywhere else where there is much vegetation, such as beach grass, use insect repellent. Inspect your body for ticks every few hours. If you find one, don't pull it off roughly. Parts of the tick may stay in place and continue to infect you. A drop of lighter fluid, kerosene, or turpentine will make the tick loosen its grip. Another method is to hold a hot needle or a lighted match near the tick until it leaves the skin. Only a few ticks spread Rocky Mountain spotted fever, but you can't tell whether the one biting you is dangerous. Take precautions against any tick bite. If you are bitten, wash the bite thoroughly with soap and water and apply an **antiseptic,** a substance that kills disease-causing organisms.

Malaria is caused by protozoa and spread by mosquitoes. It is a disease mainly of hot climates. Mosquito-control projects have greatly reduced the number of cases throughout the world. But the pesticides involved, especially DDT, have also poisoned large parts of the environment. Malaria causes attacks of severe chills followed by high fever, headache, nausea, and aches and leaves the victim exhausted when an attack is over.

Mosquitoes also spread **yellow fever** and **encephalitis** (ehn sehf uh LY tihs), or sleeping sickness. Investigations by an American Army doctor, Walter Reed, after the Spanish-American War established the role of mosquitoes in spreading yellow fever. This viral disease interferes with liver function and usually causes jaundice. In encephalitis, the covering of the brain becomes inflamed, and there may be permanent brain damage.

Pets, farm animals, and wildlife can carry diseases and infect people by biting or scratching them. Sometimes, people are in-

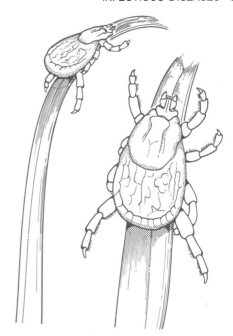

Ticks climb up on tall grass, weeds, and bushes and wait for a host to come by.

fected simply by breathing air contaminated by a pet's feces. The pet may not look or act sick, but it may carry the microbes of contagious diseases.

Rabies affects the brain and nervous system, and is fatal unless it is treated quickly. It is a disease of warm-blooded animals, including humans. Widespread vaccination of pets has held down the number of rabies cases. Wild animals, including bats, are more likely to be infected than pets. Skunks, raccoons, and foxes infected with rabies may act surprisingly affectionate with humans. Be wary of any animal that acts unnaturally. Any person bitten by an animal suspected of having rabies should have the animal examined if possible. If the animal is found to have rabies, that person should be treated for rabies. The treatment

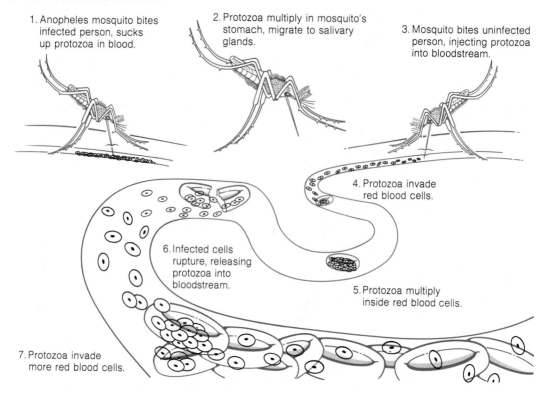

1. Anopheles mosquito bites infected person, sucks up protozoa in blood.

2. Protozoa multiply in mosquito's stomach, migrate to salivary glands.

3. Mosquito bites uninfected person, injecting protozoa into bloodstream.

4. Protozoa invade red blood cells.

6. Infected cells rupture, releasing protozoa into bloodstream.

5. Protozoa multiply inside red blood cells.

7. Protozoa invade more red blood cells.

Mosquitoes spread malaria from one infected person to another. It may be the most common infectious disease in the world.

for rabies is long and painful, so it is given only if necessary.

Many dogs are infected with **roundworms.** The eggs are deposited in the dog's feces. People, especially children, can get roundworms by touching something that has been in contact with dog feces and then touching their mouths. The eggs hatch in the person's intestines. If the condition is not treated, the roundworms penetrate the wall of the intestine. They wander through the body and settle in the liver or lungs. Occasionally they attack the eye and cause blindness. Public health officials urge dog owners to make sure their pets are free of worms and to keep them away from playgrounds.

Ringworm is actually a fungal infection, not a worm. You can get ringworm by touching either an infected person, dog, or cat or something the person or animal rubbed, such as chairs, doors, fences, or clothing.

Pet birds can carry **psittacosis** (siht uh KOHS sihs) or parrot fever. This ailment can also be spread by the feces of pigeons, chickens, and turkeys. The only way to be sure a bird is not infected is to have it examined by a veterinarian. Psittacosis is a form of pneumonia.

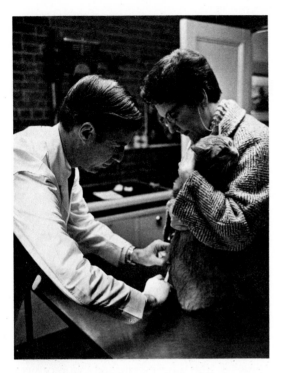

Pet animals should have periodic visits to a veterinarian for their protection and their owners'.

Farm and wild animals can infect people with other serious diseases. These diseases can be picked up by handling infected animals, drinking their milk, or walking barefoot around animal paths. Farmers can avoid these diseases by having their animals blood-tested and taking care in handling them. Pasteurizing milk and thoroughly cooking meat kill the pathogens.

SELF CHECK

1. How should a cold be treated?

2. Why is influenza more dangerous than a cold?

3. What two tests can show whether someone has tuberculosis?

4. What are the two most common venereal diseases?

5. How can you avoid catching diseases from food and water?

Protection Against Disease

11-9 Body Defenses Against Disease

Pathogens are all around—in air, in water, in food, in other people, on things we touch. Every time we breathe or eat we take pathogens into our bodies. Why aren't we sick all the time?

Skin presents the first defense against pathogens. Inside the body's natural openings, its heat and the sticky material pro-

duced by mucous membranes form another protective barrier. Tears are slightly antiseptic and wash away dirt and microbes from the eyes. If microbes enter the stomach, enough of them are killed by stomach acid to prevent many illnesses.

In spite of the natural defenses, pathogens do enter the body through irritated membranes, cuts, scratches, and punctures. They penetrate the body systems and set up infections. Then the body mobilizes another

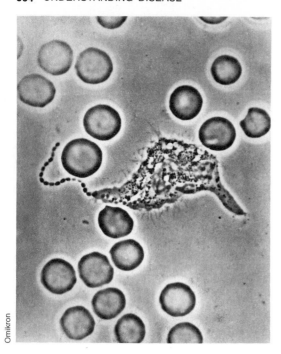

Omikron

A white blood cell destroying a chain of disease-causing bacteria in the bloodstream.

leukocyte activity and other body defenses.

Still another defense system can give a person **immunity** (ih MYOO nuh tee), or protection, from a disease. When the body detects foreign materials such as bacteria, viruses, or toxins, it develops **antibodies,** substances that fight the intruders. The lymph nodes and certain bone-marrow cells manufacture antibodies from a raw material called gamma globulin, a protein in the blood. The human body can make thousands of different antibodies. In general, an antibody is effective against only one disease. A foreign material that can stimulate the production of antibodies is called an **antigen** (AN tih juhn).

When the viruses of mumps, for example, enter the body, it creates one antibody substance that reacts to that one kind of virus. The specific antibody remains in your blood and you do not get mumps again, although you may be exposed to mumps many times. However, the mumps antibody cannot protect you against any other disease.

Some antibodies provide only temporary immunity. This is true of the common cold. Others give permanent protection. Few people get measles, chicken pox, mumps, or mononucleosis more than once.

Some antigens may come into contact with a baby developing in the mother's uterus. The developing baby creates antibodies, and the child will be resistant to those antigens. This is one reason people do not all get the same illnesses. Newborn babies are also immune to many diseases because they got antibodies from their mothers. Most of these antibodies only last a few weeks.

An immunity developed to a disease after antigens have entered the body is an **acquired immunity.** Other immunities are called **natural.** They are inherited from the parents. Your natural immunity to one or more diseases protects you when you come

defense system. The white blood cells, or **leukocytes** (LOO kuh sytz), find pathogens and destroy them. When microbes damage or poison body tissue, the infected area becomes sore and tender. The capillaries in the infected area fill with blood. Leukocytes pass through the thin walls of the capillaries and into the damaged tissue. The number of leukocytes increases automatically in response to an infection.

White blood cells surround invading organisms and prevent them from spreading. The raised, tough wall around a pimple, boil, or infected cut is created by leukocytes. The infected area fills with a thick, yellowish fluid, called **pus.** Pus from open sores can spread infection. Lymph carries some pathogens to lymph nodes, which filter out and destroy them. The fever that accompanies many infections results from into contact with a person who is in the contagious stage of that disease. There is no way you can know what your natural immunities are, however. No one should ignore precautions against infectious disease. You may not get mumps, for example, the first time you are exposed to the disease, but you may get it the next time.

Natural immunity may not give complete protection against a disease, but it may control its severity. Measles is usually a mild disease among populations that have experienced it for many generations. But when measles is introduced among people who have never experienced this disease, it is often fatal.

Some people do not have enough gamma globulin. Their bodies have difficulty fighting infections. Their lives may be threatened by diseases that could easily be controlled in a normal person. The condition cannot be cured, but victims can be protected by frequent injections of gamma globulin.

Viruses can be grown in eggs to make vaccines. Here a technician removes virus-filled fluid.

11-10 Adding to the Body's Defenses

Some microbes multiply so fast and produce so much poison that the body cannot form antibodies fast enough to prevent illness. Additional antibodies are needed. You can get them by **immunization** (ihm yuh nuh ZAY shuhn).

Vaccines are available to combat many diseases. A vaccine contains modified antigens to stimulate the production of antibodies without producing an illness. A vaccine may contain dead pathogens, as in typhoid or Salk polio preparations. The pathogens may be alive but weakened and harmless, as in smallpox and Sabin oral polio vaccine. Or antigens may be made from toxins that have been treated chemically to make them harmless but still able to cause the body to make antibodies. Such chemically treated toxins are called **toxoids.** Tetanus vaccine is a toxoid.

Like antibodies, vaccines vary in the length of time they can provide immunity. Smallpox and tetanus vaccines provide protection for only a few years. Sabin polio vaccine is believed to provide lifelong protection.

Because so many infectious diseases can be controlled by immunization, some people feel safe without being immunized. They think that the lack of disease in their community protects them. But it takes only one contact to make them sick. Doctors urge parents to have their children immunized to make sure that a chance contact will not be dangerous.

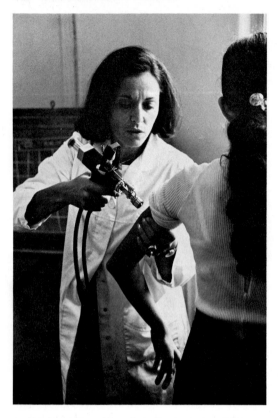

A doctor giving a flu shot. Each strain of flu requires a separate vaccine.

Once an infection has started, there are likely to be medicines available to fight it. Many antibiotics have been developed. An **antibiotic** (an tih by AHT ihk) is a substance that will kill certain microbes. Penicillin and streptomycin are antibiotics. Antibiotics do not kill viruses but are sometimes used in viral illnesses because they kill bacteria that may be slowing down a patient's recovery.

Antibiotics present several problems. An antibiotic will not kill all the bacteria present. Those that survive may become immune to the antibiotic. Antibiotics kill helpful bacteria as well as pathogens. And other pathogens that were kept under control by helpful bacteria may then cause disease. Also, many people are allergic to certain antibiotics. Before you are given an antibiotic or other medicine, you should tell your doctor whether you are allergic to it, if you know.

An antibiotic—or any other medicine—affects the body in other ways besides its desired effects. A side effect of aspirin, for example, is that it upsets some people's stomachs. Other medicines can be addictive or have other serious effects. If a pregnant woman takes certain medicines, her baby may be affected. Any medicine should only be taken if the benefits outweigh the risks. If a medicine is only available with a doctor's prescription, it is especially likely to be dangerous. So a doctor's judgment is needed. Don't take other people's prescription medicine or give anyone else your own. Be cautious if you take medicine left over from an earlier illness. If the disease is not the same, you waste time before getting proper treatment. Or the left-over medicine may have lost its effectiveness with age.

Understanding the nature of contagious diseases and developing vaccines and antibiotics have controlled many illnesses that once caused epidemics. Providing protection against infectious disease has been one of the major factors in increasing life expectancy and enabling people to live healthy lives.

SELF CHECK

1. How do leukocytes combat infection?

2. What are antibodies?

3. What is the difference between acquired and natural immunity?

4. How do vaccines prevent infectious diseases?

Health Frontier

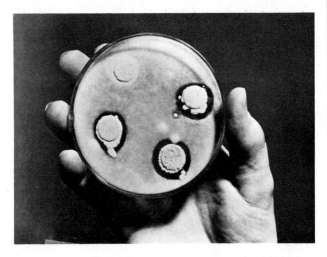

Antibiotics on three discs of paper keep bacteria from growing nearby. One antibiotic doesn't work.

Self-Defeating Cures

No antibiotic or insecticide seems to work indefinitely. Scientists must constantly change existing ones and develop new ones. The reason is that humans are not the only living things with natural and acquired immunities. Microbes and insects can and do become immune too.

Immunity in bacteria has made new problems for doctors and hospitals. Some antibiotics stop being effective after they have been used for a while. Pathogens that antibiotics once destroyed develop a resistance to them. The bacteria pass their immunity on to their descendants. For example, there are now gonorrhea bacteria that are resistant to penicillin, although it would have killed them in the past.

Staphylococcus bacteria, the kind that cause boils and other skin diseases, often infect hospital patients in spite of large doses of antibiotics. "Hospital staph" infections occur, despite increased attention to sanitation, because of the increased resistance to antibiotics.

Resistant bacteria can develop in individual people, as well as in hospital environments.

Repeated doses of an antibiotic can gradually become less effective. Many people ask their doctor for an antibiotic for every minor illness. If they overuse one of these medicines, it may not work effectively when they need it in a serious illness. The doctor may then have to prescribe a different antibiotic that has unpleasant side effects.

Flies, mosquitoes, and other disease-spreading insects have developed immunities to some insecticides. As a result, it takes bigger doses of pesticides to kill these "super bugs." Most pesticides are not very selective. That is, they kill harmless and helpful organisms in addition to the target insects. And in time they become less and less effective at killing the intended victims. Unless new chemicals are developed, whole insect populations will eventually become immune to insecticides that once would have destroyed them. More promising ways of controlling insects involve using natural controls, not pesticides. For example, draining stagnant pools where mosquitoes breed and reintroducing natural predators that were killed off by earlier doses of pesticides.

Chapter Summary

Disease may be caused by a disturbance in a body system, improperly functioning glands, environmental factors, injuries, emotional state, or pathogens. Infectious diseases that spread among people are also called contagious. The microbes that cause infectious diseases include bacteria, viruses, rickettsiae, fungi, and protozoa. The most common contagious disease, a cold, is caused by viruses. The most common contagious disease caused by bacteria is gonorrhea.

Colds are not serious, but if they are ignored they make people more susceptible to other, more serious respiratory diseases. Flu resembles a cold but is more dangerous. It leaves patients weak and susceptible to other ailments. Vaccines are available for protection against some types of flu. Pneumonia, strep throat, rheumatic fever, and tuberculosis of the lung are other diseases of the respiratory system. Infectious mononucleosis (mono) is usually mild. But it must be treated to avoid damage to the liver.

Gonorrhea and syphilis are the two most common venereal diseases. Both are curable, but the damage they do to the body cannot be reversed. No vaccine against venereal disease is available. A person may be cured and still get the disease many times again.

Pathogens in soil, water, and food cause serious diseases such as typhoid fever, dysentery, hepatitis, and tetanus. Some of these can be prevented by immunization. Good personal hygiene habits and care in selecting food and water can usually prevent these illnesses.

Pets, wildlife, farm animals, insects, and ticks spread many infectious diseases to humans. Preventive measures include medical care of animals, precautions in handling them, and prompt attention to bites and scratches.

The skin and materials it produces form the first natural barrier against pathogens. The body fights infections with white blood cells and by developing antibodies. An antibody gives protection against a specific disease. The immunity may be temporary or permanent. Vaccines stimulate the production of antibodies without causing illness. Antibiotics such as penicillin have saved many lives by killing bacteria, but they must be used with caution.

Chapter Self Check

1. How have the leading causes of death changed in the past century?

2. Why do people respond differently to a cause of disease?

3. What are some differences between bacteria and viruses?

4. Name one or more diseases caused by each of the following: bacteria, viruses, rickettsiae, fungi, and protozoa.

5. Why are the following medicines only partly effective against a cold: antihistamines, decongestants, aspirin, nasal sprays?

6. How does the body fight cold viruses?

7. Why is strep throat potentially a dangerous disease?

8. What are the symptoms of infectious mononucleosis?

9. How is syphilis diagnosed?

10. What is usually the first sign that a person has gonorrhea?

11. Why do some people think venereal disease is not serious?

12. Why do doctors usually give a tetanus booster to people who have deep or uneven wounds?

13. What are the most common ways of becoming infected with infectious hepatitis? With serum hepatitis?

14. What foods are most likely to cause food poisoning?

15. How can anyone be infected by an animal without touching it?

16. Describe the body's first defenses against pathogens.

17. What do all antibodies have in common? In what ways are they all different?

18. What pathogens can be killed by antibiotics?

19. What are some potential disadvantages of antibiotics?

20. Why should people be immunized even against diseases that are not common?

Read More About It

Fuller, John G. *Fever: The Hunt for a New Killer Virus.* New York: Reader's Digest Press, 1974. The events leading to the realization that a special maximum security lab must be used to handle the Lassa fever virus. A true story with aspects of a detective story.

Glasser, Ronald J. *The Body Is the Hero.* New York: Random House, Inc., 1976. How the body fights infectious disease. Also includes dramatic accounts of some diseases of the body's defense systems against disease.

Rosebury, Theodor. *Life on Man.* New York: Viking Press, Inc., 1969. Disproves some unrealistic ideas about cleanliness and microbes. Includes information about the importance and usefulness of microbes, as well as their harmful effects.

Wilson, David. *Body and Antibody.* New York: Alfred A. Knopf, Inc., 1972. How antibodies protect us, and what happens when this defense system does not work right. The significance of immunology in cancer, transplant surgery, and allergies.

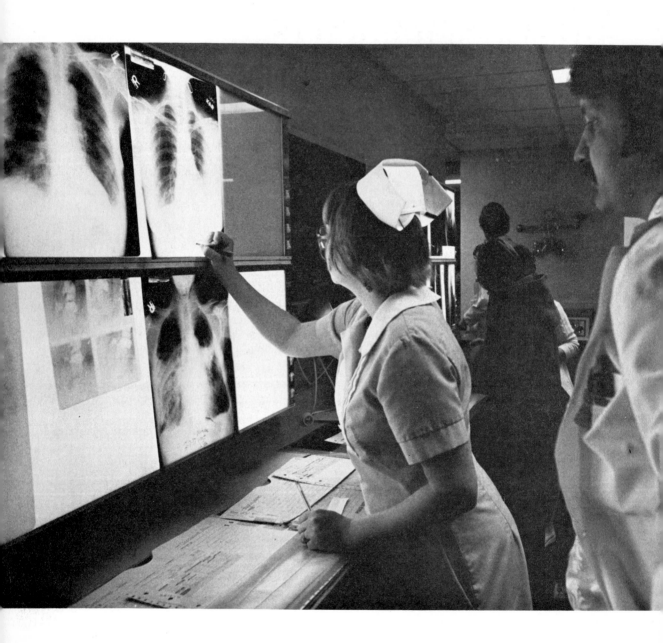

12
Malfunctions
of Body Systems

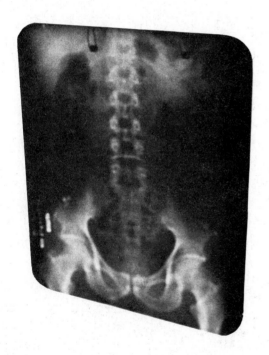

After completing the work in this chapter, you will be able to:

explain what an allergic reaction is.

describe the symptoms and treatment of diabetes and other diseases resulting from malfunctioning glands.

tell what a person who has symptoms of appendicitis should and should not do.

describe how to reduce your chances of getting a cardiovascular disease.

describe several diseases that affect the nervous system and discuss diseases that are related to emotional problems.

organize and write down your own medical history.

A Lot Can Go Wrong

The "wisdom of the body" is often given credit for overcoming disease and healing injuries. But sometimes our bodies behave in ways that seem to be unwise.

Body systems may work against us instead of for us. For example, antibodies usually give protection against disease. But antibodies may attack the body's own cells. The clotting action of blood is a life-saving process. But clots can also form inside a blood vessel and threaten life by blocking circulation.

Body organs and systems make thousands of adjustments and responses throughout life. Most of the time, this constant adjusting keeps us in good health. When a body system, or any part of it, functions incorrectly or goes out of balance, this flaw in body wisdom can make a person feel sick.

Some diseases of body systems seem to occur only in older people. Others affect mostly children. Still others seem to work on people your age. Some of these illnesses cannot be cured, but doctors have ways of controlling many of them.

Some Familiar Diseases

● **12-1 Attitudes About Illness**

Some people have difficulty knowing how to act around people who are disabled or seriously ill. Should you act the same way you would with anyone else or should you act differently? What can you say without offending? How much sympathy or extra help should you offer?

PROCEDURE

Describe your reaction to each of the following statements. Do you agree, disagree, or have some other response?

1. A seriously ill person doesn't want to see other people.

2. When you know someone is in the hospital you should go visit him or her.

3. When someone is disabled you should try to ignore the disability entirely.

4. When someone is disabled you should try extra hard to help the person with everything.

5. Most people who become seriously ill will never be the same again.

6. Certain illnesses, especially mental illnesses, are a disgrace to the whole family.

7. People who look different or act oddly should be kept out of sight because they bother some people.

DISCUSSION

1. Make a list of circumstances that could change your feelings about at least one of the above statements.

2. Does your answer to any of the state-

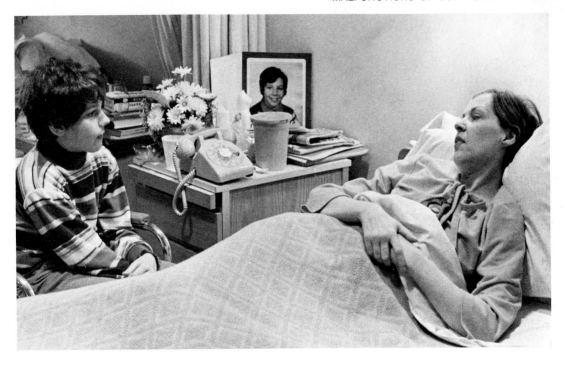

ments depend on whether the person is a member of your family? If so, how?

3. Why do you think some people feel differently from the way you feel about some of the statements?

12-2 When Immunity Leads to Disease

When your body produces an antibody in response to an invading pathogen, the antibody protects you against a disease. It works for your benefit. Antibodies can also be produced in response to other materials such as pollen, the yellow powder produced by the male reproductive organs of some plants. If you have an **allergy,** your body is extra sensitive to certain substances. It works against you. Antibodies react with the pollen, dust, or other substance. A chemical called **histamine** (HIHS tuh meen) is produced. Histamine causes the symptoms of allergy, including sneezing, coughing, and itching. Antihistamines, the major medicines for relieving symptoms of allergies, block some of the effects of histamine.

What can set off an allergic reaction? Almost anything—house dust, pollen, skin or hair shed by animals, chemicals in cosmetics, dyes, perfumes, foods, insect bites, sunlight, and medicines. Anything that sets off an allergic reaction is called an **allergen.** On the first contact with an allergen, there is no allergic reaction. The body makes antibodies. An allergic reaction may occur on the second contact with the allergen, but not necessarily. The reaction may occur years later, after many contacts.

The United States Public Health Service estimates that nearly 15 percent of the population suffers some allergic disease. The

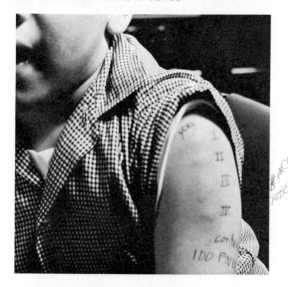

To test for allergies, doctors sometimes inject suspected allergens just under the skin. An allergic reaction may cause swelling.

respiratory system and the skin are the most commonly affected areas. Allergies can also affect the digestive tract, nervous system, joints, kidneys, and blood vessels.

The only way to prevent an allergic reaction is to stay away from the substance. If this isn't possible, medical treatment may be needed. If a person doesn't know what is causing an allergic reaction, a doctor tests the patient by applying tiny amounts of suspected allergens to the skin of the forearms. A mild allergic reaction of swelling and redness takes place at the location of the substance the person is allergic to. Once the allergen is identified, the patient can get relief from symptoms by a series of treatments to build up the body's resistance to the allergen, or by medicines that control the symptoms.

Hay fever isn't usually caused by hay and it doesn't produce a fever. The medical name is *allergic rhinitis*, which means that

an allergen sets off unpleasant reactions in the nasal passages. Sneezing, a stuffy or runny nose, watery and itchy eyes, and itchy nose, mouth, and throat are the symptoms. The symptoms can occur in any season of the year, depending on the allergen and where the victim lives. The usual allergens are pollen and the spores of molds.

Asthma (AZ muh) produces a spasm, or sudden contraction, of the bronchial tubes of the lungs. Spasms make breathing difficult. During an asthmatic attack, mucus may collect in the lungs and bronchial tubes, causing irritation, coughing, and further difficulty in breathing. People having an attack may feel as though they are suffocating. Asthmatic attacks may become so severe that the bronchial tubes and lungs are damaged. Prolonged or continuous attacks can also damage the heart. Bacteria, as well as an allergic reaction, may cause asthma. Only a medical specialist can determine the cause and treat it. Emotional tension also can cause an asthmatic attack in a susceptible person. The attacks may decrease or disappear when the emotional problems are relieved or solved. Even cases of asthma that have a known physical cause have improved when the patient's emotional pressures were relieved.

After the respiratory system, the skin is the second most common location of allergic reactions. The allergen does not have to be something that touches the skin. **Eczema** (EHK suh muh) is a rash, with itching, swelling, blistering, oozing, and scaling of the skin. Many children are subject to this allergic skin reaction. Certain foods can trigger eczema in an infant. Childhood eczema may persist for many years, disappear, and then reappear during adulthood.

The skin may react to allergens in chemicals, clothing, leather, dyes, toilet articles, cleansers, insecticides, medicines, and an almost endless list of other materials, including poison ivy. This type of allergy is called **contact dermatitis.** Mucous membranes as well as the skin are subject to allergic reactions. Emotional factors can make the symptoms of skin allergies more severe. Relief of psychological tension often reduces the allergic symptoms of contact dermatitis.

Foods or drugs can cause **hives,** itchy swellings on the skin. Large hives can cause the eyelids, tongue, mouth, hands, or feet to swell. In severe cases, there also may be difficulty in breathing, stomach pain, nausea, and vomiting. Hives may come and go in a short time or may last for months or years. Some medicines, including penicillin, can cause hives. Anyone who gets hives from a small amount of penicillin is lucky, because hives are a warning signal of allergy. A person who is allergic to penicillin should not take it again. A further dose could be fatal. People who are allergic to any medicine should tell a doctor or a nurse about it whenever a medicine might be prescribed. A different medicine can be used instead, if necessary.

In some diseases, antibodies are produced that work against the body's tissues. One such disease is **rheumatoid arthritis** (ROO muh toyd ahr THRY tihs), the most serious of the many arthritic diseases. Most of the cases are between the ages of 25 and 50, and the disease affects about three times as many women as men. It can come on suddenly or gradually. The patient feels tired and weak. There may be fever. One or more joints may become swollen, inflamed, stiff, and painful. The disease may disappear for a while and then return, perhaps in a different part of the body. Or it may never reappear. Cases may be mild, or so severe that the patient is disabled.

Rheumatoid arthritis causes inflammation of the lining inside joints. Abnormally large amounts of lubricating fluid make a joint swell. The lining grows out over the surfaces of the joint and wears away the cartilage. Scar tissue develops, leaving the joint stiff, tender, swollen, and painful to move. If the disease is not treated, the joint may become permanently deformed and immovable. Treatment includes rest, physical therapy, and medications.

Another form of arthritis, **osteoarthritis** (ahs tee oh ahr THRY tihs), is not related to the immune reaction. It is called "degenerative joint disease" because it is caused by wear and tear. It usually affects much-used joints such as the knees and knuckles.

A severe case of rheumatoid arthritis.

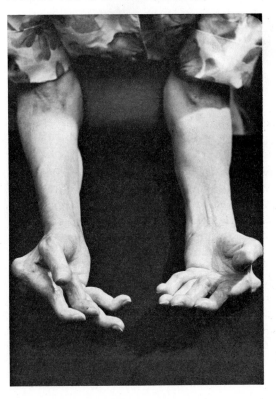

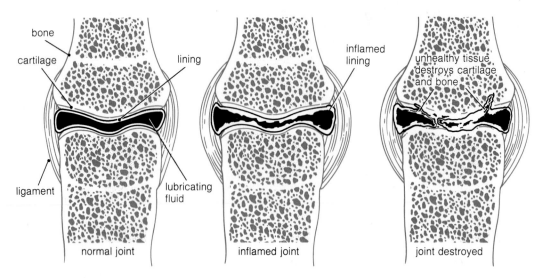

bone
cartilage
lining
inflamed lining
unhealthy tissue destroys cartilage and bone
ligament
lubricating fluid
normal joint
inflamed joint
joint destroyed

Rheumatoid arthritis attacks the lining of a joint and destroys its flexibility. It can be treated, but there is no cure yet.

Osteoarthritis rarely strikes people under 40. The cartilage in the affected joint wears away, leaving the joint painful and stiff. But osteoarthritis is much less crippling than rheumatoid arthritis because the joints do not become as limited in movement if proper treatment is started early in the disease.

12-3 When Glands Malfunction

The precision with which the endocrine glands regulate many body functions is upset when a gland produces too little or too much of a hormone. Too much production can be caused by enlargement of the gland or by a growth, called a **tumor**. It is sometimes treated by removing part of the gland. Too little production results from damage to a gland, possibly by a tumor or an infection. It is usually treated by giving the patient extra doses of the hormone. Some diseases result from a gland that malfunctions without any apparent cause.

Because it takes such small amounts of hormones to keep the body systems working properly, it is dangerous to take hormones except under a doctor's care. Even a "hormone face cream" (if it actually does contain hormones) can upset certain body

Malfunctions of the pituitary gland made two of these men the tallest and the shortest in the world.

functions. This can cause disease instead of prevent it.

The pituitary gland produces several hormones. So a malfunctioning of the pituitary can cause many different health problems. One of the products of the pituitary is growth hormone. Too much of it produced during childhood leads to **gigantism** (jy GAN tihz uhm). A person having this condition grows unusually tall but still well proportioned. If overproduction begins during adulthood, the person will not grow taller, but parts of the bone structure, especially the cheeks, jaws, hands, and feet, enlarge. The opposite condition is **dwarfism**. Other disorders also may cause dwarfism, but too little production of growth hormone is a common cause.

A person with severely bulging eyes may have too much thyroid hormone. This condition is called **hyperthyroidism** (hy puhr THY roy dihz uhm). It also causes excessive sweating, rapid pulse, and weight loss despite an increase in appetite. Someone having an overactive thyroid gland may be very irritable or excitable. The condition can be treated with medicine or by removal of part of the gland. Some medical centers use radioactive iodine to kill some thyroid cells.

Too little thyroid hormone, **hypothyroidism** (hy poh THY roy dihz uhm), in an adult makes the patient mentally and physically sluggish. The tongue may become enlarged and the skin becomes puffy, looking as though it were full of fluid. Lack of thyroid hormone in infancy produces **cretinism** (KREE tihn ihz uhm). A cretin may have an old-looking face, dull and puffy eyes, a pot belly, and a thick tongue that may protrude from the mouth. Both physical and mental development are impaired. A cretin can be treated with thyroid extract and must continue taking this medication for life. Untreated, the child will be dwarfed and mentally retarded. Therefore early treatment is essential to prevent damage.

Goiter (GOY tur) is a disease of the thyroid gland caused by iodine deficiency. It is an enlargement of the thyroid gland. The visible symptom is a swelling at the front of the neck.

Probably the most familiar disease associated with gland malfunctioning is *diabetes mellitus*, usually just called **diabetes**. If the islets of Langerhans, the endocrine glands in the pancreas, do not produce enough of the hormone insulin, the body cannot use sugar or store it efficiently. Extra sugar accumulates in the blood and urine. But it is not available to body tissues. A simple test can show sugar in the urine and alert a doctor to the possibility of diabetes. Symptoms of diabetes include excessive thirst and appetite, frequent need to urinate, fatigue, loss of weight, and itching. Diabetes also causes poor circulation, decreased resistance to infection, and slow healing of wounds.

Diabetes tends to run in families. It can show up at any age. It is most likely to occur in people over 40 who are overweight. Close relatives of diabetics should control their weight and get physical examinations every year.

Diabetes cannot be cured, but it can be controlled. People who have diabetes can live normal lives if they take care of themselves. A person who has severe diabetes may need injections of insulin several times a day, as well as a diet low in sugar and starch. A person who has very mild diabetes may only have to lose weight and eat fewer carbohydrates. Mild diabetes can often be controlled by diet plus new medications that can be swallowed instead of injected. Regular exercise is helpful because it increases the body's ability to use sugar. So less insulin is needed. Exercise also improves circulation, which helps tissues stay healthy.

Diabetes is very dangerous if it gets out of control. In the case of severe diabetes, lack of insulin may lead to a sudden increase of sugar in the blood. This causes nausea,

Carrying a card like this could save a diabetic's life. The other side of the card identifies the person and his or her doctor.

If unconscious or acting strangely I may be having a reaction to insulin or to an oral medicine taken for diabetes.

I HAVE DIABETES

If I can swallow give me sugar, candy, fruit juice or a sweetened drink. If this does not bring recovery or I can not swallow call a physician or send me to a hospital quickly for administration of glucose or glucagon.

Distributed by
AMERICAN DIABETES ASSOCIATION, INC. • 1 West 48th St., New York, N.Y. 10020

Some professional athletes have diabetes. It can be controlled by proper diet and insulin.

vomiting, and headache. In extreme cases, the person may go into a coma from which only medical attention can rouse him or her. A sudden decrease in blood sugar, called insulin shock, causes tremors, cold sweats, extreme hunger, and possibly convulsions or mental confusion. Diabetics should carry a special identification card or metal insignia, so that they can get prompt, correct, medical attention in an emergency.

12-4 Intestinal Problems

The intestines can be affected by many conditions, including infections, nervous tension, and allergies. Two problems that are potentially serious, but can be corrected easily by surgery, are appendicitis and hernia.

The appendix is a small, hollow, fingerlike organ that extends down from the large intestine. If it becomes plugged, it is likely to become infected. **Appendicitis,** or inflammation of the appendix, must receive medical attention promptly. It mostly affects people between the ages of 10 and 30, but it can strike anyone. An inflamed appendix causes severe abdominal pain, nausea, and fever. The warning signals of appendicitis should result in an immediate call to a doctor.

Anyone experiencing the symptoms of appendicitis should lie down and remain as quiet as possible until medical attention is obtained. If the pain is severe, an ice pack may be applied but not a hot-water bottle. Take nothing by mouth—no food, water, or any medicine. Be especially careful not to take a laxative, which can cause an inflamed appendix to burst. A burst appendix allows the infection inside the appendix to spread quickly throughout the abdominal area. This extremely serious and often fatal condition is called **peritonitis** (per uh tuh NY tihs). It can usually be prevented by removing the inflamed appendix. This operation is called an **appendectomy** (ap uhn DEHK tuh mee). If an appendectomy is done before complications develop, recovery is usually quick.

Another problem that may require surgery is a hernia. A **hernia** is a loop of intestine that bulges through a weak spot in the muscle tissue of the abdomen. The weak spot is usually in the groin area or at the navel. The weak spot may be present at birth, but a hernia may not appear until the muscles are strained by lifting heavy objects. The popular term "rupture" is an inaccurate term for a hernia, because a rupture means a tear. Coughing, sneezing, or

Overloaded backpacks can lead to back strain, especially during long hikes. The person below shows the right way to lift heavy objects to avoid back injuries and hernias.

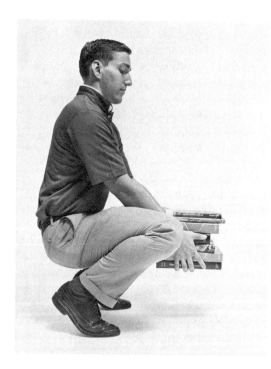

straining to pass bowel movements can make a hernia worse. Lying down with the knees up lets the hernia seem to decrease, since the intestine may slide back into place temporarily. Men are more likely than women to get hernias.

Anyone having a hernia should be treated by a doctor. An untreated hernia may strangulate. When this happens, a loop of intestine is caught so tightly that its blood supply is reduced or cut off. The cells of the intestinal wall die from lack of oxygen. This condition is as serious as a burst appendix. An untreated hernia that suddenly becomes painful is a medical emergency. It is important to be seen quickly at a doctor's office or in the emergency ward of a hospital.

A hernia is best treated by surgery to repair the muscular weakness. The commonly advertised trusses for men that press against the abdominal wall are inconvenient and often uncomfortable. An improperly fitted truss may enlarge the weakened area. Doctors oppose the use of trusses and advise instead the surgery needed to repair the weak muscle tissue. Usually the patient can go back to work two to four weeks after surgery.

Using proper techniques to lift objects will help prevent hernias, as well as back trouble. When lifting a heavy weight, face the object, keep your feet close to it, and spread your feet more than a foot (30 centimeters) apart. When lifting from the floor, bend your knees, grasp the object, and rise slowly. You should feel the effort of lifting in your legs rather than in your back. Carry loads on your shoulders, not on your hips. Avoid reaching high for heavy packages.

SELF CHECK

1. What is an allergic reaction?

2. What are some possible causes of asthmatic attacks?

3. Among diabetics, what are the symptoms of (a) too much sugar in the blood, and (b) too little sugar?

4. Why is appendicitis life threatening?

Nervous and Cardiovascular Diseases

12-5 Anemia

Anemia is any condition in which the blood cannot carry as much oxygen as it should. This sometimes means that there are not enough red blood cells, and sometimes that the red blood cells do not have enough hemoglobin. Anemia is not a disease, but a symptom of a number of disorders. Mild anemia causes tiredness and reduces the body's resistance to disease. Severe anemia leads to shortness of breath and a rapid heartbeat.

The word *anemia* means "without blood." Loss of a large amount of blood from a wound causes severe anemia, requiring transfusions to replace the blood. Constant blood loss is more difficult to detect and correct. Stomach ulcers, heavy menstrual flow, or intestinal worms can lead to anemia.

Iron deficiency is a common cause of anemia. When the body breaks down old red blood cells, the iron in them is saved and reused. Healthy men lose only a small amount of iron, which is replaced by a good diet. Women lose iron when they menstruate, so they need almost twice as much iron as men. Children need extra iron for growth. A well-balanced diet will usually prevent iron-deficiency anemia. Anyone who is often tired without an obvious reason should be examined by a doctor. If the problem is anemia, the doctor may recommend iron pills. Anyone taking iron pills should follow directions carefully because too much iron is poisonous.

Anemia can also have other causes. **Pernicious** (puhr NIHSH uhs) **anemia** results from a breakdown in the mechanisms by which vitamin B_{12} is absorbed in the body. This affects the way red blood cells develop. It was always fatal before the discovery that

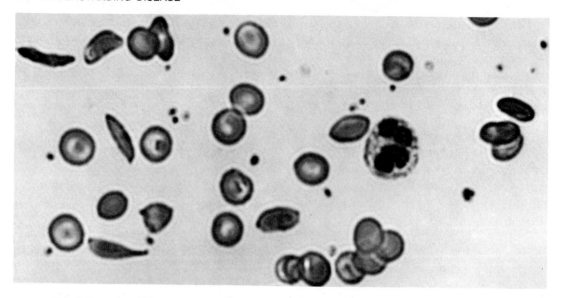

The flattened red blood cells are a sign of sickle-cell anemia.

injections of vitamin B_{12} can control it. The injections must be taken the rest of the patient's life, usually once a month.

In **sickle-cell anemia,** an abnormal type of hemoglobin makes affected red blood cells crescent shaped and unable to carry oxygen. Blood flow in small blood vessels is often blocked, causing pain. The attacks can be relieved by transfusions, but no cure for the disease has yet been found. Sickle-cell anemia is found mainly in people of African and Mediterranean descent. It is an inherited disease. People with two genes for sickle-cell anemia have the disease. People with one sickle-cell gene and one normal gene are said to have sickle-cell trait. They do not have the disease, and have no symptoms. But if both parents have sickle-cell trait, their children may inherit the disease. Oddly enough, research has shown that people with sickle-cell trait are protected from malaria. The protozoa that cause malaria cannot survive in their blood cells.

12-6 Cardiovascular Diseases

Diseases of the heart and blood vessels, **cardiovascular** (kahr dee oh VAS kyuh luhr) **diseases,** result in more deaths than all other causes combined. But research into this group of diseases has led to discoveries of preventive measures, new medications, new types of surgery, and advanced life-saving equipment.

Certain symptoms warn of the possibility of heart disease. Only a doctor can tell whether these symptoms indicate serious trouble. Someone may notice that ordinary activities are beginning to cause shortness of breath or pain in the chest. A sensation of choking or suffocation may wake a person up in the middle of the night. Swelling of the ankles may indicate that the heart cannot circulate blood effectively. Pressure pain in the center of the chest during an activity, after a heavy meal, or during cold weather is also an important symptom. So are dizziness, fainting, blue lips or fingernails, coughing up blood, or a persistent cough.

Hardening of the arteries and high blood pressure can lead to heart disease. They can occur separately, but they often go together. Hardening of the arteries, or **arteriosclerosis** (ahr tihr ee oh skluh ROH sihs), is a slow, progressive disease that may begin early in life. The linings of the arteries become thick and hard from deposits of fat, minerals, and other materials. The arteries lose their ability to expand and contract with the flow of blood. Blood moves with difficulty through the narrowing arteries, so the heart has to work harder to push the blood through them. Hardening of the arteries that supply blood to the heart makes the heart less able to do its job. Arteriosclerosis cannot be reversed, but the process can be slowed down. Exercise helps prevent build-up of materials deposited in the artery walls and develop added blood vessels. Large amounts of cholesterol in the blood seem to be associated with arteriosclerosis. Many doctors advise their patients to eat less fatty meats, dairy products, and eggs.

High blood pressure (hypertension) has been called "the silent killer." This disease rarely produces any symptoms until it is so serious that body organs are affected. Every time the heart beats, blood pressure rises and falls within a normal range. But sometimes, for various reasons, the arteries contract, and the blood presses harder against the walls of the arteries to get through, causing high blood pressure. High blood pressure is sometimes temporary, caused by nervous tension. But some people's blood pressure is too high all the time. The heart may be damaged by having to work harder. In only about ten percent of all cases of hypertension can the cause be found. A kidney ailment or a narrowing of one or more arteries may be the cause.

High blood pressure affects about one out of six adults in the United States. More women than men have hypertension, and black men are twice as likely to have it as white men. There seems to be a family tendency to have it. One high measurement of blood pressure does not mean hypertension. The measurement should be repeated later. If blood pressure is consistently high, a doctor must determine the best treatment. Medicines that can reduce blood pressure are available. A low-salt diet may be necessary. Overweight patients are advised to lose weight. Counseling sometimes helps when emotional strain causes hypertension.

An artificial pacemaker can be implanted in the chest to help a faulty heart beat rhythmically.

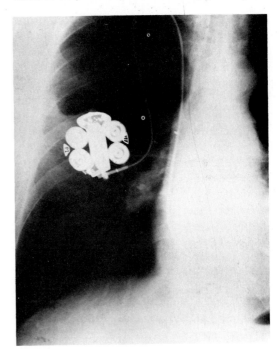

Dr. Paul Dudley White leads a "pedal for health" ride. To keep his heart strong, the famous heart specialist rode bicycles and did other strenuous activities even in his 80's.

Treating hypertension often involves more than medicines and special diet. Hypertensive people may have to change their style of life if it is too tense for them and is endangering their health.

Rheumatic fever, as you read in Chapter 11, begins with damage to the heart by streptococcal toxin. Slowly, the inner lining of the heart and one or more valves are damaged. Children who suffer rheumatic fever are often instructed to take antibiotics for a long time to prevent recurrence of streptococcus infection and to prevent damage to heart tissue. Deaths from rheumatic fever have declined during the past 30 years because of the use of antibiotics.

A **heart murmur** is a sound made by the heart in addition to its normal beat. Some heart murmurs mean that a heart valve is not functioning efficiently, because of rheumatic-fever damage or for some other reason. Other murmurs are not signs of trouble. People who have a heart murmur do not need to restrict their activities unless a doctor advises it.

Pain over and around the heart, called **angina pectoris** (an JY nuh PEHK tuh rihs), indicates the heart's need for more oxygen. Sometimes the pain spreads to the shoulder, neck, arm, or hand. Angina pectoris is not really a disease but a set of symptoms. They tell the patient and doctor of the underlying ailment—arteriosclerosis of the arteries of the heart. When the heart needs extra oxygen, the reduced blood flow can't supply it. Then the chest pains begin. Pain may be brought on by climbing stairs, excitement, or a large meal. This ailment can be treated with medicine, rest, and small meals. In some cases, surgery is performed. This operation involves bypassing the clogged coronary artery with a piece of another blood vessel, usually a section of a vein from the leg. Many angina patients live a full lifetime if they cooperate with their doctor in keeping their disease under control.

In a heart attack, or **coronary thrombosis** (KAWR uh nehr ee thrȧhm BOH sihs), the flow of blood to part of the heart is blocked by a blood clot (thrombus). A heart attack is accompanied by a sudden, severe pain in the chest. Pain may be felt also in the left arm, throat, or back. The pain may pass quickly or last for hours. Sweating, extreme weakness, intense shortness of breath, a grayish color of the skin, nausea, and loss of consciousness may accompany a heart attack.

A person having a heart attack needs immediate medical attention, beginning with first aid and continuing in a hospital. Eighty percent of people having their first heart attack survive. Gradually the area of the heart muscle cut off from its blood supply by a clot is replaced by scar tissue. During the weeks of recovery, new blood vessels form around the scarred area. Usually, the full blood supply to the heart is normal within four to six weeks. Heart-attack patients must be very careful not to over-exert themselves during the first few weeks after the attack. They can then return gradually to their usual activities. They should exercise, control their diet, and avoid smoking. They may have to change the way they live and work. Many heart specialists believe that working under pressure and emotional tensions, combined with lack of regular exercise and periods of relaxation, contributes to heart attacks.

A **stroke** is the cutting off of part of the brain's blood supply. An artery of the brain may be clogged by a clot. Or a weak spot in an artery may stretch and break. Most strokes are caused by arteriosclerosis, high blood pressure, or both. A stroke can cause confusion, difficulty in speaking, paralysis, or immediate death. Brain tissue is perma-

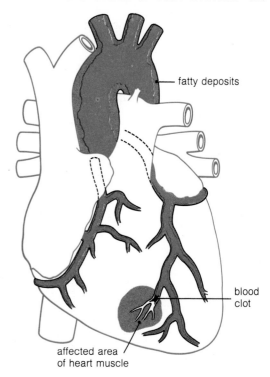

In a heart attack, a blood clot cuts off the blood supply to some heart muscle. Most victims survive their first heart attack.

nently damaged if it loses its blood supply for a few minutes. Depending on where in the brain a stroke occurs and how severe the damage is, the patient may be able to recover fully or only partially. Rehabilitation programs enable many stroke victims to recover the use of paralyzed arms or legs, or to speak normally again. Strokes do not occur only among your grandparents' generation. A stroke can happen at any age. The important consideration for people your age is that the conditions that build up over many years and cause stroke can be controlled or prevented early in life.

Most heart and blood-vessel diseases affect middle-aged or older adults, but

Paralysis can be caused by injuries and diseases of the spinal cord. Activity is good physical and mental therapy.

many of these diseases begin unnoticed in people your age. Regular physical activity, low-fat diet, and avoidance of smoking now can delay or prevent cardiovascular problems later. A tendency toward heart disease sometimes runs in families. So anyone whose relatives have heart trouble should be especially careful to stay in good shape.

12-7 Malfunctions of the Nervous System

Diseases of the nervous system may arise due to abnormalities of the nerves, injuries, or infections. Or they may accompany psychological problems.

Multiple sclerosis (skluh ROH sihs), or MS, is a disease of young adults. MS is the most common disease of the nervous system affecting young adults in North America and northern Europe. In MS, the covering of the axons of central nervous system cells is damaged. Nerve impulses traveling along these nerve pathways are interrupted. The course of the disease varies according to the location and amount of nerve cell damage. The cause of multiple sclerosis is not known. Some researchers believe that a virus causes the disease. Their theory is that the virus remains in the nervous system of babies and children until adolescence or early adulthood, and then begins to produce symptoms. Others believe that an antibody is produced that attacks the body's own nerve cells.

Double vision is often the first sign of MS. The patient may then have trouble maintaining balance and controlling the arms and legs. There may be numbness, weakness, and pain in various parts of the body. MS cannot be cured, but medicine, physical therapy, massage, and exercise keep the affected muscles in as good condition as possible. The patient's disability can lead to psychological problems, so reassurance and encouragement from friends and family is important. Since MS is a crippling but not an immediately fatal disease, its victims can lead long and useful lives.

The seizures of **epilepsy** (EHP uh lehp see) may be hardly noticeable or severe. In a *grand mal* epileptic seizure, the victim becomes unconscious. He or she may foam at the mouth and gnash the teeth. The arms and legs may stiffen and jerk violently. Bowel and bladder control may be lost. A *petit mal* attack may be a brief clouding of consciousness that passes without any further ill effect. *Petit mal* sufferers may not even know that they had an attack. The only symptom may be a brief blank stare.

You can help someone who has a severe *grand mal* epileptic seizure in these ways:

1. Lower the person gently to the floor. Remove furniture or any hard objects he or she may strike in thrashing around.

2. When the mouth is open and relaxed, you may put a folded handkerchief or roll of paper between the back teeth on one side to prevent broken teeth or a bitten tongue. Do not force anything between the teeth.

3. Do not try to move the person or to force liquids down the throat. After the seizure, urge the person to rest quietly until he or she has regained control. Hospitalization is not necessary unless the person has a series of seizures.

Epilepsy results from the discharge of excessive electrical energy from a group of brain cells. Specialists consider epilepsy a symptom, not a disease. Nearly 100 conditions have been identified as capable of producing seizures. They include brain damage at birth, high fever, poisoning, infection, insufficient sugar or calcium supply to the brain, tumors, or blows to the head.

Medicines that eliminate or greatly reduce the severity of epileptic seizures are available. Many epileptics go to school or to work with no restrictions except to take their medicine regularly. They can drive and take part in sports. A big problem for an epileptic may be public ignorance and prejudice. Many people still have a superstitious fear of epilepsy. Sometimes, known epileptics are shunned and prevented from living or working normally, even though their illness is under control. Parents and teachers may need professional advice to help epileptic children and adolescents cope with social prejudices.

Parkinson's disease is a disease of the brain that mostly affects older men and women. The brain damage that causes Parkinson's disease may be caused by a virus infection, carbon monoxide poisoning, or by arteriosclerosis. The disease appears slowly. It may start with a slight shaking of the hands or difficulty in talking. Later, the whole body may shake, muscles stiffen, and the back tend to bend forward. The face takes on a fixed, masklike appearance. Although the nervous system is affected, intelligence is not. Many victims whose jobs involve mainly mental work can continue working for many years. Treatment of Parkinson's disease includes massage, medication, and sometimes brain surgery.

Some of the causes of **schizophrenia** are psychological, some are biological. Schizophrenia can apparently be brought on by family problems and social pressures. Heredity may also be a factor. That is, the chances of becoming schizophrenic are greater for people who have schizophrenic

A special video system enlarges print so that people with very poor eyesight can read.

parents, even when they are raised by foster parents. Brain damage caused by injuries or alcoholism may also result in schizophrenia. Some schizophrenics have been found with abnormal blood and urine. Schizophrenics are treated with medicines and vitamins as well as psychotheraphy. The question of whether psychological problems cause changes in chemicals in the body, or the reverse, is far from being settled. Many researchers are studying it.

Diseases affecting the senses are common. Any of the senses can be impaired. Diseases of the eyes and the ears are considered the most serious because these senses give us most of our information. Sensory impairment may exist at birth or may result from infection or injury. Every child's vision and hearing should be tested early and regularly throughout childhood. Many problems can be corrected or prevented from becoming worse if they are treated early. At the least, the difficulty can be recognized and the child helped to make up for it. Many children with undiagnosed vision or hearing problems have been thought to be mentally retarded or uncooperative when they really were not.

Blindness in infants may have many causes, including an illness of the mother or excessive use of oxygen or medication during delivery. Of the two million blind people in the United States, 17 percent were born that way or inherited a blinding disease. In later life, cataracts and glaucoma are the most common causes of blindness. You will study these diseases in Chapter 16.

Hearing may be impaired at birth. Children born prematurely may have defective hearing, as well as other physical disabilities. Children whose mothers had German measles early in pregnancy may suffer severe hearing loss. Hearing loss can begin with an infection that spreads from the nose and throat through the Eustachian tube to the ear. An infection of the outer ear, if not treated, may eventually damage the eardrum and middle ear. Some types of deafness appear to be part of the aging process. Among older people, loss of hearing may be so gradual that the individual does not notice it for a long time. If it is noticed, many people are unwilling to admit it, even to themselves. They may complain that "people mumble," and feel offended if anyone suggests that their hearing is less than perfect. They may be afraid of losing their jobs. Many people, even small children, can be helped by hearing aids. Children who have hearing difficulties may need special training to learn to speak properly. Most school districts have specially trained teachers to help children with defective hearing.

SELF CHECK

1. What is anemia?

2. How can you reduce your chances of getting heart disease?

3. What is a stroke?

4. What age group is most susceptible to multiple sclerosis?

5. Is epilepsy always severe?

Other Diseases of Body and Mind

12-8 Birth Defects

By now you know about dozens of systems, organs, tissues, and body functions. Something could go wrong with any of them when they are developing, before a baby is born. Almost everyone has something that is not quite perfect. For most people it is minor: a birthmark, crooked teeth, a weak knee, an allergy.

A few babies are born with severe defects. A defect that exists at birth is called a **congenital defect.** An organ may be missing, improperly formed, in the wrong place, or may not work well. If the defect is very serious, the baby will die before birth or soon after. Some birth defects do not show up until adolescence or even middle age. Many defects can be corrected or improved by treatments such as surgery, medication, and special diets. Glasses and orthodontia are often used.

Birth defects can be caused by many factors, such as disease in the mother or drugs she takes during pregnancy, exposure of either parent to radiation before concep-

tion, genetic abnormalities, and lack of oxygen during birth. German measles during the first three months of pregnancy is particularly dangerous. The baby may be born deaf, mentally retarded, or with cataracts or a defective heart. Young women are advised to be immunized against German measles early in their lives so that they will be immune during pregnancy. Syphilis can also cause birth defects. Doctors can test for some genetic problems early in pregnancy.

Some congenital abnormalities of the heart do not show up until later in life, but some are obvious at birth. A "blue baby" has a condition leading to a lack of oxygen in the blood. There may be a hole in the tissue of the wall separating the chambers of the heart. The hole allows oxygen-rich blood from the lungs to mix with oxygen-poor blood from the rest of the body. The body cells do not get enough oxygen. Many congenital heart defects can be corrected by surgery.

Brain damage may occur before or during birth. It may be caused by lack of oxygen, premature delivery, head injury, or

Given help and understanding, cerebral palsy victims can keep minds alert and spirits strong.

infection of the brain or its covering. **Cerebral palsy** is partial paralysis and lack of muscle coordination resulting from brain injury. The condition often affects speech. So the victims may appear to be mentally retarded. With medical help, physical therapy, special education, and encouragement from their families, they can learn to talk, walk, and feed and dress themselves. Like people suffering from other disabilities, palsied children need to be treated as people first. They can grow up to enjoy useful lives if they are not ignored, shunned, or pitied because of their disability.

A **cleft palate** is a split in the roof of the mouth. A **cleft lip** (formerly called a "harelip") is a split in the upper lip. These conditions result from the failure of the two sides of the face to join together properly during development before birth. They cause difficulty in eating and speaking. Surgery can correct the defects before the child learns to talk. Speech therapy is often necessary. With early treatment, most children born with a cleft lip or palate can achieve a normal appearance and speech.

Mental retardation is a term used loosely in describing people who show less than normal ability to learn and don't adapt to needs of everyday life at a rate society expects. A few people cannot learn to do even the simplest tasks for themselves and must be cared for as if they were babies. However, most retarded people are only mildly retarded. They can learn to take care of themselves, make a living, and lead useful lives. Mental retardation has many causes. Many are not understood, but others can be prevented. For example, some metabolic and endocrine disorders can be detected at birth and treated before any damage is done.

Children who have speech problems or emotional illnesses often have difficulty learning even though they are not retarded. Speech therapy or counseling may allow such children to act normally and to overcome their learning disabilities.

12-9 Psychosomatic Illnesses

Every physical problem has psychological effects. If you come down with the flu the day before you have to play in an important basketball game, you may be depressed or angry. Someone who has heart disease or cancer is likely to be very frightened and depressed.

Emotional problems affect the body too. Changes in respiration, circulation, diges-

"Sorry your ulcer flared up, Joe. The work's piling up on your desk."

tion, and other body processes often accompany emotional changes. When you are tense or afraid, you may get a headache or an upset stomach. A person living under constant fear and tension may develop a serious illness, such as a stomach ulcer.

Physical illnesses caused by emotional problems are often called **psychosomatic** (sy koh soh MAT ihk) **illnesses.** The word *psychosomatic* comes from the Greek words for "mind" and "body." Headaches, stomachaches, obesity, and diarrhea (frequent, excessive, and watery bowel movements) can be psychosomatic illnesses. These same disorders may have physical causes too. Some psychosomatic illnesses disappear quickly, but others become a "way of life" and become more severe as the person

grows older. Psychosomatic illnesses are not imaginary. The pain and discomfort are real and may require treatment by a doctor. The psychological problems that cause the discomfort should be resolved with the help of counseling.

Many diseases are related to the emotions. People who are tense and overworked are more likely to develop high blood pressure or heart disease. People who have asthma or epilepsy are more likely to have an attack when they are upset.

When people speak of **ulcers,** usually they are referring to open sores in the inner lining of the stomach or of the duodenum, the small intestine near the stomach. The medical name for this is *peptic ulcer.* When digestion occurs normally, the stomach lining

A life filled with tension and strain often leads to ulcers, high blood pressure, and other diseases.

protects itself against its own strongly acid digestive juices without difficulty. If too much is produced, or if the juice contains too much hydrochloric acid, this substance may damage the lining of the stomach or the intestines. Once an ulcer forms, it continues to be irritated unless it is treated. An ulcer patient may become seriously ill if the ulcer breaks through the stomach or duodenum wall and bleeds or allows digestive juices to escape into the abdominal area.

Ulcers are a characteristic twentieth-century disease. Competitive adults, who work under great pressure and are often dissatis-fied with their accomplishments, make up most of the ulcer patients. But students also may suffer from ulcers. Young soldiers subjected to extreme hazards and anxieties in combat may develop ulcers too.

The most common symptoms of ulcers are pain and discomfort in the upper abdomen, usually a few hours after eating. These pains decrease when food is eaten, especially milk or other acid neutralizers. Severe symptoms may include nausea and vomiting. If the ulcer bleeds, the blood may be vomited or passed out of the body through the rectum.

Ulcers can be successfully treated and cured. The process may take a long time. Medical treatments include rest, a special diet, and medicines to reduce the amount of digestive juices produced in the stomach and to neutralize the stomach acids. In severe cases, a surgeon may remove the ulcerated portion of the digestive tract. Ulcer patients are advised to give up smoking, because smoking irritates the lining of the stomach and duodenum. Alcoholic beverages usually are not allowed. Ulcer patients should find ways to reduce the emotional tensions that trigger the production of their physical symptoms.

In **ulcerative colitis** (UHL suh ray tihv koh LY tihs), ulcers, or sores, occur in the lining of the colon. The most common symptoms of ulcerative colitis are severe diarrhea and abdominal pain. (However, diarrhea is more often a symptom of infection in the digestive tract or emotional tension.) Weakness and loss of weight usually accompany this disorder. Ulcerative colitis is most common among young adults. It is associated with stress, emotional upsets, and worry. People who get this disease usually are tense, very serious, and very competitive. They need help in learning how to relax.

Circulatory and nervous disorders may also be psychosomatic. Doctors believe that tension headaches and **migraine** (MY grayn) **headaches** are sometimes caused by emotional difficulties. Migraine headaches are very painful. The pain usually occurs on one side, but it may occur on both or shift from side to side. Nausea usually accompanies the headache.

Migraines show how complicated the cause of a disease can be. People who worry about doing their work perfectly or who are repressing their anger are most likely to suffer from migraine headaches. But some people report freedom from headaches on weekdays while they are working, and suffer on weekends when they have fewer responsibilities. Many sufferers get migraine attacks when they eat chocolate or cheese. Their bodies apparently produce too little of an enzyme needed to break down certain chemicals in these foods.

Senility (sih NIHL uh tee) is the gradual mental and emotional deterioration that affects many elderly people. Senile people may suffer losses of memory, confuse the present with the past, and be unable to recognize old friends and members of their family. They may burst out suddenly with joy, rage, or despair for no apparent reason. They may become suspicious of people.

Doctors formerly believed that most senility was caused by brain damage due to hardening of the arteries in the brain. Now, specialists in diseases of the elderly believe that psychological factors are at least the partial cause of senility. Older people may feel that they have become useless and withdraw from everyday life. An environment in which the person feels loved and needed can help prevent or delay many of the symptoms of senility.

12-10 Investigating Your Medical History

Many times throughout your life you are likely to be asked questions concerning your health and medical history. Insurance applications, college admission forms, and job and military application forms require you to know quite accurately your medical past. Will you have this information readily at hand? Or will you have to resort to trusting your memory, guessing, or writing "I don't know"? There are also times when a doctor may need to know your medical history in order to treat you properly and even to avoid harming you.

PROCEDURE

Why not take this opportunity to bring your personal medical record up to date? In answering the items listed below, write down what you can remember for sure. Look up what you don't know and file the information away carefully for future additions and reference. The time will be well spent. You don't have to bring your record into class. It is for your own private use. Be sure to write the date you make this record. Save your record and make changes in it when necessary. Next to each change put down the date you write the change.

1. List the diseases you have had.

2. List the immunizations, vaccinations, and booster shots you have had, including the dates.

3. List your allergies.

4. Write down any family illnesses you know of, particularly those discussed in this chapter.

5. Record any injuries you have suffered.

6. Describe any surgery or extended medical care you have had.

7. Describe any hearing or sight impairments, and what correction is used.

8. Write down your blood type.

9. Describe any health problems you have now and any medication you are using.

SELF CHECK

1. What are some causes of congenital defects?

2. Why should the term "mentally retarded" be used very cautiously?

3. Describe a person who is likely to have a psychosomatic illness.

Chapter Summary

An allergic reaction usually involves the skin or respiratory system, but it may affect other body systems or organs. An allergy results from the extra sensitivity of the body to environmental antigens. Rheumatoid arthritis is related to the production of antibodies that work against the body's own tissues.

One of the most familiar health problems involving a malfunction of an endocrine gland is diabetes mellitus, the disease resulting from under-production of insulin. Diabetes can be controlled but not cured. Failure to control diabetes results in circulatory problems, low resistance to infection, and eventually, death.

Appendicitis, hernia, and peptic ulcer are among the most common problems of the digestive system. Anemia can be caused by a deficiency in red blood cells, loss of blood, deficiency of iron and other nutrients, or misshaped red blood cells.

Many diseases of the heart and blood vessels begin at an early age. Ailments such as high blood pressure and hardening of the arteries may not produce any symptoms for many years. Heart damage caused by childhood rheumatic fever may not reveal itself for 15 or 20 years. Heart attack and stroke need immediate hospital care.

Multiple sclerosis is crippling but not fatal for many years. The symptoms of epilepsy, another disease of the nervous system, may be severe or mild.

Abnormal chemical makeup of blood and urine, as well as emotional difficulties and family and social pressures, are thought to cause schizophrenia.

Diseases involving any of the senses may be present at birth or may be caused by infection or injury. Other birth defects include abnormalities of the heart, cerebral palsy, cleft palate, and mental retardation.

Psychosomatic diseases may involve almost any part of the body. Ulcers, colitis, migraine headaches, and asthma are all influenced by the emotions. The slow process of senility is believed to result from both psychological factors and reduced blood flow due to hardening of the arteries of the brain.

Chapter Self Check

1. What are some common allergens?

2. What body systems are most often affected by allergies?

3. How can an allergic attack be prevented?

4. How is rheumatoid arthritis related to antibodies?

5. How can diabetes be controlled?

6. What should *not* be done if someone has symptoms of appendicitis?

7. What is the best treatment for hernia?

8. List some common causes of anemia.

9. What symptoms may indicate heart disease?

10. Why is high blood pressure sometimes called "the silent killer"?

11. What causes angina pectoris?

12. What are heart-attack patients advised to do when they leave the hospital?

13. Describe the effects of multiple sclerosis.

14. Name some conditions that can produce epileptic seizures.

15. Describe some causes of hearing loss.

16. Why should a child's vision and hearing be tested at a young age?

17. What is a "blue baby"?

18. How should a person who has cerebral palsy be treated?

19. What is a psychosomatic illness?

20. How does a peptic ulcer form?

Read More About It

Edwards, Jesse E. and Goott, Bernard. *The Illustrated Coronary Fact Book.* New York: Arco Publishing Company, Inc., 1973. The normal circulatory system, diseases that affect it, and preventive measures people can take. Well illustrated.

Griffith, Valerie Eaton. *Stroke in the Family.* New York: The Delacorte Press, 1970. Actress Patricia Neal recovered from a series of strokes with the help of the author. Discusses rehabilitation for stroke victims.

Kruger, Bert. *Aging in America.* Boston: Beacon Press, 1973. The emotional problems of aging as well as the physical and psychological effects of aging.

Lowenstein, Bertrand E. and Preger, Jr., Paul D. *Diabetes: New Look at an Old Problem.* New York: Harper & Row, 1976. The nature and effects of diabetes and the care needed in taking insulin and other medications.

Miller, Benjamin F. *Freedom From Heart Attacks.* New York: Simon & Schuster, Inc., 1972. Important facts and theories about how genes and environmental conditions are related to heart disease.

13

The Dangerous Environment

After completing the work in this chapter, you will be able to:

describe the effects of pollution, noise, and overcrowding on human health.

explain what cancer is and what some of the causes are.

describe some treatments for cancer.

discuss ways of avoiding or reducing environmental health hazards.

Pollution Is Everywhere

In late 1976, an atomic bomb was test-exploded in China. Wind blew radioactive fallout eastward. Several days later, rain carried some of it to the ground in Pennsylvania, halfway around the world. Radioactivity was detected in cows' milk. Health officials tested milk frequently to see if the radioactivity reached a dangerous level. They also warned people to wash vegetables from their gardens very carefully before eating them.

Pollution travels all over the world. Radioactive wastes, factory wastes, oil spills, car exhaust, and sewage spread as far as the North Pole and the middle of the Pacific Ocean. And some of these materials will stay around for thousands of years.

Pollution is materials in the wrong place. Lead, for example, is used for batteries and pipes. In gasoline it keeps car engines from knocking. But in the air it is a deadly poison.

You already know a lot about pollution. You have seen dirty air and polluted water. You know that pollution affects animals and plants. This chapter focuses on how pollution, noise, and overcrowding affect people's health. You will also learn how to protect yourself and others against pollution.

Pollution and Health

13-1 Air and What Else?

What is in the air you breathe? Where is the air the cleanest? The dirtiest? A simple investigation can help determine some of the things in the air in your school and elsewhere in your community.

MATERIALS

petroleum jelly
tape or clothespins
white paper strips

PROCEDURE

1. Your class will be divided into groups of two or three. Each group will choose a location at which to test the air. Each group will

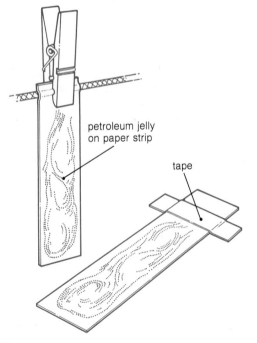

petroleum jelly
on paper strip

tape

The air in a city is a lot like a dump. All sorts of unwanted materials are discharged into the air we breathe.

have to visit their location twice: once to set up the test and again to collect the sample. The groups should try to choose a variety of sites, indoors and out.

2. At the location where you have chosen to leave your air tester, smear one side of a strip of paper with the petroleum jelly. Leave one end clean so you can handle the paper easily. Use tape or clothespins to fasten the paper in place. Some papers should be left flat and others vertical. Record where you leave the paper, the time, and the date.

3. After you have left your paper, record each day's weather—temperature range, wind, relative humidity, and precipitation.

4. Before your next health class, collect the paper. On the clean part, write where the paper was and whether it was flat or vertical. Bring it to class, and let everyone examine it.

DISCUSSION

1. What locations left the most dirt on the papers?

2. What locations were the cleanest?

3. Were the vertical papers as dirty as those that were placed flat? What reasons can you give for your answer?

4. Do you think specific weather conditions affected your results?

5. What do the papers indicate about the air we breathe?

6. What could be done to improve the condition of the air in any of the locations that seem to be especially dirty? If these suggestions are practical, what are you going to do about them?

13-2 Air Pollution

Clouds of pollution six miles (ten kilometers) high have been found over parts of North America. Some places have more air pollution than others, but no place is free of it. Air pollution has many sources—cars, furnaces, crop dusters, factories, power plants. Some pollutants (materials that pollute) have obvious effects such as making your eyes burn. Others are harder to detect, but build up and cause trouble slowly.

Some pollutants are poisons. Others, such as dust and asbestos fibers, collect in and block small tubes in the lungs. In addition to causing disease, air pollution also makes some existing diseases worse. For people whose respiratory systems are already damaged by diseases such as asthma, pollutants may cause dangerous blocking of bronchial passages. Lung tissues may become coated with mucus. Thousands of people who had lung diseases died during severe episodes of air pollution. Children are more vulnerable to air pollution than adults because they are growing, have smaller air passageways, breathe faster, and are closer to the ground. Children who are undernourished are in particular danger because their resistance to disease is reduced.

There are many different materials in polluted air. This section will discuss some of the most common and dangerous ones.

Carbon monoxide is a colorless, odorless, tasteless gas. It is formed in combustion reactions when fuel does not get enough oxygen to burn completely. A major source is automobile engines that are not properly tuned. When carbon monoxide is inhaled, it combines with hemoglobin. Carbon monoxide combines with hemoglobin more readily than oxygen does. So it takes the place of oxygen in the red blood cells. The body tissues are deprived of oxygen.

Symptoms of carbon monoxide poisoning are headache, dizziness, weakness, blurred vision, and possibly nausea. Someone who inhales a large amount of carbon monoxide

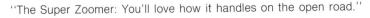
"The Super Zoomer: You'll love how it handles on the open road."

Where does dust in the air come from? Sand pits, smokestacks, car tires wearing away, volcanoes . . . you can add to the list. The bicyclist's protective mask keeps dust out of his lungs.

becomes unconscious and may die of suffocation. People who have heart or lung diseases are in particular danger because their bodies may get barely enough oxygen anyway. A person who has been overcome by carbon monoxide needs fresh air. Artificial respiration may be necessary. (You will learn about artificial respiration in Chapter 15.)

People can get carbon monoxide poisoning from an automobile engine running in a closed garage, a gas heater that is not vented to the outdoors, or a faulty stove or furnace. Carbon monoxide from a car engine can get into the car through the heater or ventilator. Always drive with a window slightly open. In slow, heavy traffic, exhaust gases from the car ahead may be drawn into your car, so try not to drive too close. Smoking in a closed car produces significant amounts of carbon monoxide. Drowsiness caused by carbon monoxide is thought to contribute to many automobile accidents.

Lead poisoning affects the stomach, the brain, and the nervous system. In children it can lead to brain damage. Symptoms include stomach cramps, mental depression, and convulsions in children. Lead poisoning can be diagnosed by a blood test. The most

Poor people usually suffer most from pollution. They often live near highways, factories, and dumps and trash-filled vacant lots that are set on fire.

important treatment is to prevent further exposure to lead. Medication is used in severe cases. The earlier the problem is diagnosed, the better off the patient is.

Lead gets into the air in the exhaust of cars that burn gasoline containing lead. Tires and many paints also contain lead, which enters the air as they wear away. Children who play near highways and bridges may breathe dangerous amounts of lead. (Children can also get lead poisoning by eating chips of lead-based paint.) People who jog beside a highway inhale lead as well as carbon monoxide.

Sulfur dioxide is produced when sulfur is burned. Coal and fuel oil often contain large amounts of sulfur. So do many metal ores.

Breathing sulfur dioxide leads to lung diseases. Many people have died when smog containing sulfur dioxide settled on a city or town. Factories often have very tall smokestacks so that sulfur dioxide will be diluted and carried away by wind. Some factories wash the sulfur dioxide out of their exhaust gases with a spray of water. They produce sulfuric acid, which the factories can sell. There are laws limiting the amount of sulfur in fuel, but sulfur dioxide levels in the air sometimes rise dangerously high.

Nitrogen oxides are produced in car engines and electric power plants. These oxides react with moisture in the lungs, forming acids. Nitrogen oxides also react with other air pollutants to form products that burn the eyes and irritate the lining of the nose and lungs. Emission-control devices on automobiles reduce the amount of carbon monoxide and nitrogen oxides that are produced. But they make a car use more gasoline. Also, the increasing number of cars means emissions are still high.

Dust and **fibers** in the air, such as asbestos fibers, become lodged in the smaller bronchial tubes. They stay there for years, causing irritation and swelling. Eventually, they can clog air passages so that not enough air gets into the lungs. The victim coughs, becomes short of breath easily, and is more susceptible to lung diseases such as bronchitis and cancer. If the condition is discovered early, further damage can usually be prevented by protecting the patient from the dust. Diamond cutters, rock drillers, and asbestos-products workers are most likely to be exposed to dangerous amounts of dust. Besides masks and good ventilation, these workers should have regular chest X rays.

Although workers in certain industries are most likely to be affected by materials in the air, anyone can be affected. If you use paint, cleaning fluid, or spray cans, be sure you are in a well-ventilated area. When you use a power saw, sander, or anything else that produces dust, wear a face mask. Avoid breathing heavily polluted air as much as you possibly can.

13-3 Water Pollution

Practically every kind of liquid or solid waste product, from sewage to lead, gets dumped into water. Agricultural pesticides and fertilizers get washed into streams. Dust from the air falls into water, and gases become dissolved in it. As a river flows along, it becomes more and more full of chemicals. Recently a photographer demonstrated that water from the Mississippi River contained enough chemicals to develop film.

Tap water has been treated to remove some of the dangerous materials. Most community water departments filter out solid particles, and add chlorine or ozone to kill bacteria. But many materials that were dissolved in the river or lake are still in the water when you drink it. These materials may include pesticides, detergents, acids, minerals, and radioactive materials.

Salt used to melt ice on roads gets washed into streams and remains in tap water. The sodium in the salt can be harmful to people who have high blood pressure or heart disease. Water softeners, which make water better for washing, also add sodium to water. Sodium in water is not in table salt form, so the water does not taste

The daily discharge of wastes into sinks, toilets, and drains is
as big a pollution problem as oil spills in the sea.

salty. But it is still potentially harmful. Water softeners should be installed only on the hot water line.

Some water systems have lead pipes. If the water is slightly acidic, when it sits still in the pipes it will dissolve some of the lead. Water departments are starting to treat the problem by making the water less acidic. Meanwhile, if your water system has lead pipes, run the water for two or three minutes before taking any for drinking or cooking, especially early in the morning, to wash away the lead dissolved in the water.

Water you drink is not necessarily free of pathogens. Even water from a clear mountain spring may be contaminated. When you are camping, or any time you are not sure the water is safe, boil it before you drink it. When the United States Public Health Service studied local water systems, they found that most local officials did not test enough water samples. About one-eighth of the systems had too many bacteria

in their water. Viruses are more difficult to kill than bacteria. But no state government or federal agency has made rules about testing water for viruses.

Some people buy bottled water for drinking. It is usually labeled as coming from a spring. Often it does, but in some cases tests of bottled water show that it is nothing but expensively packaged, fraudulently advertised tap water. Before buying any bottled water, read the label to see if the source of the water is listed.

Water containing irritants or pathogens can be dangerous to swim or bathe in as well as to drink. Fungus infections and rashes can develop from skin contact with polluted water. Pathogens can be swallowed or can enter the body through a cut or scratch. If a lake, river, or beach area is posted "not safe for swimming," heed the warning.

People can also take in dangerous materials when they eat fish from polluted water.

Everything has to go someplace, so we can't escape our wastes. They wash up on the beach and blow back in the wind.

For example, fish may contain mercury compounds, which are dumped into water as waste from many industrial processes. Mercury affects the nervous system. Small doses can cause headaches and numbness. Larger amounts can lead to brain damage, birth defects, and death.

There is not much you can do to protect yourself against mercury and other harmful chemicals that get into fish and shellfish in amounts too small to detect. But you should avoid eating fish caught in waters you know are badly polluted by industrial wastes. Warnings have been issued on these waters.

13-4 Will Everybody Please Quiet Down!

Noise is a pollutant too. People who are subjected to loud noise—whether from machinery or from rock music—suffer hearing loss. Enough loud noise causes permanent damage by destroying cells in the inner ear. Many young people who constantly listen to loud rock music have suffered as much hearing loss as people 65 years old.

Noise causes adrenalin to go into the bloodstream, making blood vessels constrict. This increases blood pressure and pulse rate. It can make cardiovascular problems worse. Loud noise makes people tense, irritable, aggressive, and less able to concentrate. So it may contribute to accidents and stress-related diseases such as stomach ulcers. Even fairly quiet sounds such as conversation or traffic can interfere with sleep and make you feel tired in the morning.

A problem with noise is that people don't agree on what is noise, or what is too loud. Someone may say that he has to play music loudly to feel it, but complain when you do the same thing. You may be bothered when a neighbor starts her motorcycle early in the morning.

Loud noises that you like can cause hearing loss just as effectively as loud noises you hate.

You can protect yourself more effectively against loud noise than against many other environmental health hazards. Avoid exposing yourself to loud, continued noise. Try setting the television, radio, or stereo at a lower volume. Carpets and drapes can absorb and screen out some noises. It may also be possible to put some noisy home appliances, such as washing machines, away from the areas of the house or apartment where your family spends most of its time. Some new products carry noise-level labels. Advertisers are starting to emphasize how quiet their products are. Before your family buys any appliance, try to find out what brands are quietest.

When you can't control your environmental noise, try to get away from it. Choose the quietest part of your home for studying and sleeping. Some people use earplugs when no quiet location can be found.

13-5 Overcrowding

Scientists once put eight mice in a large cage. As the mice produced young, the scientists gave them plenty of food and water, but no more space. The population grew to 2200 mice, all crammed into the space that was ideal for eight. The crowded mice fought with each other. Cannibalism became common, although there was plenty of food. Female mice stopped taking care of their young. Finally they stopped having babies at all. In the end, overcrowding led to the death of the whole population.

Some scientists feel that the mice experiment can tell us a lot about human behavior in overcrowded situations. Of course it cannot tell us everything about overcrowding. People who live in high-density areas, such as Holland and Japan, have developed ways of behaving so that they interfere with each other as little as possible. Overcrowding

alone is not necessarily disastrous, but overcrowding plus poverty usually produces crime, disease, and other serious social problems.

People live in cities because jobs, schools, stores, and social activities are there. There have been cities for thousands of years. People in cities used to burn soft coal in their stoves, dump sewage in the streets, and drink water from wells in the middle of town. The cities were full of smoke. And diseases such as typhoid were common. Cities are cleaner now, but there are still many kinds of pollutants. As people become more aware of the problems, they can work to solve them.

Many of the problems of cities are problems of crowding. Disease spreads faster when people live and work close together. Crowding and the noise it produces lead to stress. Many people in cities cannot afford medical care and nutritious food, so they

A private place in a crowd—a tree shared with a friend.

are more susceptible to disease. Automobiles in traffic jams produce hazardous amounts of lead, carbon monoxide, and other pollutants.

The problems of cities are very difficult, but people are taking action on some of them. One area in which there has been progress is giving people more room to move around. There is increased pressure on city governments and builders to set aside parks and play areas. Schools are encouraged to leave their open areas available for community use. Cars have been banned from some busy shopping streets. Neighborhood groups turn trash-covered vacant lots into playgrounds and gardens.

There is increasing awareness of people's need for privacy. Everyone needs to be alone sometimes to think. People find privacy in places like bathtubs, apartment house roofs, and libraries. If you don't have a place where you can be alone, try to find one. You might want to discuss the problem with your family. Probably everyone in your family would like more privacy too.

SELF CHECK

1. How do these air pollutants affect health: carbon monoxide, lead, dust, and fibers?

2. How can tap water endanger health?

3. How does noise affect the circulatory system?

4. Why are people in crowded cities more susceptible to disease than people living in the country?

Cancer

13-6 What Is Cancer?

Normal cell division is orderly and limited. A child's cells divide frequently enough to keep the child growing at a proper rate. An adult's cells divide when new cells are needed—for example, to replace worn-out blood cells or to heal an injury. When enough new cells have been produced, cell division stops. No one knows how the body regulates cell growth.

Occasionally a change occurs in the DNA in a cell nucleus. Such a change is called a **mutation** (myoo TAY shuhn). A mutation produces a cell that behaves differently from its parent cell. Mutations can occur by themselves or be caused by radiation or chemicals. Most mutations are harmful, and cause the cell to die. Other cells with mutations are destroyed by the body's defense systems. Sometimes, however, a mutation leads to a kind of cell that does not die and does not stop dividing when it should. It becomes a lump or mass of cells, called a **tumor.**

A **benign** (bih NYN) **tumor** has a wall around it. Cells cannot escape from it and move to other parts of the body. A benign

Normal bladder cells (left). The nuclei of cancerous bladder cells (right) enlarge and crowd out the rest of the cell contents.

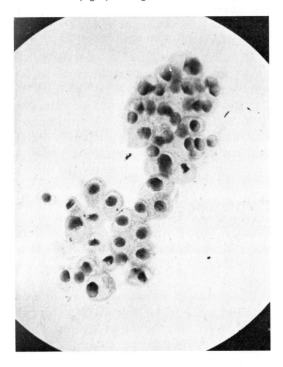
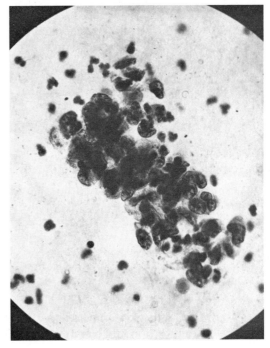

tumor causes problems if it grows large. It may take up enough space to interfere with the functioning of body organs. If so, it can be removed by surgery, usually without complications.

A **malignant** (muh LIHG nuhnt) **tumor** is not confined. Fragments of it may break off, move through the bloodstream or the lymphatic system, and start growing in other parts of the body. A malignant tumor is called a **cancer.** If cancer is discovered early in its development, before it spreads, it can often be removed. After it spreads, it becomes more difficult to cure. Besides crowding body organs, malignant tumors rob healthy cells of their blood supply. Cancer of a vital organ, such as the liver or lungs, eventually prevents it from functioning properly. An uncontrolled malignant growth-is almost always fatal. In rare cases, the growth of cancer cells stops on its own. No one is sure why this happens. Certainly, no one can depend on its happening.

There are four major types of cancer. A **carcinoma** (kahr suh NOH muh) is a growth that begins in tissues that cover or line organs, such as the skin or the lining of the lungs, uterus, breast, or intestines. If a growth begins in supporting tissue, such as bone or muscle, it is called a **sarcoma** (sahr KOH muh). A third type, **lymphoma** (lihm FOH muh), results from abnormal growth in the lymph nodes.

The fourth type, **leukemia** (loo KEE mee uh), is a cancer of the blood-forming tissues in the bone marrow, spleen, and lymph nodes. There is overproduction of leukocytes (white blood cells). There may be 100 times the normal number of leukocytes in the blood, but they are not able to perform their job of fighting infection. The number of red blood cells and platelets is reduced because the white cells crowd them out. The patient becomes anemic and susceptible to infection and bleeding. Acute leukemia appears suddenly and advances rapidly. There is also a slower-developing (chronic) form. There is no prevention for leukemia yet. Cures are beginning to look more promising. By using new experimental drugs, doctors have been able to achieve symptom-free periods and apparent cures in many patients.

Cancer is not contagious. Doctors, nurses, and researchers have never caught the disease from patients. The family and friends of a cancer patient do not have to worry about catching cancer from the patient either.

13-7 Carcinogens in the Environment

The actions of people seem to be the cause of many cancer cases. Substances released into the environment by industry, cars, and waste disposal; tobacco smoke; certain medications; chemicals used in industrial processes; sunbathing; even some of the components in our food—all have been associated with cancer.

The most recent scientific opinion is that environmental factors are responsible for up to 85 percent of all cancers. A substance that can cause cancer is called a **carcinogen** (kahr SIHN uh juhn). Environmental factors that cause cancer are difficult to detect and prove. After the first contact with a carcinogen, many years may pass by before an individual shows symptoms of cancer. By then, the person may have changed jobs several times, moved to another part of the country, and be living in a much different way from his or her lifestyle during the time when the first contact was made with the carcinogen.

Until recently there was no overall government policy in the United States for testing and regulating the sale of new chemicals that could prove harmful. In late 1976 a bill

The price of convenience is very high. Spray paint contains ingredients that are harmful when inhaled. And the gas in the can escapes into the upper atmosphere, where it damages the ozone layer. The ozone layer is needed to screen out harmful ultraviolet radiation from the sun.

was signed into law that requires testing of new chemicals before they are allowed to be sold.

No one knows for sure whether it takes a certain amount of a carcinogen to cause cancer. Most safety laws are based on the idea that there are safe levels of carcinogens, below which there is no risk. But many experts say that even a very small amount of a carcinogen will cause cancer in a few people. Also, some carcinogens accumulate in the body. So a very small exposure over a long period of time may result in a build-up of a carcinogen to a dangerous amount in the body.

A few carcinogens are well recognized. One is tobacco smoke. Cigarette smoking causes at least 80 percent of lung cancer cases—about 73,000 cases in the United States each year. Lung cancer is almost always fatal. Smokers also have a greater risk of getting cancer of the larynx, mouth, esophagus, and bladder.

Reduction of air pollution would remove another major cause of cancer, as well as other lung diseases. In some industrial cities, there is so much of the carcinogen benzopyrene in the air that people living there breathe in the equivalent of the smoke of five or six cigarettes a day.

Some industrial processes produce carcinogens. These substances may not result in symptoms of cancer for 20 to 30 years. Some workers who applied fluorescent paint to watch dials when they were young, licking the paintbrushes as they worked, developed cancer of the mouth or throat when they were middle-aged.

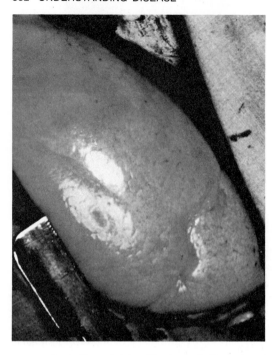 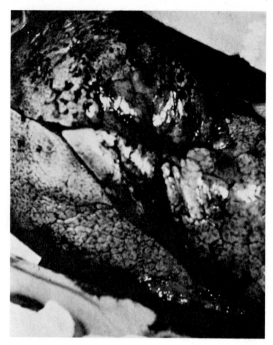

A section of a healthy lung (left) and a dirty lung (right).
Breathing polluted air is likely to cause dirty lungs and increase
the chances of getting a respiratory disease.

Vinyl chloride, a gas used to make a plastic called polyvinyl chloride (PVC), has been found to be a cause of liver cancer. New standards were set up so that workers would be exposed to less vinyl chloride. More recently, scientists have questioned the safety of PVC. PVC tends to have some molecules of vinyl chloride left in it. The vinyl chloride can escape into foods and cosmetics in PVC containers. PVC liquor bottles have been banned in the United States. PVC food wraps, containers, and water pipes are being studied.

Many carcinogens work in combination with other materials to produce cancer. Asbestos, used in construction and insulating materials, can cause several types of cancer. Asbestos workers have a very high rate of lung cancer, but only if they also smoke. The combination of asbestos and smoke leads to 92 times as many cases of lung cancer as asbestos alone.

Some foods are believed to contribute to cancer. Some researchers suspect that there is a connection between the amount of beef fat that people eat and risk of getting cancer of the colon. Diets with too much sugar or too little roughage may also be involved. Many food additives are suspected of being carcinogenic. A few have been banned and others are being tested. Some are called safe by some experts and dangerous by others.

Certain drugs have also been linked with high cancer rates. After World War II, thousands of women were given the synthetic hormone diethylstilbesterol (DES) during pregnancy to prevent miscarriage. Some of their daughters developed cancer of the vagina during adolescence. The use of hormones by middle-aged women to reduce the discomforts of menopause now worries some cancer specialists. They believe that the medicine may contribute to cancer of the uterus. Therefore women taking these hormones must have frequent medical examinations.

The safety of birth-control pills is being questioned. Drugs used to prevent rejection of organ transplants have been found to be carcinogenic. Other medications, used in less serious medical cases, also are being examined to discover if they are cancer-causing chemicals.

X rays and other forms of radiation, in high doses, can cause leukemia and other forms of cancer. To reduce the risk of cancer, doctors avoid having their patients X-rayed unless it is necessary, and they keep the dosage of radiation as low as possible. Ultraviolet radiation from the sun increases the risk of skin cancer.

If every human carries the potential for cancer in his or her body, why doesn't

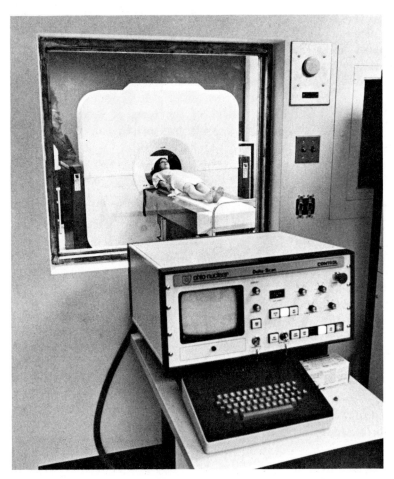

A special X-ray machine controlled by a computer can take large numbers of pictures but still keep the radiation dose of the patient down to a low level.

everybody become a cancer patient? The answer seems to be that some people are more susceptible than others. Some families tend to have high rates of particular forms of cancer. The strength and efficiency of an individual's defense systems partially determines whether malignant cells will form and live. Improperly working endocrine glands may make an individual prone to cancer. Some doctors believe that psychological factors are significant too. They suggest that people with certain emotional characteristics, such as tenseness and a tendency to avoid expressing their feelings, are prone to cancer.

Different environmental factors, including available food, influence the kinds of cancer that occur and the rates at which they occur. Age, race, nationality, and social and economic class also influence the kinds of cancer that occur and the rates at which they occur.

13-8 Symptoms and Treatment of Cancer

Cancer produces different symptoms, depending on its location and stage of development. Pain is usually not a symptom during early stages of cancer. If you or any member of your family experiences any of the following conditions for more than two weeks, a doctor should be consulted.

Cancer's Danger Signals

Unusual, persistent bleeding or persistent discharged substance
A lump or thickening in the breast or elsewhere
A sore that does not heal
Persistent change in bowel or bladder habits
Persistent hoarseness or cough
Persistent indigestion or difficulty in swallowing
Change in a wart or mole

These conditions do not necessarily mean cancer, but a doctor can find out and treat the problem, whatever it is. Diagnosis starts with a complete physical examination, including blood and urine tests. The doctor will ask about the patient's medical history and illnesses of relatives. If there is a problem with the lungs or the digestive system, X rays may be taken.

The final test for cancer is to look at some cells from the suspected area. For some organs, such as the uterus, a few cells can easily be scraped off and examined. The **Pap test** is a standard part of a physical examination for women. Cells are scraped from the narrow, lower end of the uterus. The Pap test can detect cancer of the uterus while the cancer is still completely curable. If cancer of the lung or intestine is suspected, cells for testing can be obtained through a lighted tube inserted into the body. Some other organs can be punctured with a long needle through which cells can be drawn out. Occasionally surgery is required to get cells to be tested.

If diagnosed early enough, many forms of cancer can be treated. But the question of when a patient should be regarded as cured is not easy to answer. For most forms of cancer, a patient is usually considered cured if the disease has not occurred again five years after treatment. However, some patients are regarded as cured after one to three years. Other patients have to be checked for longer than five years. The five-year survival rate in the United States now is about 35 percent of all cancer patients. Some doctors believe that this rate could be 50 percent if all malignancies were diagnosed early enough for treatment to be effective.

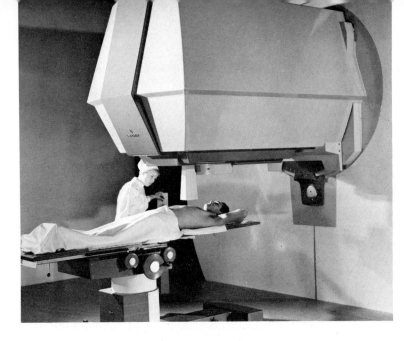

Radiation can kill or cure. Here a patient receives radiation therapy to kill cancer cells or at least slow down their growth.

The goal of cancer treatment is the complete removal or destruction of the malignant cells. If the disease is diagnosed early enough, this can be done before any part of the body has been seriously damaged. In advanced cases, extensive surgery may be necessary.

If surgery is not possible, as in some cancers of the lymphatic system, a doctor may decide to use radiation treatment. The goal of **radiation therapy** is to attack cancer cells that are deep in the body. X ray, radon (a radioactive gas put out by radium), cobalt, and high-voltage therapy are types of radiation treatment. The radiation dose must be carefully controlled because the treatment can damage healthy cells as well as malignant ones. Cancer cells are usually more sensitive to radiation and are destroyed first.

A third method of treatment is **chemotherapy** (kehm oh THEHR uh pee), the use of powerful chemicals. Some chemicals help slow down the malignant growth. Others destroy healthy cells along with cancerous cells, but they destroy the cancerous cells more rapidly. In some cases, two or three types of treatment are used together or alternately. In the case of breast cancer, surgery may be followed by both X rays and chemotherapy. The goal is to eliminate any malignant cells that may have invaded the circulatory or lymphatic system after surgery. Treatment for leukemia may include chemotherapy, radiation therapy, and transplants of healthy bone marrow from another person.

Cancer frightens most people more than the possibility of having a heart attack, which is three times as likely to happen. Some people are so afraid that they will not get a physical examination for fear that cancer may be discovered.

Cancer patients usually face terrible uncertainties about whether their treatment will work. Every aspect of a cancer patient's life is affected. Families of cancer patients, as well as the patients themselves, need special help and counseling. Since cancer may afflict a person for many years, the patient's family has to learn how to help him or her. But family members also need to know how to avoid having their own lives completely disrupted by the strain.

Health Frontier

"It Can't Happen to Me!"

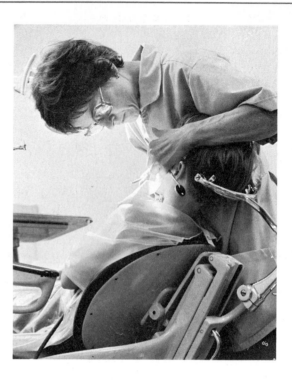

People in the health professions sometimes have to work with dangerous chemicals. They should know the dangers of these materials. You might expect that they would be extra careful. Yet health workers have a high rate of illness and death from exposure to chemicals.

Ordinarily, tooth fillings are made of a mixture containing mercury. The mercury is in a form that is not dangerous to the patient. But preparing fillings can be dangerous to the dentist. Several studies have shown that many dentists have high levels of mercury in their bodies. Mercury can cause nerve disease and psychosis.

Doctors and nurses who work in operating rooms are continually exposed to low concentrations of anesthetic gases. They experience a high rate of liver and kidney disease and cancer. Their children are more likely to have birth defects.

Some of the most dangerous chemicals are used in laboratories that do research and medical tests. Many laboratory workers do not follow even basic safety precautions, such as using hazardous materials only in areas with good ventilation. Not surprisingly, laboratory workers have a significantly increased rate of death from cancer.

Why do these things happen? Sometimes it is because of ignorance. Only half of all hospitals have formal safety training. But even people who are well aware of the dangers can be affected. Of course, not even the best precautions available can protect a person completely. But a major factor seems to be carelessness. People tend to think that accidents, poisoning, and cancer only happen to other people. They mentally get used to working with a dangerous material. But their bodies don't.

13-9 Cancer Prevention

Cancer research has been carried out for many years, conducted by governments, universities, the American Cancer Society, and private laboratories. The goals in the past have been to find cures for cancer. Now, new emphasis is being placed on preventing cancer. Environmental carcinogens are being identified. Attempts are being made to eliminate them, and people are advised on how to avoid known carcinogens.

The fact that carcinogens are present in everybody's environment allows people to take preventive action. Here are some ways people can reduce their chances of getting cancer.

Don't start to smoke. If you already smoke, stop. Or at least smoke less or switch to low-tar cigarettes.

A high-fat, high-carbohydrate, low-roughage diet contributes to overweight, diabetes, and cardiovascular disease. It is also associated with some cancers. Eat less animal fat, substitute chicken or fish for hamburgers, eat more fresh fruits and vegetables, and use whole-grain breads and unrefined, unsugared cereals.

Check the labels on food. You can't avoid all additives unless you grow your own food. But you can reduce the amount of flavor enhancers, colorings, and preservatives that you eat.

Don't over-expose yourself to direct, intense sunlight. Light-skinned people especially are likely not only to suffer painful sunburn, but also to increase the possibility of developing skin cancer.

Be alert to the cancer danger signals you read about in the last section. Tell your family about them. If your parents and grandparents know about possible dangerous symptoms, they can stop worrying about vague aches and pains that "could be cancer." Knowing about the symptoms of this group of diseases and avoiding as many risks as possible is the most effective way of coping with this environmental hazard.

SELF CHECK

1. What is the difference between a benign tumor and a malignant tumor?

2. Name some environmental factors that are considered causes of cancer.

3. What are three major treatments for cancer?

4. What can a person do to try to reduce his or her chances of getting cancer?

Pollution and You

• 13-10 How to Reduce Pollution

By now you know many reasons why you should avoid pollution, and some ways you can. You can help reduce pollution too. One way is to become an alert consumer. Before you buy anything—from a deodorant to a car—think about its effects on the environment. You may be able to buy a product that pollutes less. If a product needs to be improved, write to the company and tell it how. Remember to think about safety, too, when you use products.

People are in the habit of keeping unused rooms and buildings lit up at night, even though it wastes electricity and adds to pollution. That habit—like the habit of throwing cans away instead of recycling them—can be broken.

Soon you will be eligible to vote. Even now, you can influence government decisions, especially local ones. Find out what the pollution problems are in your community. Does the city need better sewage treatment? Do the owners of a factory say they will have to close down if they are ordered to clean up? Are new laws needed? Are existing laws being enforced? Choose a local pollution problem and find out as much as you can about it. Think of some questions and suggestions. Then write or talk to the appropriate government officials.

Some pollution is inevitable. Every process produces waste products. But usually the waste can be reduced or used so that it does not become pollution. In this activity you will examine the effects on the environment of things people do, and consider ways to reduce pollution.

PROCEDURE

On a separate piece of paper, make a table like the one below. Think of several things people do and the wastes that are produced. Fill in the table with your ideas. It has been started for you.

DISCUSSION

1. What are some health hazards of the activities you listed? How could the hazards be reduced?

2. Choose one of the ways of reducing waste that you listed. Would reducing this waste be likely to cause any new problems as a side effect?

3. Do people do anything that produces no pollution at all?

ACTIVITY	WASTES	DISPOSAL OF WASTE	HOW TO REDUCE WASTE
Driving a car	Carbon monoxide, nitrogen oxides, unburned gasoline, used oil, oil on roads, shredded rubber from tires, asbestos from brakes, old cars	Exhaust into air, old cars and tires to junkyards, some recycling	More efficient engines, keep engine tuned, drive less, drive more slowly, more recycling
Heating buildings			

Copy This Table on a Piece of Paper

Chapter Summary

Pollution is not new, but in the twentieth century people have begun to pollute their environment so badly that life itself is threatened.

The sources of air pollutants include cars and trucks, furnaces, factories, power plants, and nuclear explosions. Some pollutants are immediately noticeable. They make people cough or make their eyes burn. Others, like radioactive particles, can cause serious health effects without any early symptoms.

Chemicals from industry and agriculture get into tap water. Eating fish from polluted water can make people sick.

It is easier to protect oneself against noise than against most other environmental hazards. People living in overcrowded conditions are subject to disease, stress, and other health hazards.

Cancer is uncontrolled cell growth that is not confined. If it is diagnosed before it spreads to other parts of the body, it can often be removed. After it spreads, cure becomes difficult or impossible.

About 85 percent of all cases of cancer are believed to be caused by environmental factors, including substances that people eat, drink, inhale, or are exposed to where they work. Many industrial processes and materials, drugs, food additives, and other chemicals are tested when they are suspected of being carcinogenic. Some products are banned. People are warned against using others, such as cigarettes, that are known to cause several forms of cancer.

Individuals can reduce their chances of getting cancer by avoiding as many as possible of those substances that are known or strongly suspected of being carcinogenic.

Chapter Self Check

1. List three products you use and describe how they can lead to pollution.

2. Describe the effects of air pollutants in the lungs.

3. Why is carbon monoxide an especially dangerous substance?

4. Describe the effects of lead poisoning.

5. How can people avoid lead poisoning?

6. What are some effects of noise on emotions?

7. What factors make overcrowding a health hazard?

8. What is the difference between normal and abnormal cell division?

9. How do malignant tumors affect body organs?

10. Name and describe the four major types of cancer.

11. Among smokers, what parts of the body are most likely to become cancerous?

12. Name at least two common industrial materials that are now known to be carcinogens.

13. What medications are being questioned as possible carcinogens?

14. Patients need X rays for diagnosis, but X rays themselves increase the risk of cancer. How do doctors try to solve this problem?

15. What are some ways the body keeps itself from getting cancer?

16. List the seven danger signals of cancer.

17. What are some methods a doctor uses to learn if a patient has cancer?

18. What is the most important factor in treating cancer successfully?

19. How have the goals of cancer research changed in recent years?

20. What are some ways an individual can avoid or reduce environmental pollution?

21. Is it possible to live in a completely pollution-free environment?

Read More About It

Commoner, Barry. *The Closing Circle.* New York: Alfred A. Knopf, Inc., 1971. How the environmental crisis happened and what can be done about it. The author believes people may not survive if problems of the environment are not solved.

Ehrlich, Paul R., and Anne H. Ehrlich. *Population, Resources, Environment,* Second Edition. San Francisco: W. H. Freeman & Co., 1972. A detailed discussion of how a rising population, limited food supply, and abuses of the environment affect each other.

Schroeder, Henry A. *The Poisons Around Us.* Bloomington, Indiana: Indiana University Press, 1974. Reference on toxic metals in food, air, and water.

Shimkin, Michael B. *Science and Cancer.* Washington: U.S. Department of Health, Education, and Welfare Publications No. 1162, 1969. The many kinds of cancer and the weapons available to fight them. Chapters on environmental carcinogens and the relationship between nutrition and cancer.

Walbott, George L. *Health Effects of Environmental Pollutants.* St. Louis: C. V. Mosby Co., 1973. Discusses air, water, and food contaminants: their nature, sources, and effects on humans.

14
Preventing Accidents

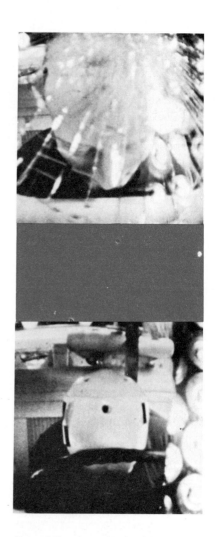

After completing the work in this chapter, you will be able to:

identify causes of accidents.

describe the do's and don't's of safe driving and motorcycling.

explain rules of pedestrian and bicycle safety.

identify home safety hazards and describe ways of preventing home accidents and fires.

describe safety rules for water sports and boating.

One of the dummies in these staged car crashes was wearing a shoulder harness. Which one wasn't?

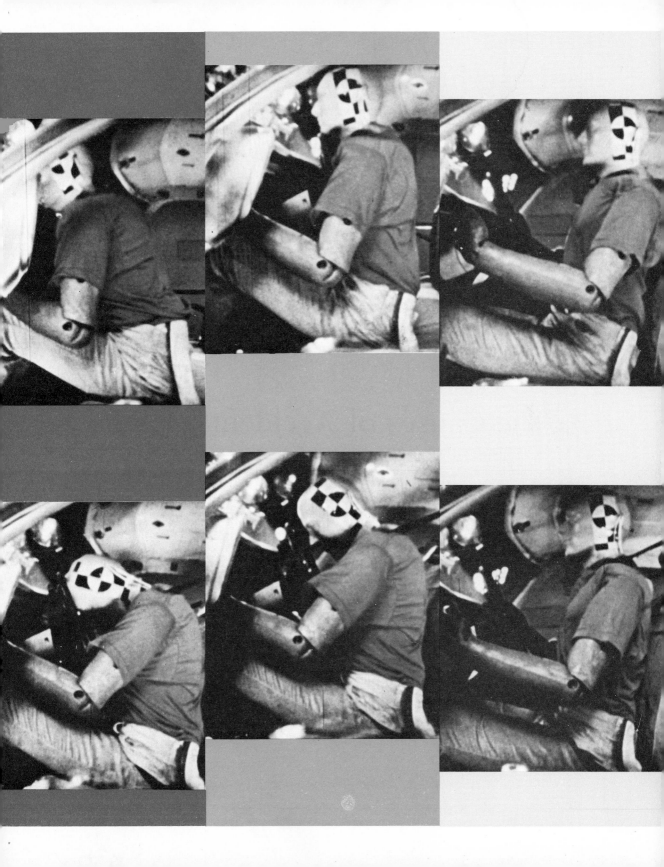

Descents and Falls

On February 20, 1962, Colonel John Glenn, Jr., the first American to orbit the earth, was catapulted into space. Later that same day he piloted his spacecraft through its flaming descent to a successful plunge into the Atlantic Ocean.

Two years later, John Glenn was replacing a bathroom mirror in his apartment when the glass started to slide from his hands. As he moved to catch it, he slipped and fell. "When I came to," he said, "I found myself kneeling in a heap of broken glass and a pool of blood."

Does this story make you think that even a trained, careful person is helpless against luck or fate? Maybe stories like this make you feel that accidents are inevitable. They aren't. Accidents are unexpected events, but they are not caused by bad luck or uncontrollable fate. Accidents have causes, and most accidents can be prevented when the causes are identified and eliminated. A descent from space, for example, is a controlled fall, not an accidental one.

Both knowledge and attitude are important in preventing accidents. Knowledge about how accidents are caused can enable you to prevent many of them. And a state of mind that lets you be alert to hazards, regardless of what you're doing, can save your life.

The Causes of Accidents

14-1 Accidents and the Death Rate

Accidents are a leading cause of death among people of all ages. In recent years, over 100,000 people have been killed in accidents in the United States and 13,000 in Canada each year.

Among people under the age of 25, accidents are the number one cause of death by a dramatic margin, as you can see in this table.

You can learn several things from the table:

1. Accidents are responsible for more than 50 percent of the deaths of people in the 15–24 age group.

LEADING CAUSES OF DEATH IN THE U.S. 15–24 AGE GROUP

CAUSE OF DEATH	NUMBER OF DEATHS		
	Male	Female	Total
All Causes	35,729	12,074	47,803
Accidents	**19,526**	**4,674**	**24,200**
Motor-vehicle	12,502	3,403	15,905
Drowning	2,180	210	2,390
Poison (solid & liquid)	834	254	1,088
Firearms	734	98	832
Other	3,276	709	3,985
Homicide	4,354	1,223	5,577
Suicide	3,378	907	4,285
Cancer	1,653	1,054	2,707
Heart disease	674	418	1,092
Other	6,144	3,798	9,942

from *Accident Facts*, 1976 Edition, National Safety Council

2. For the 15–24 age group, no diseases are among the top three killers. (This is true of no other age group.)

3. Among accidents affecting 15- to 24-year-olds, motor-vehicle accidents far outnumber all others.

4. Male accident victims in this age group far outnumber females. Eighty percent are males. (For the general population, males make up 70 percent of all accident victims in the United States.)

For Canadians, the picture is very similar. Accidents are the leading cause of death for young people, and male accident victims greatly outnumber females.

Disabling accidental injuries affect many more people than fatal accidents. Nearly 11 million people, about the population of Illinois, were disabled in accidents in 1975. A **disabling injury** is an injury that keeps a person away from her or his usual occupation at least one day beyond the day of the accident.

The cost of accidents in one year, including medical expenses, property damage, insurance administration costs, and loss of pay, is over $47 billion.

Accidental deaths in fact outnumber wartime fatalities. About 635,000 United States soldiers were killed in all wars between 1900 and 1976. During those same years, more than 2 million civilians died in motor-vehicle accidents alone.

Why are there so many accidents? Why are so many young people accident victims? And why are so many more males than females involved? The following sections will help you answer these questions.

14-2 Ability, Attitude, and Accidents

There are situations that require certain physical abilities or skills, special knowledge, or special effort and attention. When a person is not up to the demands of such a situation, an accident is likely to occur.

Physical limitations are responsible for many accidents. Elderly people, for example, may fall because their vision or sense of balance is poor. Poor eyesight and poor hearing are common causes of accidents among all age groups. Slow reaction time is another. **Reaction time** is the amount of time between the instant you sense something and the instant you do something

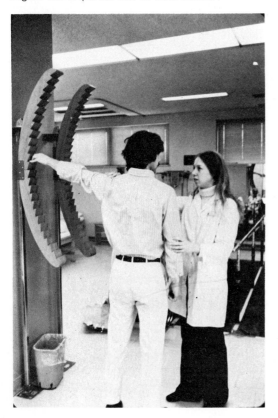

Physical therapy helps many accident victims regain full or partial use of their limbs.

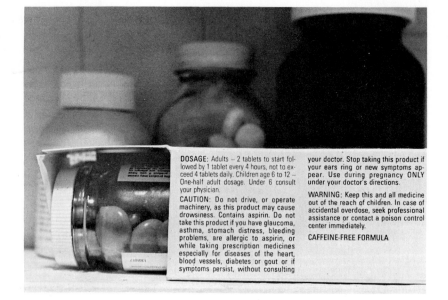

DOSAGE: Adults – 2 tablets to start followed by 1 tablet every 4 hours, not to exceed 4 tablets daily. Children age 6 to 12 – One-half adult dosage. Under 6 consult your physician.

CAUTION: Do not drive, or operate machinery, as this product may cause drowsiness. Contains aspirin. Do not take this product if you have glaucoma, asthma, stomach distress, bleeding problems, are allergic to aspirin, or while taking prescription medicines especially for diseases of the heart, blood vessels, diabetes or gout or if symptoms persist, without consulting your doctor. Stop taking this product if your ears ring or new symptoms appear. Use during pregnancy ONLY under your doctor's directions.

WARNING: Keep this and all medicine out of the reach of children. In case of accidental overdose, seek professional assistance or contact a poison control center immediately.

CAFFEINE-FREE FORMULA

Many medicines, such as antihistamines, carry warnings that they can cause drowsiness.

about it. Having slow reaction time makes it more likely that a person will not be able to get out of the way of unexpected dangers. Some medicines have the side effect of slowing down reaction time. It is wise to find out if this is true of a medicine that you must take.

Two major causes of accidents are tiredness and alcohol or drug use. Alcohol is a contributing factor in over half of all traffic fatalities. People who are sleepy, drunk, or otherwise not fully alert take dangerous—and foolish—risks when they try to drive or do anything else that requires more coordination and judgment or faster reactions than they are capable of. Even during a simple activity such as walking on a smooth, level path, a hiker who is overtired can have a bad fall.

Attitudes and personality have a lot to do with accidents. People who like to take chances may jump on the tailgate of a moving truck or race a car against another car down a narrow road. This isn't the same as knowing how to enjoy adventures. Mountain climbers, white-water canoeists, and professional racers seek adventure, but the good ones know what they are doing. They know the specific dangers they face and they take appropriate precautions.

A few people unconsciously invite accidents. Such individuals may dislike themselves and have an urge toward self-destruction. Others may need attention badly and may unconsciously want to hurt themselves or others as a way of getting attention. Even a momentary burst of hostility or anxiety can bring with it an unconscious wish for something bad to happen to someone.

Lack of attention or carelessness is a significant cause of accidents. The inattention may last only a few seconds, but that's long enough to be hurt or killed. Emotional upsets can result in accidents by taking a person's attention away from what she or he is doing. A depressed, worried, or angry person may not be able to focus her or his attention well enough to drive a car or to use a sharp knife safely.

Carelessness isn't associated only with unpleasant thoughts and feelings. Thinking about the weekend, looking forward to a party, or just enjoying a pleasant day can distract anybody. Being alert and paying attention to where you are and what you're doing are good habits to form in order to stay out of accidents.

● **14-3 Investigating Your Safety Fitness**

Among the reasons people have accidents might be that they lack the vision and quick reactions needed to take all the action necessary to prevent accidents. The following activities will help you determine the degree to which you have these necessary physical abilities.

A. PERIPHERAL VISION

Peripheral (puh RIHF uhr uhl) **vision** is the distance you can see all around you when you are directing your gaze straight ahead. When you say that you saw something "out of the corner of your eye," you are referring to your peripheral vision. The better your peripheral vision is, the larger your **field of vision** is, and the faster you will see things to your side. How good is your peripheral vision? Here is a chance to test it.

MATERIALS

large table or desk	scissors
masking tape	white paper
ruler	yardsticks or meter sticks

PROCEDURE

1. You will work in teams. Using white paper, cut several strips two inches (five centimeters) long, and one-half inch (one and one-half centimeters) wide.

2. Place two yardsticks or meter sticks flat on a large table or desk with their one-inch (one-centimeter) ends together. The other ends should be four and one-half feet (one and one-half meters) apart. Tape them down to hold them in position.

3. Have the person being tested place her or his chin on the table with eyes looking

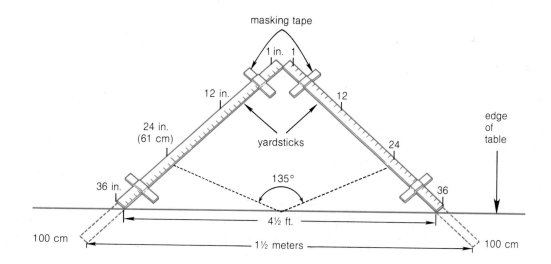

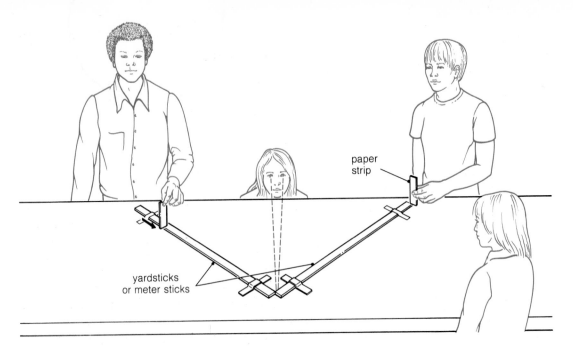

paper strip

yardsticks or meter sticks

directly at the point where the yardsticks or meter sticks meet, as shown in the picture.

4. Have one person stand at the end of each measuring stick, slightly behind the one being tested. Each tester will hold one strip of white paper vertically.

5. The two testers will silently agree on which of them will slowly move the strip of paper along the top of the measuring stick, starting at the 36-inch (100-centimeter) mark. The person being tested should not know whether the strip will appear on the left or on the right side. One other person should watch to make sure that the person being tested keeps her or his eyes gazing at

the point where the sticks meet. Stop moving the strip when the person first sees it.

6. Copy the table below on a piece of paper. Record in the table under "Trial 1" the distance at which the person taking the test first saw the strip of paper, and whether the strip was on the left or the right side. Round off to the nearest inch (or centimeter).

7. Repeat steps 3–5 four more times, making sure that not all five trials come from the same side. Record the results for trials 2–5 in the table. Calculate the average number of inches (or centimeters) for seeing the paper strip for the five trials, and record it in the table under "Average Distance."

NAME	TRIAL 1		TRIAL 2		TRIAL 3		TRIAL 4		TRIAL 5		AVERAGE DISTANCE
	Side	Distance	Side	Distance	Side	Distance	Side	Distance	Side	Distance	
			Copy This Table on a Piece of Paper								

DISCUSSION

1. Detecting the paper strip at the 24-inch (61-centimeter) mark or earlier means that the person being tested has a field of vision of 135 degrees or more, as shown on page 367. The minimum safe field of vision is about 135 degrees. Judging from your average distance, do you have a field of vision of 135 degrees or more?

2. Using everyone's average distance, calculate the entire class average. Is the average field of vision for the class 135 degrees or more?

3. List some ways in which good peripheral vision contributes to safe living.

4. What can be done to make up for poor peripheral vision?

B. DEPTH PERCEPTION

It is important in many everyday activities to be able to determine with some accuracy how far something is from you. How accurately you judge such distances is a measure of your **depth perception.**

MATERIALS

chair
chalkboard eraser
  or similar object
long table
pencil

masking tape
ruler
yardstick or meter
  stick

PROCEDURE

1. Place a pencil near one end of a long table and to one side of center, and tape it down, as shown in the picture. Then place a second object such as a chalkboard eraser at the other end of the table and to the other side of center. You will try to match up the second object and the pencil using your depth perception.

2. Sitting three feet (about one meter) away from the eraser end of the table, bend forward so that your eyes are level with the two objects, rather than above them. Use a yardstick or a meter stick to push the eraser or similar object until the far end of it looks exactly even with the pencil. Push gently so that the object does not move forward too far.

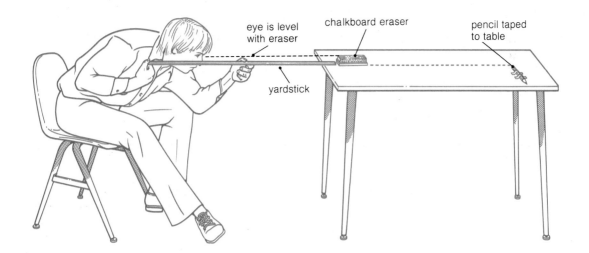
eye is level with eraser — chalkboard eraser — pencil taped to table — yardstick

3. Measure the actual distance between the pencil and the far end of the object you have moved, as shown here.

4. This distance is the distance you were off, or the amount of error. Record this distance in a table like the one below, under "Both Eyes, Trial 1."

5. Repeat steps 1–3 twice more. Record the results for trials 2 and 3 in the table. Average your three distances of error and record it in the table under "Both Eyes, Average."

6. Repeat steps 1–5 using one eye only. Cover the other eye with your free hand. Record all your results in the table under "One Eye Only."

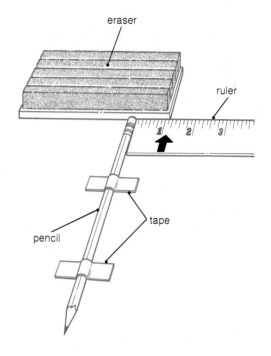

DISCUSSION

1. An error of one and one-half inches (about four centimeters) or less means depth perception that is probably good. Do you have good depth perception with both eyes?

2. Calculate the class's average error using everyone's average for both eyes. Is the average depth perception (with both eyes) for the class good?

3. How does depth perception using both eyes compare with that when using just one eye?

4. Look back at the results of the peripheral vision test. Is there any indication that individuals who have good depth perception also have good peripheral vision?

5. Make a list of activities and skills in which depth perception is important for safe and successful participation.

NAME	BOTH EYES				ONE EYE ONLY			
	Trial 1	Trial 2	Trial 3	Average	Trial 1	Trial 2	Trial 3	Average
				Copy This Table on a Piece of Paper				

RIGHT FOOT

NAME	TRIAL 1	TRIAL 2	TRIAL 3	TRIAL 4	TRIAL 5	TRIAL 6
		Copy This Table on a Piece of Paper				

C. REACTION TIME

Avoiding accidents frequently involves the ability to react quickly to a potential danger. How quickly do you react and move?

MATERIALS

chair
paper cup or similar lightweight object
yardstick or meter stick

PROCEDURE

1. Copy the table above on a piece of paper twice. For the second table change the title to "Left Foot."

2. Sit with your feet flat on the floor. Begin straightening your right knee and move your right foot forward about 12 inches (30 centimeters), as though it were on the accelerator of a car. Look straight ahead.

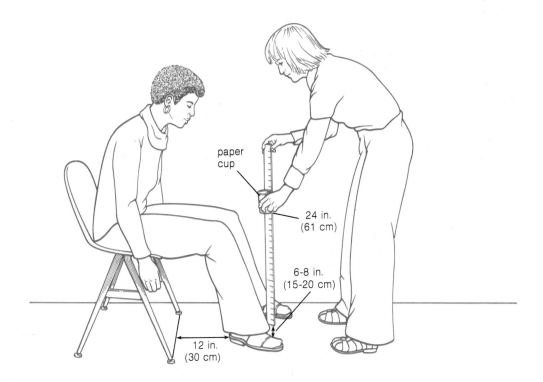

paper cup

24 in. (61 cm)

6-8 in. (15-20 cm)

12 in. (30 cm)

3. Your partner will hold a yardstick or a meter stick upright 6 to 8 inches (15 to 20 centimeters) to the left of your right foot.

4. As your partner drops a lightweight object from the 24-inch (61-centimeter) point on the measuring stick, move your foot quickly to the left as you would in braking a car. Keep your heel close to the floor and try to intercept the object with your foot before it hits the floor.

5. Record the trial as successful or unsuccessful by writing "yes" or "no" in the "Right Foot" table under "Trial 1." Do at least six trials. Record the results for trials 2–6 in the table.

6. Repeat steps 2–5 using your left foot. Record all your results in the "Left Foot" table.

Jaywalking—what a way to test reaction times!

DISCUSSION

1. Rate yourself as "good" if you successfully intercept the object with your foot at least four out of six times. Was one foot much better than the other? Why? Was the better foot "good"?

2. Did people in the class feel awkward using the less-favored foot? Why or why not? For the class as a whole was the favored foot "good"?

3. Give examples of other parts of the body that must react quickly to stimuli in certain situations.

Your class has now measured three ways that people respond to stimuli. Good scores on these tests should help a person avoid accidents. Bad scores indicate a likelihood for accidents to happen.

On the average, does your class score acceptably well? Looking at the scores as a whole, would you judge that the people in your class would tend to have a lot of acci-

dents? People your age *do* tend to have more accidents than people of other age groups. How can you account for that?

Look back at the class results on the three tests. Do average scores for males and females differ? The table in Section 14–1 showed that males have more accidents than females do. How do you account for that?

SELF CHECK

1. What is a disabling injury?

2. What are some physical limitations that are responsible for many accidents?

3. How does the abuse of alcohol and other drugs lead to accidents?

4. How do attitudes affect accidents?

5. In what ways are peripheral vision, depth perception, and reaction time important in accident prevention?

Accidents With Vehicles

14-4 Why Motor-Vehicle Accidents Occur

The combination of driver, vehicle, environment, and driving situation determines whether an accident will occur. These are typical accidents about to happen:

Joe Mendoza is driving home on twisting and narrow roads. He can hardly see in the heavy, evening rain. He has been on the go since five o'clock in the morning and can think about nothing but getting into bed. All of a sudden a car comes toward him around the curve and veers onto Joe's side of the road.

Connie Simmons is driving a rented car back from her vacation. There is a lot of fast traffic on the freeway. Connie is impatient with the stop-and-go of the cars ahead. She sees an open stretch in the left lane and instantly steers toward it. Unfortunately, the side rear-view mirror in this car does not reflect the angle of view she is used to, and she hasn't seen the fast-moving truck that is coming up just behind her to the left.

Sooner or later, they will both be sorry he isn't watching the road.

Lisa Fremont is late for her after-school job. She jumps into the car. She doesn't bother with her seat belt because she's going only a short distance. She wonders if her brother has had the brake lights fixed. Traffic is very heavy, and it looks as though Lisa won't be able to find a parking space. When she sees one, she suddenly slams on the brakes. Lisa hasn't noticed the van just behind her, and it turns out that her brake lights aren't working.

George Spector is the first in his class to turn sixteen and get his driver's license. At the birthday party someone suggests that they all go for a drive in her parents' car and get some pizza. Seven people jam into the car and George takes the driver's seat. The evening is beautifully clear and there is no traffic. George steps on the gas and the group cheers. But when he comes to a right turn, he loses control of the unfamiliar power steering. He tries to brake—but he hits the gas pedal instead.

Some causes of motor-vehicle accidents are well publicized: alcohol, recklessness, excessive speed, defective equipment, lack of familiarity with equipment, and skidding on wet or icy roads. Which of these are at fault in the cases just described? What other factors contributed to these accidents? Could the drivers in these cases have reached their destinations safely? What could they have done better?

14-5 Driving Safely

Safe driving is a skill. It is also a set of habits and attitudes. Developing proper driving techniques can go a long way toward keeping you safe. In addition, if you know in advance what to do in emergencies, you can make the right decision fast when dangerous situations arise. You can increase your safety by learning also how to check the condition of some important equipment in your vehicle. Most important of all to safe driving is being firm with yourself and never letting yourself drive beyond your ability.

If a driver-education course is offered in your school or community, take it. You will have classroom instruction in traffic laws. Driver training behind the wheel, with a qualified instructor, will help you develop confidence and necessary skills, including techniques for handling a car to avoid danger. Successfully completing the course also pays off financially. Automobile insurance premiums for people your age, especially males, are high. People who successfully complete a driver-education course usually can get automobile insurance coverage at a lower cost than people who learn to drive only with a friend or a member of the family.

Here are some suggestions for good driving. You will hear much more about them in a driver-education course.

Concentrate on your driving. Don't let emotions, day-dreaming, conversation, music, or pets or other passengers distract you—even for a second. If you should find your mind wandering while you drive, do something about it. Slow down. Talk to yourself. Say, for example, "I see a traffic light ahead. I will now put my right foot on the brake pedal. . . ." It is useful to develop a personal routine for helping yourself concentrate that you can fall back on when you're having trouble.

Be sure you are in suitable physical condition to drive. Have you misplaced your glasses? Are you feverish? Do you have a headache? Are you too tired? Have you had a drink? Have you used drugs? Are you experiencing side effects from any medication? If the answer to any of these questions is "yes," you are taking a big risk by driving.

Stop when you are tired. Get out of the car and walk around. Wash your face at a rest area. Have something to eat or some coffee or tea. Drive with the window open for fresh air. Whenever possible, have a licensed passenger drive.

Obey traffic signals and signs. Do not try to save time by racing through lights or going through stop signs. Signal all turns and lane changes.

Drive at appropriate speeds. Drive at the speed of traffic. Slower drivers and speeders have more accidents than those who drive with the mainstream of traffic. Do not exceed speed limits. When the speed limit in the United States was lowered to 55 miles (88 kilometers) per hour, highway deaths declined considerably.

Observe other drivers. Be on the alert for speeders, tailgaters, road hogs, and drivers who don't signal properly or who go through red lights or stop signs. Be watchful at intersections even if you have the legal right of way.

Watch the road and the weather. Potholes, curves, changes in lane marking, and sudden rain, snow, or high wind can be dangerous. Observe cars in front of and behind you. But don't limit your vision to the car right ahead. It will pay to glance farther up the road when you can, to see if problems lie ahead.

Don't tailgate. A good general rule is to keep one car length of space ahead clear for every 10 miles (16 kilometers) per hour of speed when visibility and road conditions are good. Keep the view ahead and behind you unobstructed.

Control your passengers' behavior. Movement and noise in the car can be dangerous.

Testing tire design with cameras and a glass "road." Even well-designed tires don't grip a wet road tightly at moderate speeds.

Be firm in getting passengers to cooperate. After all, if you are the driver, you are the one who is responsible for any accident.

Use your seat belt and make sure that passengers use theirs. People who refuse or fail to use seat belts take unnecessary risks, even on short rides.

Keep your car ventilated, even during cold weather. Exhaust fumes may leak carbon monoxide into the passenger compartment.

Keep your car in safe driving condition. Before you get into your car, check for signs of trouble. Water or oil marks underneath could indicate a leak. See that the tires look properly inflated and that no glass is near them. Check that the headlights, taillights and windows are all free of dirt, ice, and snow.

If you're going on a long trip, make sure that there is enough water in the battery and enough coolant in the radiator. Also check the engine oil, transmission fluid, and brake fluid levels. Check the condition of the fan belt. If you don't know how to check these things, have someone else do it for you.

When you get into the driver's seat, check the windshield wipers, seat belt, and turn signals. Always be on the watch for any special lights the car has that signal a failure in the engine or brakes.

Have the car checked regularly. Either learn to check tire pressure, shock absorbers, and other equipment yourself or have it done. The required yearly or semi-annual inspection in many states is not frequent enough to catch things that break, rot, or simply fail to function.

14-6 The Special Hazards of Motorcycling

The speed, excitement, power, and economy of motorcycles have made them popular in many countries. But the chance of being killed is four to seven times as great for even a careful motorcyclist as for a car driver. About 88 percent of all motorcycle accidents involve death or injury. The comparable figure for other motor-vehicle accidents is 8 percent.

Special reflective tape and fabric can be attached to motorcycles, helmets, and clothing to make motorcyclists more visible at night to pedestrians and other motor-vehicle drivers.

Injuries resulting from a collision between a motorcycle and a car, or from being thrown from a motorcycle, are likely to be severe and long-lasting. Even with a strong helmet and protective clothing, a motorcyclist is lucky to be able to walk away from an accident.

Here are some things a motorcyclist can do for self-protection:

Know how to operate the motorcycle correctly. (Hold a valid operator's license.)

Wear a helmet and protective clothing and footwear. (Some states require motorcyclists to be helmeted.)

Be as visible as possible. Wear reflective strips on clothing at night.

Keep the motorcycle in good operating condition. Check brakes, lights, turn signals, and tires regularly.

Drive extra-defensively. Motorists sometimes don't see motorcycles until it is too late to avoid an accident. And some drivers think it's fun to crowd a motorcyclist.

Don't play games in traffic. Don't startle or antagonize motorists by darting past or weaving in and out of lanes. Use the turn signals.

Owners of smaller motorcycles sometimes try to make them do everything a large motorcycle can do. This practice often causes accidents. Smaller motorcycles have more trouble with potholes, stones, and slippery patches on roads. Drivers need to know what their vehicles can do and should not try to exceed the limits.

14-7 Safety Afoot

Walking is the safest way of going anywhere, but pedestrians can have accidents too. Sidewalks are usually safe, so long as you watch where you're going. But when walkers, bicycles, cars, buses, and trucks all crowd into the streets, pedestrians can be hurt.

Crossing at intersections, with a green or a "walk" light, doesn't eliminate the need to watch for drivers in a hurry. Many ignore red lights and stop signs. Some make right turns on a red light. In some states this is legal, provided the car has first come to a complete stop and the driver has checked traffic. Dodging traffic in the middle of a street or "playing chicken" with a motorist is a game people sometimes play with their lives.

If you walk where there are no sidewalks, stay close to the left-hand side of the road, facing traffic. Avoid walking alone at night. If you can't avoid it, try to find brightly lit streets. At night, stay near the curb and wear light-colored, visible clothing. Be alert, even in neighborhoods where you don't expect to be robbed or assaulted, or to find heavy traffic.

Many people your age are involved in accidents or are robbed, kidnapped, or sexually assaulted when they hitchhike or give rides to hitchhikers. Some states prohibit hitchhiking on certain roads, especially on interstate and other major highways. Hitchhikers may be picked up by a drunk or careless driver and be hurt in an accident. A driver or hitchhiker may be looking for someone to rob or rape. Police and school officials warn students against hitchhiking. Thumbing a ride—or offering one to a hitchhiker—is one risk you don't have to take.

14-8 Better Bicycling

Next to walking, bicycling is the easiest way of getting around. And more communities are setting aside bicycling paths for recreation. In some towns and cities, sections of

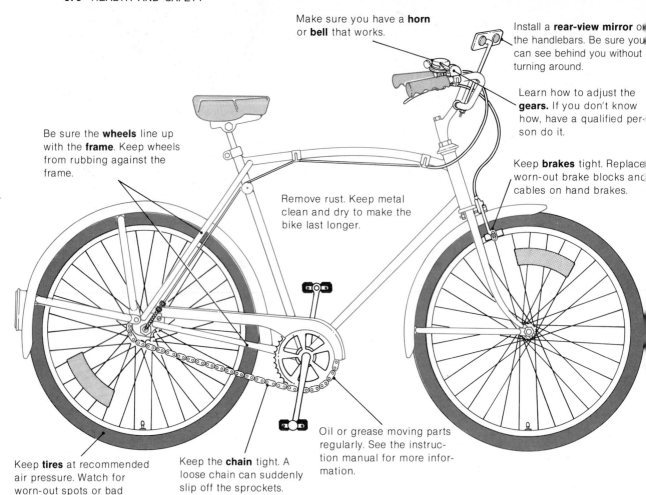

Make sure you have a **horn** or **bell** that works.

Install a **rear-view mirror** on the handlebars. Be sure you can see behind you without turning around.

Be sure the **wheels** line up with the **frame**. Keep wheels from rubbing against the frame.

Remove rust. Keep metal clean and dry to make the bike last longer.

Learn how to adjust the **gears.** If you don't know how, have a qualified person do it.

Keep **brakes** tight. Replace worn-out brake blocks and cables on hand brakes.

Keep **tires** at recommended air pressure. Watch for worn-out spots or bad bruises.

Keep the **chain** tight. A loose chain can suddenly slip off the sprockets.

Oil or grease moving parts regularly. See the instruction manual for more information.

roads are open at times to bicyclists only, usually on weekends.

You can keep a bike in good condition by following the recommendations in the picture above.

An old and completely wrong rule of bicycle safety was that you should ride a bicycle facing traffic. Don't do it. When you ride a bicycle in the street, stay close to the curb on the right-hand side of the street. Don't swerve suddenly to the left.

When you are riding a bicycle, you can easily see the lights of a car or truck at night, but drivers may not see you at all until they are almost on top of you. Be sure that you have reflectors or reflecting tape on the bicycle so that drivers can see your bicycle at night. Wear light-colored clothing so that you will be more visible to drivers. (Your clothing should not have loose parts that can get tangled in the wheels, pedals, or chain.)

Expert bicyclists keep well back from moving cars. Motorists may stop suddenly. Do not ride past the right side of a stopped bus; you may hit passengers getting out of

Learn how to signal when you are turning or stopping in traffic.

the bus. Be alert for pedestrians who might walk out from between parked cars and for car doors that might open in front of you without warning. Watch out for dogs; they may snap at your legs and cause accidents. Avoid driving too fast down hills or on rough or slippery roads.

Bicyclists as well as drivers should follow traffic laws. Stop at red lights and stop signs. Signal before you turn or stop. Be sure you know all traffic laws that apply to bicycles in your community. Don't play games with drivers who want to pass you. Let them go by.

You should be careful of pedestrians when you ride a bicycle. Some bicyclists like to scare pedestrians. Whizzing close to pedestrians, especially older people, can make them fall.

If you and your friends want to play games with bicycles, find a place where there are no cars or pedestrians. Bicyclists, motorists, and pedestrians can be a hazardous mixture when care is not taken by all.

SELF CHECK

1. What are three factors that contribute to motor-vehicle accidents?

2. What are the advantages of taking a driver-education course?

3. Give at least five suggestions for good driving. Name at least three things a motorcyclist can do for self-protection.

4. Under what circumstances can walking be hazardous?

5. How can bicyclists make themselves more visible at night?

6. What safety features should bikes have?

Accidents at Home and at Play

14-9 Preventing Accidents in Your Home

You might think there's no place like home for feeling safe. Maybe home feels safe because there are no warning signs posted. But the high number of deaths and injuries in homes every year proves that people need to recognize unmarked hazards and learn how to avoid accidents.

Parents and older brothers and sisters have to protect young children. Keep poisonous substances such as household cleaners and insect sprays out of reach of youngsters. Medicines, too, should be kept out of reach of young children. Close off unused electrical outlets with special covers. Store plastic bags, matches, knives, and sharp tools out of children's reach.

An agency of the United States government regulates the safety aspects of more than 10,000 products, from detergents to snowmobiles. If you have a question about the safety of any appliance, chemical, tool, or child's toy in your home, you can write to the United States Consumer Product Safety Commission, Washington, D.C. 20207. You can also ask for their Banned Products List, which describes dangerous products.

If only your feet had eyes!

Someone in your family may have bought one of those products before the agency made their sale illegal. In Canada, questions and complaints may be sent to the Department of Consumer and Corporate Affairs, Canadian Building, 219 Laurier Avenue West, Ottawa, Ontario K1A 0C9.

Consumers need to use products carefully, as well as to avoid buying dangerous ones. Many items can be hazardous if used incorrectly. When you buy anything for your home that could be hazardous, read the directions and warranty. If you think any product is unsafe, report it to the proper agency. Many cities, states, and provinces have consumer safety bureaus. These agencies, as well as federal bureaus, can become more effective if people report badly made, unsafe, contaminated, and otherwise hazardous products.

Carefully examining your house or apartment may turn up many situations that could cause injuries. A few areas in the home to inspect for safety conditions are listed in this table.

14-10 What to Do About Fires

About 85 percent of all fires occur in homes. And 80 percent of the people who die in home fires are overcome by smoke, superheated air, and carbon monoxide.

Here are some ways you and your family can make your home safer from fire:

Keep matches and lighters out of children's reach.

Place ashtrays wherever people smoke.

Don't smoke in bed, lying on a sofa, or reclining in a chair that invites you to go to sleep.

Get trash out of the basement, closets, attic, garage, and hallways.

Only use flammable materials, such as

WHAT TO CHECK	WHAT TO DO
Outdoors	Cracked and broken concrete and blacktop should be fixed. Porches and steps should be kept in good condition. Outdoor lights also help prevent tripping and falling.
Lighting indoors	Keep passageways and stairs lighted. Stairs should have light switches at both top and bottom. Rooms should have a light switch near the door.
Rugs	Small rugs on smooth floors slide easily. Tacks, paints, sprays, and special mattings are available to make small rugs stay in place.
Basement	Keep basement stairs and handrails in good repair. Never leave any objects on the stairs. Don't let toys, tools, boxes, bicycles, trash cans, or flammable substances clutter the basement.
Bathroom	Keep dangerous substances away from young children. Keep smooth floors dry. Keep used razor blades off sinks, countertops, and cabinet shelves. Use non-skid mats or devices in the bathtub and shower.
Kitchen	Highly polished floors are slippery. Put knives and other tools away when you are finished using them. Place broken dishes and glasses in the garbage immediately. Be sure the stove and other appliances are turned off when they are not being used. Keep toys and other objects out of the working area as much as possible.

cleaning fluids, in an open area, away from any flame or spark.

Keep curtains and drapes away from an open flame and from electrical appliances, such as toasters and heaters.

One reason home fires kill thousands each year is that many people panic. They run if their clothing is burning, jump out of a window before fire fighters can put up a ladder or spread a net beneath them, or try to put out a spreading fire rather than call the fire department. Many deaths and injuries could be avoided if families reviewed together what to do in case of fire.

The general rule for putting out fires is to cool the burning materials or smother them by cutting off their supply of air. This can be done with water, by throwing something over the fire, or by use of a chemical fire extinguisher. Certain newer home fire extinguishers, labeled good for Class A, B, and C fires, can be used on all types of fires, including grease, gasoline, and electrical fires. Other extinguishers are good only for specified types of fires. If you have a home extinguisher, be sure you know where and when *not* to use it. Be sure it is recharged as necessary. An all-purpose, home fire extinguisher can be bought inexpensively.

If the contents of a wastebasket or trash can catch fire, use a fire extinguisher or pour water on the flames. When the fire seems to be out, get the container outdoors. Leave it there until you are certain the fire is out.

Clothing treated with a flame retardant will char but not burn (right). Untreated clothing does catch on fire easily (left).

The spray from a small home fire extinguisher, being tested here, doesn't last long. But it may last long enough to put out a small fire.

If fat or grease in a pan on a stove or in an oven catches fire, turn off the gas or electricity. First, try to smother the fire with a nonflammable lid, tray, or other object. Never throw water on a grease fire; water spreads burning grease. If you cannot smother the fire, throw baking soda or salt on the flames. If you have a suitable fire extinguisher, use it as gently as possible so as not to splatter burning fat all around.

If someone's clothes are burning, stop him or her from running or thrashing around. Have the person lie on the floor or ground and throw a rug, coat, blanket, or any other heavy material over the clothing to smother the flames.

If a fire is spreading through a house, everybody has to leave fast. Very young children, elderly people, and the sick need help getting out. All other members of the family should get out on their own, through the nearest, quickest exit. Don't stop to rescue anything you own, no matter how valuable. If you are in a smoke-filled room,

crawl on the floor, where the air is clearer and cooler. If possible, hold a wet cloth over your nose and mouth. A dry cloth is the next best protection.

Even if you successfully put out a small fire, call the fire department to have a professional check. A fire you thought was out might start up again hours later. If any fire cannot be controlled very quickly, get out of the house and call the fire department. Many people over-estimate their ability to deal with home fires.

Once out of a burning building, don't try to go back in. Fire fighters can rescue anyone in the building more quickly and efficiently than untrained people can.

14-11 Electrical Hazards

Any electrical equipment can cause electrical shock if it is not installed or used properly or if wiring inside or outside the

During a thunderstorm, don't stand under a lone tree; tall objects are often hit by lightning. Stay away from water, including beaches, pools, and baths. The safest places to be are indoors or in a car.

equipment becomes worn. The more electric current an appliance or tool uses, the more potentially dangerous it is.

To be installed correctly, electrical equipment should be **grounded.** This means that it is electrically connected to the ground by a special wire to protect you from electrical shock. In case a malfunction develops while the equipment is in use, this wire will carry the current away from you safely. The most effective grounding device is the special three-pronged plug that is used with a three-wire grounded electrical outlet. Most new appliances and power tools come with this type of plug.

When using electrical equipment, follow these rules to prevent electrical shock:

Never use electrical equipment near water. Electric shavers should not be used in the bathtub. Do not place electrical appliances such as a hairdryer or a radio on the edge of the bathtub. Many small kitchen appliances such as electric fry pans should not be immersed in water, even if they are not plugged in, unless the instructions say they may be placed in water.

Follow all instructions or warnings that come with electrical equipment. If in doubt, ask someone who knows about electricity and wiring before you hook up or use unfamiliar equipment.

Rubber-soled shoes and dry hands should become a habit when you use electrical devices, but they alone cannot always protect you against ungrounded equipment.

Electricity can cause fire as well as electrical shock. To prevent fire, follow these rules:

Do not leave appliances such as toasters and irons operating unattended. Turn them off when you are done with them.

Do not leave lamps at the edge of tables. Do not leave lamp and other appliance cords where they may be tripped over and pulled down.

Do not overload circuits in your home or rely too much on extension cords. Plug-

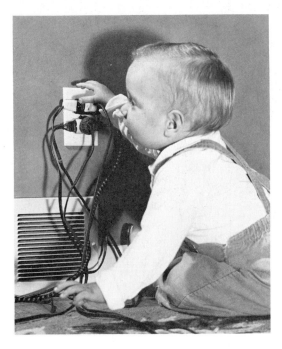

Overloaded circuits can start fires inside walls. The danger to this child is obvious.

Power lawnmowers present a special danger. They can throw sharp objects and stones with the speed of a bullet and severely injure or kill the user or a bystander several feet away. Always wear sturdy shoes when you use a power mower. Turn the motor off and disconnect the spark plug wire before you try to clear matted grass or other material from the blades. If your mower is gasoline operated, fill the tank outdoors, not in a garage or shed.

Use safe, sturdy ladders, long enough for you to reach comfortably without stretching, when you paint, repair, or reach for anything. A small step stool or a short ladder can be used indoors.

Many paints, paint removers, adhesives, solvents, cleaners, and other household materials are poisonous. They must be used only in a well-ventilated area and should never be inhaled deeply. Read the directions on the cans or bottles carefully before you use any of these products. Some of the chemicals used to propel aerosol products can damage the heart, circulatory system, kidneys, or liver.

ging things directly into wall outlets is safer.

All home wiring should be kept in good repair. Do not run wires under rugs.

Always use the right size fuse. Do not substitute a coin for a blown fuse.

14-12 Using Tools and Equipment Correctly

Hand and power tools can cut, rip, bruise, and puncture skin, muscle, and bone. Some power tools have automatic shutoff devices and other safeguards, but accidents still occur. Often the accidents could have been prevented through the use of a hard hat, safety goggles, or heavy gloves and other protective clothing.

Check lawns for small rocks and other potential flying missiles before mowing.

After watching hundreds of shoot-outs on TV, who needs to learn how to handle a gun? Everyone who has one.

14-13 "I Didn't Think It Was Loaded."

More than half of the accidental deaths caused by firearms occur in the home, not in the fields and woods among hunters. Most of the accidents involve adolescents and adults, not children. The deaths and injuries occur mostly among people who handle firearms carelessly, fool around with them, or dare other people to fire them. Most accidental deaths and injuries from firearms could have been avoided.

Firearms are sometimes kept in the home for protection or for hunting. They should always be treated as though they were loaded. If there are young children in the house, weapons should be locked up. Just hiding firearms isn't good enough. Young children can find practically anything.

Gun safety means knowing the weapon thoroughly. Know how it works, its safety features, and its hazards. A weapon should be stored away from its ammunition, which also should be locked away. When you clean a gun, always keep the muzzle pointed away from yourself and other people, in a safe direction, up or down. The safest method is to clean a weapon in a room by yourself, or outdoors where you are sure that no one else is around.

Air rifles, pea shooters, pellet guns, and other weapons are hazardous also. Personal protection devices, such as tear-gas cartridges, can endanger friends and innocent strangers. Handle any type of potentially harmful device with the same regard for safety as you have for pistols, rifles, and shotguns. Remember that bullets, BB's, and slugs can travel long distances.

14-14 Don't Make Waves

Swimming, boating, surfing, and water-skiing are popular outdoor activities. Yet many people who participate don't bother to learn or to follow the basic rules of water safety. They "make waves" through carelessness, lack of consideration, and lack of knowledge. The results include accidental injuries and drownings. Thousands of people drown every year. Half of them are in the 15–24 age group, and about ten times as many young men drown as young women.

Taking these precautions will make swimming safer:

Always have a friend nearby when you swim.

Stay out of the water immediately after a meal, or when you are overheated, tired, or chilled.

Before you dive at a strange place, check the depth. Find out whether the bottom is sandy, muddy, or rocky.

Stay close to shore, a float, or a boat, unless you are an experienced long-distance swimmer.

Work up slowly to long-distance swimming. You need to be in good physical condition for a long swim in strong ocean waves or rapid river currents. Have another good swimmer with you or a friend in a boat beside you.

The first rule of boating safety is to know how to swim well and handle yourself in the water. Can you swim for ten minutes while fully clothed? Can you put on a personal flotation device while treading water? Do you know how to use a buoyant cushion

If a boat or a canoe capsizes, do you know how to right it and get back in, or what to do if it can't be righted and emptied out?

correctly? You can learn these and other skills, including lifesaving techniques, at Red Cross classes, community recreation centers, summer camps, or a YWCA or YMCA.

If you have non-swimmers in your boat, require that they wear life jackets at all times. Good swimmers should also wear life jackets in hazardous conditions such as rough water. If you are operating a boat, you need to watch constantly for swimmers, scuba divers, and other boats.

There are "rules of the road" for rivers, bays, lakes, and the ocean as well as for highways. The United States Coast Guard Auxiliary puts out many publications on boating safety. "Federal Requirements for Recreational Boats" (CG-290) and "Recreational Boating Guide" (CG-340) are useful

leaflets and pamphlets. You can write for them to the Superintendent of Documents, Government Printing Office, Washington, D.C. 20402, or check your telephone directory for a local branch of the Coast Guard Auxiliary.

Do you think you could save a drowning person? You don't have to be a swimmer to be a rescuer. If at all possible, throw a rope, life preserver, strong wooden plank, or a rope of knotted clothing to a person struggling in the water. Pull the person to a boat, a float, or shore.

Strong, skilled swimmers can use swimming rescues. The first thing you have to know about lifesaving techniques is how to control the victim. People in trouble usually struggle in the water. They thrash around. When you approach a panicky person, she or he will try to grab you for help. Your good intentions aren't enough. You have to know how to approach a struggling person and how to hold her or him so that you can help. Otherwise you will be pulled under the water yourself.

The second lifesaving skill involves knowing how to pull the victim from the deep water to a safe place. You can learn how in a lifesaving course. Your strength, knowledge, and skill can enable you to control and rescue someone in serious trouble.

SELF CHECK

1. What areas of a home may be unsafe?

2. What are the two basic principles for putting out fires?

3. How can you best protect yourself in a smoke-filled room?

4. Explain how electrical equipment is grounded. How does this protect someone who is using the equipment?

5. What is the cause of most accidental deaths and injuries from firearms?

6. Describe precautions to take in water sports and boating.

7. What places should you stay away from to avoid lightning during a thunderstorm?

Chapter Summary

Accidents cause more than half of the deaths among people between 15 and 24 years old. This number could be reduced if people understood the causes of accidents and developed the skills, habits, and attitudes to prevent them. Physical limitations, fatigue, drug use, inattention, and emotional difficulties can all lead to fatal and disabling accidents. Bad luck is not the cause of most accidents.

The driver, the vehicle, the environment, and the driving situation are all involved in traffic safety. Driver-education courses offered in schools and communities help people develop safe driving skills, habits, and attitudes. Motorcyclists have to be especially careful since nearly all motorcycle accidents result in injury or death. Pedestrians need to be alert to their surroundings. Bicyclists can avoid accidents by keeping their bicycles in good condition and by following traffic laws and the rules of bicycle safety.

Many home accidents occur because people have a false feeling of safety at home. A careful inspection of a house or an apartment may turn up many potentially dangerous situations. Children and elderly people especially need to be protected from hazards in the home. A serious home hazard is fire. Knowing how to prevent fires, how to control a fire if one occurs, and how to get out of a burning building safely would reduce the number of deaths and injuries. Electrical equipment should be installed and grounded properly to prevent electrical shock or fire. Power tools, equipment, and firearms in the home should be used only with the knowledge of how they work and with the proper safety precautions.

Swimming, boating, and other water sports can be made safer by following water safety rules. Knowing how to swim is the basic rule. Knowing other skills and lifesaving techniques make water sports more enjoyable and safer.

Chapter Self Check

1. Why do people have accidents?

2. What is reaction time? What does it have to do with safety?

3. Why is attitude important in accident prevention?

4. Describe some ways a driver can deal with fatigue.

5. Why are young males charged much higher automobile insurance premiums than young females?

6. If you were driving, how would you handle the following situations: (a) your friends are wrestling in the back seat; (b) you seem to get all the red lights and there is very little traffic; (c) another driver is tailgating behind you and blowing her horn; (d) it begins to rain hard.

7. What things should you check in a car to make sure that it is in safe driving condition?

8. What are some special hazards of driving a motorcycle?

9. If you are walking along a country road where there are no sidewalks, where is the safest place to walk?

10. Why is hitchhiking potentially dangerous?

11. What are some hazards of bicycling?

12. On what side of the road should you ride a bicycle?

13. What special precautions should be taken in the home to protect babies and young children?

14. What United States agency regulates the safety aspects of consumer products?

15. What precaution can you take to avoid using a safe product in an unsafe way?

16. Describe some ways to prevent fires in the home.

17. What should you do in the event of a grease fire?

18. What is the best way to help someone whose clothing is on fire?

19. What is the purpose of a three-pronged plug and matching outlet?

20. In what ways are power lawnmowers potentially dangerous to the user and to people nearby?

21. Why do the labels of many solvents and cleaners warn the user to use them only in a well-ventilated area?

22. What factors can make water sports and boating dangerous?

Read More About It

Accident Facts. Chicago: National Safety Council, revised annually. Statistics on accidental deaths and injuries at work, on the highways, in the home and school, on farms, and at recreational places. Includes some Canadian statistics.

American National Red Cross. *American Red Cross Life Saving and Water Safety.* New York: Doubleday & Company, Inc., 1956 (reprinted often). Much useful, authoritative information. The textbook for Red Cross lifesaving training courses.

Fales, Jr., E. D. *The Book of Expert Driving.* New York: Hawthorn Books, Inc., 1970. Car-handling techniques used by professional drivers. What it takes to be a "good" driver.

Fire Protection Handbook. Chicago: National Fire Protection Association, revised periodically. Approved practice in fire prevention and protection.

Greenbank, Anthony. *The Book of Survival: Everyman's Guide to Staying Alive and Handling Emergencies in the City, the Suburbs, and the Wild Lands Beyond.* New York: Harper & Row, 1968. Almost every kind of accident and how to handle it.

McFarlane, John W. *It's Easy to Fix Your Bike.* Chicago: Follett Publishing Company, 1972. Many aspects of bicycle maintenance and repair. Illustrated with step-by-step photographs.

15
First Aid

After completing the work in this chapter, you will be able to:

define first aid and describe what you should do first in any emergency.

describe the first-aid care for shock and severe bleeding.

explain the importance of immediately restoring breathing and heartbeat and describe methods for doing it.

describe first-aid methods of dealing with various types of poisoning and burns.

explain ways to treat injuries to bones, joints, and muscles.

describe first-aid care for various types of wounds, and explain the uses of dressings and bandages.

How Can You Help?

You are camping. Suddenly, a friend drops an axe on her foot. Bright red blood spurts forth. Pressure on the wound fails to stop the bleeding. You are far from a telephone. What do you do to save her life without injuring her in any additional way?

Your young brother pokes a fork into an electric toaster to pull out a burning crust. He screams with pain and falls to the floor. You rush over to him and find that his breathing has stopped. Can you save his life?

Emergencies aren't planned. But a knowledge of simple first-aid measures can enable you to save a life when the unexpected occurs. In the most serious emergencies, such as heavy bleeding or suffocation, five minutes is the limit within which a life will be saved or lost. What is done within those five minutes can sustain a person until a doctor or other medically trained person arrives.

First aid is not medical treatment. It is knowledgeable help in the critical time between an emergency and the beginning of professional medical treatment.

Shock and Bleeding

15-1 First Aid in an Emergency

The aid given to a sick or injured person before a doctor is available is often of vital importance. **First aid** is the health-related help that must be given *first* in any emergency. Often a doctor cannot get to the scene of an accident or sudden illness. Victims may have to wait for skilled medical attention until they can be taken to a hospital or other emergency treatment center. At any time you may be faced with a situation in which your own life or another person's life depends on your knowledge of first-aid procedures.

Major emergencies in which immediate first aid is crucial are shock, severe bleeding, suffocation, heart stoppage, and poi-soning. First aid is also needed for burns, fractures, and wounds. Some first-aid procedures are simple and require little skill. Others are more complex and require in addition to skill a clear head, quick thinking, and decisive action. Everyone should take a first-aid course.

In all emergencies follow two important rules:

1. *Keep calm.* If the sight of blood or the sound of someone in pain makes you shaky, sit down and take a moment to recover. You will be able to work more quickly and effectively if your mind is clear.

2. *Get help quickly.* If possible, have someone call a hospital, doctor, or the police or fire department while you are giving first aid.

"I asked for help, not company!"

First aid requires knowledge and good judgment in order for you to act correctly and decisively. Good judgment also determines the least amount of action necessary to save a life. The necessary action can be simple. Maybe an injured or sick person just has to be kept warm and quiet.

15-2 Don't Move Victims Unnecessarily!

In general, a victim of a severe injury *should not be moved* until medical help arrives. If a driver or a passenger is trapped inside a car, turn off the ignition to prevent fire. Make the victim as comfortable as possible, but do not try to pull or push out of a vehicle anyone who is caught tight.

Sometimes before first aid can be supplied, however, a victim must be moved away from a life-threatening situation, such as fire, traffic, or poisonous gas. In this case, first make a quick check of injuries. Place any available blanket or coat under the victim and drag him or her gently to safety. If the person must be lifted, all parts of the body should have equal support. Move the person the shortest possible distance to safety.

Many accident victims have been crippled because well-intentioned friends or bystanders moved them incorrectly or

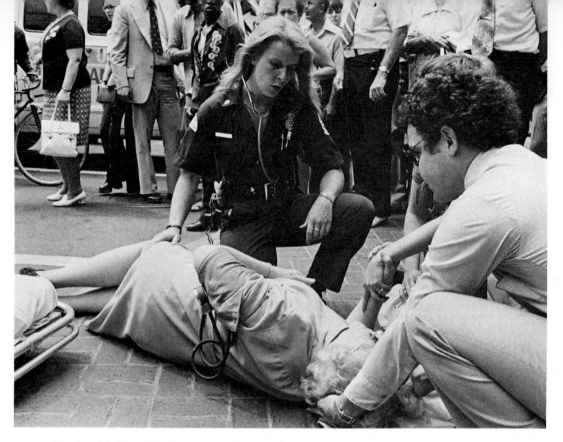

People with first-aid training check for possible injuries before moving a victim.

jammed them into the back seat of a car to take them to a hospital. They would have been better off lying quietly until an ambulance or doctor arrived. Certain types of fractures, such as those of the neck, back, or hip, can result in permanent disability or death if the injured person is moved incorrectly before skilled help arrives.

15-3 Going Into Shock

When someone has been severely injured in any way, the body may respond by going into **shock.** There are many different kinds of shock, but in general the word refers to a serious slowdown of the circulatory and nervous systems. Shock is dangerous because the brain and other organs don't get enough blood. If it is not treated, it may cause death.

Shock should not be confused with fainting, which is a temporary loss of consciousness unaccompanied by the symptoms of shock. A person who has fainted should be kept lying down. Loosen any tight clothing and don't let people crowd around the victim. If the victim does not recover right away, get medical help.

Shock symptoms may take only a few minutes or an hour or more to develop. They include sluggishness; moist skin (and pale skin for light-skinned people); drooping eyelids; vacant and dull eyes with large

Getting injured people out of difficult situations may require trained personnel and special equipment.

pupils; a weak, rapid, or irregular pulse rate; shallow, rapid breathing; thirst; and perhaps nausea or vomiting.

Shock can be fatal even though the injury or other event that produced the shock may not have been critical. Shock can result after any accident, especially one in which a large amount of blood has been lost or pain is severe, or if there has been a crushing injury.

Immediate first-aid measures may prevent shock or reduce it. It is most important to keep the victim warm, quiet, and lying down. The head should be lower than the rest of the body unless a head injury or breathing difficulty is involved. Cover the victim with a blanket or coat to maintain normal body temperature. If the victim is fully conscious, provide warm drinks, un-less internal injuries are suspected, or unless the victim is vomiting. Get medical help immediately.

Anxiety and pain may accompany shock. You should try to reduce the agonizing pain of a fracture, burn, or other severe injury, by giving proper first aid. You can help to relieve anxiety by talking reassuringly to an accident victim. Distracting him or her from pain and fear can reduce shock and is an important part of first-aid care. Talk about something other than the injury.

Action to prevent shock should be taken immediately after any accident has taken place. Sometimes people who do not appear to be severely injured go into shock an hour or so later. Many times the shock could have been reduced or prevented if precautions had been taken earlier.

15-4 Severe Bleeding

An excessive loss of blood from any severe cut or wound is especially dangerous. Shock can result from severe bleeding. A person who has a cut in a major artery in the thigh, groin, or neck can die within five minutes if the flow of blood is not stopped. The natural clotting process that stops the loss of blood from a small cut may not work in time to stop the spurts of bright red blood from a major artery, or the steady flow of darker blood from a big vein.

The simplest and most effective way to stop severe bleeding quickly while waiting for medical help is to apply direct pressure on the wound. Use a dressing made from a thick, soft pad of gauze, if available. Otherwise, use a clean handkerchief, or a piece of cloth torn from clothing. If necessary, the bare hand may be used. Work fast.

In almost all cases, direct, steady pressure on and around the wound will stop bleeding. It is important to keep the pressure steady. Do not stop applying pressure to look at the injury. If an arm or a leg is bleeding, raise it above the level of the heart, unless fractures are present. If blood soaks into the dressing on the wound, apply other layers of cloth and continue applying pressure. Do not remove the blood-soaked dressings underneath. Once the bleeding has slowed or stopped, tie the dressings firmly with tape or strips of cloth. Treat for shock. Only a doctor should remove first-aid dressings from the wound.

If the bleeding is from an arm or a leg and direct pressure does not control it, you may exert pressure with your fingers or hand over the nearest artery pressure point. These **pressure points** are areas where arteries may be pressed against the underlying bone to reduce bleeding.

A **tourniquet** (TOOR nih kiht) is an extremely tight bandage around an arm or a

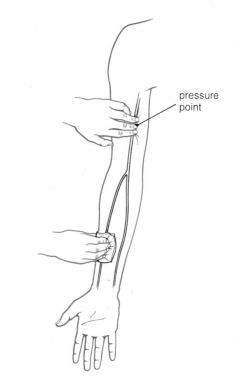

pressure point

To stop severe bleeding from an arm or leg wound, find a pressure point and apply pressure.

leg applied to stop the flow of blood into the limb. It is a very dangerous device and should be used only with great caution, and only if *all* other measures have failed. Reduction of blood flow due to a tourniquet can quickly damage tissues and cause loss of the arm or leg. **Gangrene** (GANG green) is the destruction of tissue due to complete, prolonged loss of circulation. Use a tourniquet only when a limb has been severely cut or mangled and pressure on the wound or on a pressure point does not stop the flow of blood.

When a tourniquet is needed, it should be applied close to the wound, on the side nearer the heart. Any wide, flat piece of cloth long enough to circle the arm or leg twice may be used. Wrap the cloth once around the limb and then tie it with a half-knot. Place a small stick over the half-knot and complete the knot around the stick. Tighten the tourniquet by slowly twisting the stick until the device is just tight enough for bleeding to stop. Then tie the ends of the cloth around the limb to fasten the tourniquet. Attach a note to the victim giving the time when the tourniquet was fastened. The tourniquet should not be loosened except by a doctor.

A tourniquet should never be covered by bandages, clothing, or blankets. Ambulance or hospital personnel may not notice it in time to loosen it, and gangrene may develop as a result.

SELF CHECK

1. What are the two basic rules that you should follow in any emergency?

2. When should an accident victim be moved and when should a victim not be moved?

3. What are the symptoms of shock?

4. Describe three methods of stopping bleeding and tell when each should be used.

Suffocation and Heart Stoppage

15-5 Artificial Respiration

If a person has stopped breathing for any reason at all, such as from apparent drowning, electrical shock, or other accident or illness, begin artificial respiration immediately. **Artificial respiration** is a method of stimulating breathing in someone who is temporarily unable to breathe unaided. Even after a person appears to have suffered **asphyxiation** (as fihk see AY shuhn), or suffocation, the heart may continue to beat for a few minutes. Within those few minutes, if someone gives artificial respiration, the victim's life may be saved.

The easiest, most direct, and most effective way to combat asphyxiation is to force air from your own lungs into the victim's mouth through a kind of artificial respiration called **mouth-to-mouth resuscitation** (rih suhs uh TAY shuhn).

Use the following steps when mouth-to-mouth resuscitation is needed:

1. Place the person on his or her back and clear the mouth of any visible obstructions.

2. Tilt the head back. When the head is tilted back, the tongue is pulled away from the back of the throat and the air passage to the lungs is open. This simple movement alone helps some people to begin breathing.

3. Pinch the nostrils shut as shown on the next page.

4. Take a deep breath and place your mouth directly over the victim's mouth, forming a tight seal. Exhale into the victim's

Mouth-to-Mouth Resuscitation

mouth until the chest expands. If the chest does not expand, check the tilt of the head to make sure the air passage is open. If this does not help, roll the victim onto one side and slap the back to dislodge possible obstructions. Try mouth-to-mouth resuscitation again.

5. When the victim's chest expands, turn your head to the side, and listen for the air escaping, letting the victim exhale without your help. Repeat the cycle for each new breath. If the victim is an adult, blow vigorously 12 times a minute into his or her mouth. For an infant or small child, blow gently 20 times a minute through both mouth and nose. For young children, it may be necessary to press the abdomen gently to help exhalation.

6. When the victim first begins to breathe again, time your efforts with that breathing.

7. After the victim is breathing well, watch him or her carefully, since the breathing may stop again. Treat the victim for shock and get medical care.

Even if the victim does not soon begin to breathe without aid, artificial respiration should be continued until a doctor decides it is no longer necessary.

In some victims of asphyxiation, especially those who have suffered electrical shock, the lungs are clear, but the part of the brain that controls respiration remains paralyzed for several hours. Such people must have help in breathing throughout the long time they remain unconscious.

Mouth-to-mouth resuscitation presents little health danger to the rescuer. However, a rescuer who is fearful about the process may cover the victim's mouth with a layer of a handkerchief or other cloth before beginning mouth-to-mouth resuscitation. The layer of cloth will not reduce the effectiveness of the resuscitation.

For those unfamiliar with or reluctant to use mouth-to-mouth resuscitation, the **chest pressure–arm lift method** provides good movement of air into and out of the lungs. It also must be started immediately, for a delay may mean death. It is not as effective as mouth-to-mouth resuscitation. Also, the rescuer may tire and need to be relieved, whereas one can continue mouth-to-mouth resuscitation for an hour or more without becoming overly tired.

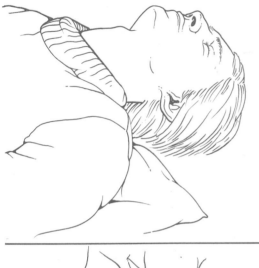

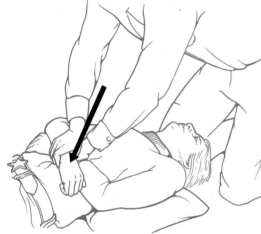

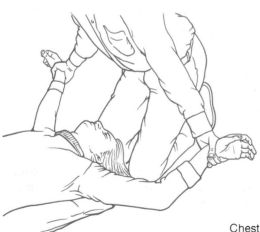

Chest Pressure–Arm Lift Resuscitation

Follow these steps to carry out the chest pressure–arm lift method:

1. Place the victim on his or her back. Put something under the shoulders so that the head drops back. Clean all foreign matter out of the mouth. Turn the head slightly to one side. If a helper is available, have him or her hold the victim's head so that the jaw juts out.

2. Kneel above the victim's head. Hold the victim's wrists, cross them on the lower chest, and press down. This should force air out of the lungs.

3. Pull the victim's arms up and back as far as possible. This should expand the lungs and fill them with air.

4. Repeat this cycle 10 to 12 times a minute. Check the victim's mouth frequently for obstructions. Every few minutes, stop to see if the victim has started to breathe alone. If so, continue to help by moving the arms with every breath. Get medical help.

15-6 Choking

Ordinarily, the trachea closes automatically when a person swallows. Occasionally, a piece of food or other object will accidentally lodge in the upper part of the throat. If the object is not dislodged, the person can die from having the air supply cut off. The victim's immediate reaction is to choke and probably to panic. If possible, calm the victim and encourage him or her to cough up the object. The obstruction may be high enough in the throat that it can be pulled out with the fingers. This is risky, though, because you could push the object farther down the victim's throat. Be very careful.

If the choking person cannot talk and is clearly not getting air, have him or her lie face down with the head over the edge of a table or bed, or on one side. For a baby or a small child, you should hold the victim upside-down or over your lap, with the upper body hanging down over your legs. Then slap the person hard on the back between the shoulder blades. If this fails to dislodge the object and the victim still cannot breathe, start mouth-to-mouth resuscitation immediately and get medical help. You may be able to force enough air past the obstruction to keep the person alive until medical help arrives.

A newer method recommended by some doctors is called the **abdominal thrust** or the **Heimlich maneuver.** Stand behind the choking victim (someone else may have to help hold the person upright) and wrap your arms around the abdomen, as shown on the next page. Give a sharp thrust upward with the thumb side of your fist. Be careful! You can easily break the victim's breastbone. The idea behind this method is that when a person chokes, the lungs contain some trapped air. Compressing the lungs quickly by squeezing upward can increase the air pressure in the trachea and throat and force the object out, similar to popping a cork out of a bottle. If the victim is too big for you to circle your arms around the abdomen, wrap your arms higher up.

CAUTION! Doctors disagree on the best way to help someone who is choking. No method can be guaranteed to work. The abdominal and chest thrust can injure lungs and organs. Use this method only if all other measures have failed. Practice the arm positions shown, but do *not* practice the actual thrust on anyone. If you are giving first aid, use the method that you know most about and can manage with confidence.

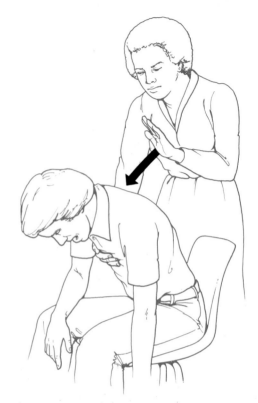

Hard slaps may dislodge an object caught in a person's throat. Another method is the abdominal thrust shown on the far right.

15-7 Heart Attacks and Heart Massage

A heart attack, or coronary thrombosis, is accompanied by pain in the chest. Pain may be felt also in the left arm, throat, or back. The pain may pass quickly or last for hours. An attack may also have these symptoms: intense shortness of breath, sweating, extreme weakness, a grayish color of the skin, nausea, and loss of consciousness.

A person who seems to be having a heart attack should sit or lie down, whichever is more comfortable. Loosen any tight clothing. Watch for symptoms of shock. If the

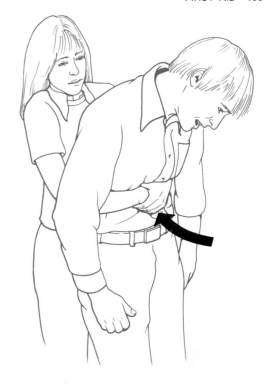

victim is not breathing, begin artificial respiration. Give oxygen if it is available. If the victim has medicine prescribed by a doctor for a heart condition, and is conscious, help the person take it. Keep panic-stricken relatives and friends away.

If a doctor cannot come immediately, the person should be taken at once by ambulance to a hospital, preferably one that has a unit for the specific care of heart attacks.

Electrical shock, apparent drowning, suffocation, or heart attack can stop the heartbeat, or make it so weak and irregular that the person quickly loses consciousness. When the heart stops beating, artificial respiration will not help, because the blood cannot deliver oxygen to the brain and other tissues. To find out whether a victim's

heart is still beating, take the pulse, as described in Chapter 2. If you cannot feel any pulse, put your ear on the victim's chest over the heart. If the heartbeat has stopped, massage applied on the outside, known as **closed-chest heart massage,** may get the heart beating regularly and save a life.

Since the brain is permanently damaged if it is not supplied with blood for as short a period as five or six minutes, speed in beginning closed-chest heart massage is absolutely essential. Heart massage squeezes the heart between the rib cage and the spine. It is a dangerous technique that usually results in rib fractures. A rescuer should use closed-chest heart massage *only when the heart is not beating.* Training in closed-chest heart massage is available in some schools

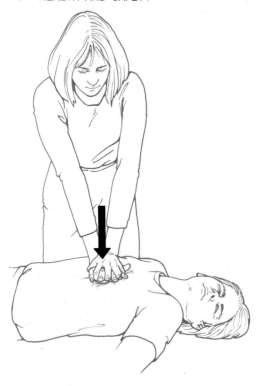

Closed-Chest Heart Massage

and from the Red Cross. You can call the American Heart Association for information about training in your community.

Use the following steps for closed-chest heart massage:

1. If you are sure the victim is unconscious (no pulse, no sign of breathing, no response to being called), give four quick mouth-to-mouth breaths.

2. With the victim on a flat, hard surface, face up, position yourself at his or her side and place your hands as shown in the picture. Your fingers should not press on the victim's chest. Do not place your hand over the very end of the breastbone.

3. Bring your shoulders directly over the victim's breastbone, keep your arms straight, and press firmly downward, a min-imum of one and one-half to two inches (three and one-half to five centimeters). If the individual is a baby or a very young child, apply pressure with the fingertips only and press down on the breastbone not more than about one and one-half inches (three and one-half centimeters).

4. Push down 80 times a minute. When you relax the pressure, keep your hands in place.

5. If a second rescuer is available, he or she should use mouth-to-mouth resuscitation. The most effective way of combining these first-aid techniques is to apply five chest compressions followed immediately by one mouth-to-mouth breath. The rhythm of five to one should be kept up as long as neces-sary, or until medical help arrives.

6. If only one rescuer is available, he or she must perform both mouth-to-mouth resus-citation and closed-chest heart massage. The rhythm then should be fifteen chest compressions followed by two full mouth-to-mouth breaths.

Even if the individual remains uncon-scious, closed-chest heart massage may get enough blood circulating to prevent brain damage. It is important to continue until a trained health professional can take over.

15-8 Electrical Shock

Take special precautions in giving first aid to a victim of electrical shock. A mistake can result in two injuries or deaths instead of one. If the victim is in contact with elec-tricity through a live wire or a defective appliance, do not touch him or her until the electric current has been turned off. You should never try to remove the victim your-self from the source of the electrical shock if electric current is still on. Even if you had

Downed power lines can cause severe injuries, even death, to
people who accidentally touch them—including would-be rescuers.

on dry rubber gloves and stood on something dry you could be badly shocked yourself. You could move a person to safety using a dry stick or rope, but it's risky.

Severe electrical shock can paralyze the part of the brain that controls respiration. Once the victim is no longer in contact with the source of electricity, he or she may need artificial respiration for a very long period of time. If breathing is normal, the victim should be kept warm, quiet, and partially propped up.

The electrical shock also may disturb the natural heartbeat rhythm, so that instead of beating regularly, the heart muscle fibers merely twitch irregularly. Closed-chest heart massage may also be necessary, in addition to artificial respiration.

SELF CHECK

1. Describe the complete process of mouth-to-mouth resuscitation.

2. What are the disadvantages of chest pressure–arm lift resuscitation?

3. What should you do for someone who is choking?

4. When should closed-chest heart massage be used as an emergency first-aid procedure?

Poisoning

15-9 Oral Poisons

Poisons are most likely to enter the body through the mouth. However, some toxic (poisonous) substances can be absorbed through the lungs, the skin, or accidentally by injection.

Once in the digestive system, poisons act in different ways. Strong acids and corrosive materials such as lye burn and corrode the tissues they touch. They "eat away" the esophagus and can seriously burn the stomach. Sleeping pills and alcohol, if taken in large enough doses, act like poisons by slowing down the central nervous system. Some poisons can slow down breathing or heartbeat. First-aid procedures differ for various types of poisons. It is important to know what poison has been taken and what type of action is called for.

Always check the label of any poisonous chemical. It tells you what to do if someone accidentally swallows it or gets some of it in the eyes or on the skin.

The public health departments of many cities have established Poison Control or Poison Information Centers. These centers maintain up-to-date files of the contents of dangerous products. By telephoning one of these centers, a rescuer can quickly get accurate information on the best first-aid treatment to give to a poison victim. Obtaining information is also important if you do not know the poison involved. You can describe the symptoms and receive advice about the best possible treatment. Keep the phone number handy. These centers are listed in the telephone directory yellow pages. If you cannot call one of these centers, call a doctor, hospital, or police or fire department for information on treatment.

If a rescuer deals quickly and correctly with the particular type of poison the victim has taken, a doctor can complete the treatment with medicines that counteract the poison. First aid largely determines the success of the doctor's treatment.

Here are the most important first-aid measures to counteract any type of poison that has been swallowed:

1. Dilute the poison. Give the victim one or two glasses of milk, or water if milk is not available. A smaller amount should be given to a small child. Speed is essential.

2. Unless the victim has swallowed strong acid, lye, kerosene, or gasoline, you should then induce vomiting. Having the victim vomit will help to clean out the stomach. Insert your finger in the victim's throat to make him or her vomit. You should do this immediately after the poison has been diluted and before it can take effect. If your finger does not cause vomiting, give the victim an **emetic** (ih MEHT ihk), a medicine that causes vomiting. A household medicine cabinet should include syrup of **ipecac** (IHP uh kak) for causing vomiting. This emetic can be purchased at a drugstore without a doctor's prescription.

If the victim does vomit, keep some of the vomited material so that it may be medically examined to determine the poison. The vomit sample should be brought with the victim when she or he is taken to be treated.

3. It is important *not* to induce vomiting, however, if someone has swallowed lye,

acid, kerosene, or gasoline. Lye and acid will further damage the esophagus if they are forced up from the stomach. Kerosene and gasoline are not extremely dangerous in the stomach, but if they are vomited, their fumes may be drawn into the lungs. In the lungs these substances become deadly. People who have swallowed one of these substances should be given an **antidote,** a substance to counteract the effects of the poison.

If the victim has swallowed a strong acid, give him or her a glass of milk, water, or a solution of one tablespoon of milk of magnesia in one cup of water. For an alkali such as lye, milk is the best remedy, but water or fruit juice is acceptable. If you are not sure whether to induce vomiting and cannot reach a Poison Control Center, dilute the poison as much as possible with milk or water. Do not give any other antidote. The old-fashioned solution known as the "universal antidote" should not be used.

4. Use olive oil or egg white to soothe the burned lips, mouth, and skin of someone who has swallowed a strong acid or alkali.

5. Save the container and any remaining poison for medical examination. A doctor may have to identify the poison before starting treatment with antidotes. Sometimes manufacturers have to be telephoned to learn the chemical makeup of a trademarked substance.

6. Get medical attention quickly.

An overdose of any medicine or drug constitutes a case of poisoning. For a baby or a very small child, a handful of aspirins can cause serious illness or death. Anyone who has swallowed too much of a medicine or drug, including sleeping pills, should be helped to vomit.

Someone who has taken too many sleeping pills may be drowsy. Support and walk him or her around the room until recovery begins. Notify a doctor; do not take full responsibility yourself. If the victim is conscious, offer as much strong, black coffee as he or she will drink. Do not try to force any liquid into the mouth of an unconscious person. Anyone who is unconscious needs immediate medical help, preferably in a hospital.

The reaction to an overdose of a medicine or drug may not occur immediately. If your suspicion is aroused by the sight of an opened medicine bottle, call a doctor immediately. The doctor will want to know what the medicine or drug is, how much was swallowed, and how much time has passed since it was taken. The rescuer may not know all of this, but any information will be helpful.

15-10 Gaseous and External Poisons

Someone who has inhaled carbon monoxide, hydrogen cyanide, methane, carbon tetrachloride, or other toxic gas fumes needs fresh air immediately. Turn off or remove the source of gas first and be on guard against the danger of fire or explosion. Then open windows and doors and move the victim to fresh air. Use artificial respiration if breathing is very weak or has stopped. The victim should be wrapped in blankets to maintain body temperature and prevent shock. Keep him or her quiet.

If a poisonous or irritating chemical has touched the skin, the substance should be washed off immediately. Every second counts. Place the person under a faucet, hose, or shower for several minutes. If the substance has touched the victim's clothing, soak the clothing with water and remove it, taking care not to touch any contaminated portions yourself.

If poison has entered the eye, hold the eyelid open and flush the eye with a continuous stream of water for at least 15 minutes. A running tap may be used.

15-11 Insect and Other Animal Bites

Insect bites are common during warm weather. Bees, wasps, hornets, lice, flies, and mosquitoes; and spiders, scorpions, and ticks can cause much discomfort and even death. As you learned in Chapter 11, some of these bites can infect you with serious diseases. Other bites, although not infectious, can still require prompt action. A person who knows first-aid measures for bites and stings can relieve discomfort, prevent or reduce infection, and possibly save a life.

The sting of a bee, wasp, hornet, or yellow jacket usually causes only a local reaction with pain, redness, and swelling around the

Hornet

Honey Bee

Yellow Jacket Wasp

Scorpions

Black Widow Spider

puncture. The stinger can be removed by pulling it out gently with fingers or tweezers. Do not squeeze the area. Squeezing spreads the poison. If you cannot remove the stinger easily, have a doctor do it. Ice or a cold, wet cloth will help relieve the pain. To relieve the itching, apply a paste made of baking soda and water, or a soft pad of gauze or other cloth moistened with diluted ammonia, or one of the calamine lotions available in drugstores. If the itching is severe, a doctor can recommend medication.

A few individuals are so allergic to the stings of wasps and bees that their lives can be endangered. If a stung person collapses or there is serious swelling, first-aid help should be given immediately and continued until a doctor arrives or the victim reaches a hospital. Treat for shock. If the sting is on an arm or leg, a fairly tight, squeezing bandage should be placed near the bite on the side closer to the heart. Loosen the bandage for one minute out of every ten. People who know that they are allergic to insect stings

Copperhead

Cottonmouth or Water Moccasin

Rattlesnake

Coral Snake

should ask a doctor for medication to be used in such an emergency.

Most scorpions and spiders in mild climates are harmless, but their tropical relatives can be poisonous. The scorpion of the United States South and Southwest hides in cool places indoors and outdoors. When surprised, it stings with its tail. Usually, the sting causes only some pain, with swelling and discoloration. Sometimes a poisonous sting causes almost no swelling or discoloration. At first, there may be only a local tingling sensation, but soon the poison causes nausea, abdominal cramps, and convulsions. Some people may die from a poisonous scorpion sting.

A scorpion victim should lie down. If the sting is on a limb, a squeezing bandage should be applied near the sting on the side closer to the heart, as for a bee or wasp sting. Apply ice to the wound. Do not give the victim alcohol to drink or let him or her walk.

The female black widow spider is shiny black with a red mark on its abdomen. The bite of this poisonous spider causes sharp pain throughout the body in a short time, followed by sweating, shortness of breath, nausea, and cramps. First-aid treatment is the same as for a scorpion sting. Most individuals who are bitten by a black widow spider recover after medical treatment.

Snakebite is much less frequent than insect bites, although the poisonous snakes shown on page 409 live in many parts of the United States and Canada. Their bites can be avoided by following two rules:

1. Wear high shoes or boots in snake-infested areas.

2. Never put your hand onto a rock ledge or in a hole without first looking to see if a snake is there. If you cannot see up to a ledge, poke around with a stick to frighten away any snake enjoying a sunbath.

In the event of a poisonous snakebite follow this procedure:

1. Apply a tourniquet near the bite on the side closer to the heart to slow down the spread of the poison.

2. Keep the victim lying down and quiet, with the bitten part lower than the heart.

3. Apply ice or cold packs to the bitten area to relieve pain and to slow down the action of the poison.

4. Get medical attention as soon as possible.

A serious animal disease that can be given to people by animal bites is rabies. Rabies can be prevented in pets by having a veterinarian give your pet an anti-rabies shot. Any warm-blooded wild animal or pet may have rabies, even one that looks healthy. Wash an animal bite thoroughly. If the animal is found to be sick with rabies, a doctor can start treatment to prevent the victim from getting this disease. If the victim develops a fever, pain, or soreness around the wound, get medical attention.

15-12 Poisonous Plants

There are about 60 varieties of poison ivy, poison oak, or poison sumac. They cause allergic reactions in four out of five people. Since anyone who spends any time outdoors in the summer can hardly avoid areas where one of these plants grows, you should learn to recognize them on sight.

Every part of the **poison ivy** plant is poisonous at all times. The oily, resinous sap may spread indirectly to human skin from clothing, garden tools, or the fur of household pets. The smoke from a brush fire containing poison ivy can injure the skin

A

B

A. Poison Ivy
B. Poison Sumac
C. Poison Oak

C

and is extremely dangerous if inhaled or if it affects the eyes.

The symptoms of poison ivy may become prominent in several hours, or they may require days to appear. The affected skin area reddens, itches, and then forms small blisters, which give off a watery fluid. The condition may last over a period of several weeks.

Washing thoroughly with hot water and soap after contact with poison ivy often prevents the symptoms. If the symptoms do develop, the skin should be treated with baking soda mixed in water, with a cold pack, or with any of several commercial preparations containing calamine. If the attack is serious, you will need to get a doctor's help.

The symptoms of **poison oak** and **poison sumac** are similar to those of poison ivy, as are the ways of preventing and treating these conditions.

Destroying these poisonous plants if they grow near places where you live and work is one safety measure. This should be done carefully, with a chemical spray. A local branch of the Audubon Society or another conservationist group is a good place to call to find out a spray you can use that will cause as little environmental damage as possible. Because the smoke can be harmful, the plants should *never* be burned. If poisonous plants are not destroyed chemically, they should be uprooted completely. Just cutting them down is useless; they will grow back from the roots. As an extra precaution, all clothing worn when spraying poisonous plants should be washed thoroughly in strong, high-alkali soap or dry-cleaned before being worn again. Be sure to warn the dry cleaner.

SELF CHECK

1. What is a Poison Control or Poison Information Center?

2. Why do gaseous and external poisons need immediate attention?

3. What are some examples of poisonous household materials?

4. How would you give first aid to a person who is apparently allergic to a bee sting?

5. How would you recognize symptoms of poison ivy, poison oak, or poison sumac?

Burns, Fractures, and Bandaging

15-13 Burns and Smoke Inhalation

Some of the most common emergencies are burns. If a person's clothing or hair is on fire, have him or her roll on the ground. Running will only fan the flames and increase the danger. Pour water, milk, or any other nonflammable liquid on the flames. Do not leave a victim burning while you look for water. If there is no water nearby, throw a blanket, heavy coat, or rug over the flames to put them out.

Help a person in a smoke-filled room to a window or an exit, whichever is appropriate. The air is freshest at floor level, so crawling across the floor is the safest method of moving through such a room.

Burns may be caused by contact with dry heat such as fire, or moist heat in the form of steam or hot liquid. They may also be caused by chemicals, lightning, or the sun's rays. Burns are classified as first, second, or third degree, depending on the extent of damage to the tissue. A first-degree burn reddens the skin. It can be serious if it covers a large area of the body. A second-degree burn reddens and blisters the top layer of skin, the epidermis. It is a serious burn. A third-degree burn destroys the epidermis and dermis. It causes the skin to have a white or charred appearance. It is a major burn.

For first-degree and small second-degree burns, run cold water over the burned area to relieve the pain and prevent further burn damage. Do not use ice water or put ice

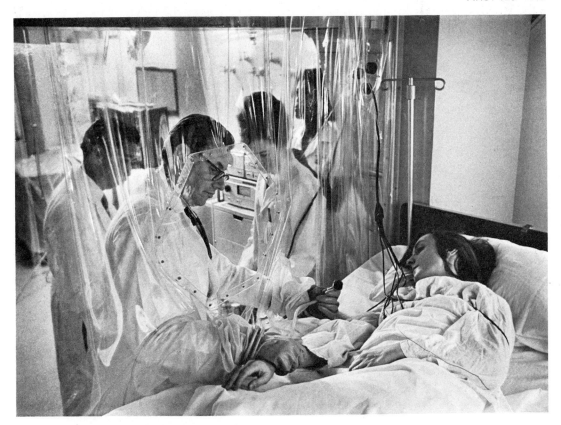

Badly burned patients can be kept in a sterile environment called a "burn island." Gloves and long sleeves attached to the plastic wall allow medical care without the risk of infection.

cubes directly on the skin. An antiseptic medication that relieves pain may be used. Do not use butter, lard, or any other greasy ointment on a burn since it is difficult to remove. After the pain eases, put dry dressings of clean gauze, towels, or sheets on the burned area. A doctor should always be called to treat any extensive burn as soon as possible after first aid is given.

To reduce shock, the victim of a third-degree burn should lie down. Place the victim's head and chest a little lower than the rest of the body, unless he or she is having trouble breathing. In that case, raise the head and shoulders slightly. Wash your hands and apply thick, dry pads of sterile gauze over the burned areas. Use clean cotton cloth if gauze is not available. Protecting the burned area from air helps to relieve pain, and the sterile or clean covering reduces the danger of infection and helps prevent the loss of body fluids. Get medical help immediately.

If the victim of a serious burn is conscious and can swallow, give fluids. Do not attempt to remove charred clothing from the burned area or to touch the skin. Do not apply medication of any kind to severely burned skin. You may make the condition worse or more difficult to treat later.

Keep yourself covered up in very cold weather. Fingers, toes, faces, and ears are the first parts to get frostbitten.

15-14 Too Much Heat or Cold

Vacation time often tempts people to rush down to the beach on a hot day and stay there for several hours without adequate protection against the sun and heat. Carelessness can result in severe sunburn or in heat stroke. Sunburn requires the same kind of first aid as for any kind of burn. Symptoms of **heat stroke** are sudden collapse, high body temperature, dizziness, headache, hot and dry skin, red or flushed face, difficulty in breathing, and rapid pulse. Body temperature may rise to 110°F (43°C). The victim may lose consciousness.

First-aid measures for heat stroke include placing the victim in a shaded, cool place and removing most of his or her clothing. Sprinkle cool water on the victim to reduce body temperature. A garden hose is useful. Get medical attention.

Strenuous activity combined with excessive exposure to the sun or other source of intense heat can cause **heat exhaustion,** a different condition from heat stroke. Under very high temperatures, the body perspires heavily to maintain its normal temperature. This excessive sweating removes large quantities of fluid and salt from the body. When the fluid and salt supply is reduced far below normal, heat exhaustion results.

The first symptoms of heat exhaustion are headache and a feeling of weakness and dizziness. The victim may feel nauseated and may suffer cramps in the muscles of the arms, legs, or abdomen. The victim may turn pale. The skin is cool and moist from perspiration, and pulse and breathing are rapid. Body temperature remains normal or slightly below normal. The victim of heat exhaustion may feel confused and have trouble coordinating his or her body movements.

To help a victim of heat exhaustion before medical help is available, have him or her lie down quietly in a cool place and loosen the clothing. Give a teaspoonful of salt dissolved in a large glass of tomato juice or water. Repeat three or four times at 10- to 15-minute intervals. Do not give too much salt at once or vomiting may result.

People who are physically active in the summer can help prevent heat exhaustion by drinking plenty of fluids, including salty drinks. Heat stroke and heat exhaustion can occur indoors as well as outdoors. Industrial plants where unusually high temperatures cannot be avoided often supply salt tablets at drinking fountains.

Winter can cause difficulties, also. Sunburn of the face can be a winter hazard from reflection of the sun's rays off the glistening snow. A more serious hazard is **frostbite,** a condition resulting from freezing. Usually the first areas to freeze are the nose, ears, cheeks, fingers, and toes. The flesh feels cold to the touch, and the frozen parts feel numb. (For a light-skinned person the frozen parts turn pale.) There may be some prickly or itching sensation as the circulation of the blood slows down. However, a person suffering frostbite may feel no warning pain and may not realize that anything serious is happening.

To help someone who has frostbite, cover the frozen part with warm clothing, or warm it between your hands or under an armpit. The frozen area must be warmed rapidly but gently. If facilities are available, place the frozen part in lukewarm water. Do not use hot water or a hot water bag, or place the victim near a hot stove or open fire. Get medical help for the victim immediately.

Never rub a frostbitten area with snow. Frozen tissues are easily damaged, perhaps permanently. Treat frozen fingers and toes with the utmost care and gentleness.

15-15 Fractures and Dislocations

Any injury that makes moving a limb or joint painful should be regarded as a fracture, or break or crack, until X rays show that it is a different injury. A broken bone is called a **closed fracture** (simple fracture)

Keep closed and open fractures from moving. Open ones also need care to prevent infection.

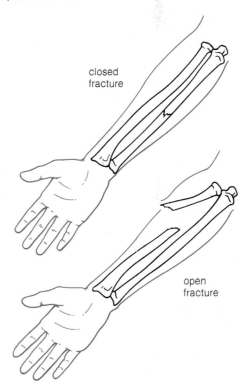

closed fracture

open fracture

when the skin is not broken. If the bone punctures the skin or if there is a connecting wound, this constitutes an **open fracture** (compound fracture).

Someone with broken bones can go into shock. To prevent shock or reduce it, keep the victim warm and quiet. For fractures of any kind the best first-aid treatment is to keep the victim lying down quietly until a doctor or ambulance arrives. Do not attempt to change the position of the bone or move the victim until the exact nature and extent of the injury are known. Only a doctor should try to set a bone. An X-ray examination is usually necessary before a doctor can know how to handle the fracture. It is extremely dangerous to move a victim who may have a fracture of the back or neck.

If a person who has a fracture must be moved or if there is going to be a long wait before a doctor or ambulance comes, the injured area should be **splinted** in the position in which you find it. Splinting helps prevent further damage to the injured area. A thick board, pole, rolled-up newspaper or magazine, or any other sturdy support may be used for this purpose.

A splint should extend beyond the joints above and below the fracture. It should be padded with a soft material, and bandaged to keep the joints and the bone ends from moving. After splinting, a broken leg should be tied to the other leg, and a broken arm to the body. The bandage should be tight enough to keep the fracture from moving but not tight enough to interfere with circulation. Examine the splinted part regularly while waiting for medical help. If a person's broken arm is splinted and the hand becomes cold or pale, the bandage must be loosened gently.

Dislocation occurs when a bone is moved from its normal position at a joint. It can take place at any movable joint. It can result from a stretching or tearing of the joint tissue. A sudden wrench may push the bone out of joint, or out of place. Dislocations are most likely to affect the fingers, knees, jaw, shoulders, hips, elbows, and wrists. Symptoms of dislocation are pain around the joint, swelling, inability to use the joint, and usually a distortion of the normal shape of the area. To prevent shock, keep the victim quiet and warm until medical help arrives. Keep the dislocated bone from moving. Splint it if necessary.

15-16 Strains and Sprains

A **strain** involves a painful stretching of a muscle or of a tendon. Any sudden, violent movement can cause a strain. Taking a wrong step and twisting an ankle or attempting to lift a heavy weight and slipping can painfully strain one or more muscles, such as one of the muscles of the back.

One of the most common types of strain involves the lower part of the back. This strain usually results from improperly lifting a heavy weight. Treatment for muscle strain includes rest for the injured area, gentle massage, and the application of heat with warm, wet cloths, a hot water bottle, or an electric heating pad.

A **sprain** occurs when ligaments around a joint or between connecting bones are torn. A sprain may be mild or cause severe pain and loss of ability to use the affected part of the body. The injured area swells, and the skin becomes red or reddish blue. The ankles, wrists, fingers, shoulders, hips, and knees are the parts that are most often sprained. Sprains frequently result after a sudden twist or wrench. Sometimes only a careful medical examination, including X rays, can distinguish between a sprain and a fracture.

First-aid treatment for most sprains calls for helping the injured person lie down. Raise the injured arm or leg above the level of the heart. Apply cold cloths or an ice pack to the area for as long as necessary to keep the swelling down, perhaps one-half to one hour. Repeat as necessary. Medication that reduces pain may be required for sprains. Do not put a sprained area into hot water.

What if you don't know whether the injury is a strain or a sprain? Whether you know or not, help the victim to be more comfortable. Then have a trained medical person examine the injury to decide what treatment is necessary.

15-17 Skin Wounds and Bandages

Any wound should be cleaned carefully to prevent infection. The method of treatment depends on the type and seriousness of the wound. There are several types of wounds.

An **incision** (ihn SIHZH uhn) is a smooth cut. Some deep incisions may damage muscles, tendons, and nerves. If an incision is long and deep, control the bleeding and get medical help immediately. The incision may require stitches to help it heal properly and to prevent bad scarring.

A **laceration** (las uh RAY shuhn) is an uneven cut in which the skin is torn. Damage to tissue is more severe than in an incision, and there is great danger of infection. Clean and cover a small laceration with a clean soft pad of gauze or cloth. If the laceration is large get medical help. Do not remove any torn pieces of skin.

A **puncture** is a hole produced by a sharp object's piercing through skin layers. A puncture does not produce much bleeding, but there is great danger of infection. Clean a puncture with soap and water, cover it with a clean, soft pad of gauze, and have it checked by a doctor or nurse.

An **abrasion** (uh BRAY zhuhn) is a scrape that produces damage to the outer layers of skin. An abrasion does not produce much external bleeding, but there is a danger of infection. Clean an abrasion and cover it with a light, clean, soft pad of gauze. If an abrasion is large get medical help.

Dressings are placed directly over a wound. They may be plain or medicated. Small dressings often have a gauze pad with adhesive to hold them in place. Dressings are sold in sterile packages. Large pads and other products also make first-aid dressings and bandaging relatively simple. If commercial dressings are unavailable, a sterile pad or several thicknesses of gauze, or at least the cleanest cloth available, should be used as a dressing to cover a wound.

A **bandage** is used to hold a dressing in place, to hold a splint securely, to rest an injured limb, or to control bleeding, as in a tourniquet. If a bandage is needed to hold a dressing in place, it should be tied securely but not tightly enough to interfere with circulation. Bandages should never be placed in direct contact with an open wound.

Bandaging can be complex. Years ago, much time was spent teaching the techniques of elaborate bandaging. Today, doctors and nurses emphasize simplicity. A bandage does not have to look attractive to be useful. It must be clean, but does not have to be sterile. Bandages applied during first aid are temporary, and a doctor will probably remove them.

A strip of clean gauze or cloth rolled into a tight spool constitutes a **roller bandage.** Roller bandages are sold in many different lengths and widths. A short length of the roll may be used for a simple cut. Several feet of bandage may be needed if an arm or a leg must be bandaged for its entire length.

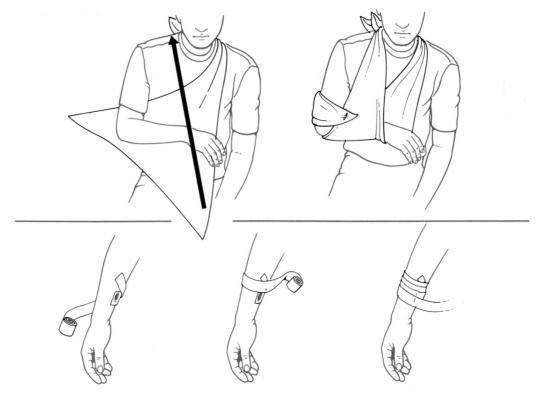

Two useful bandages are slings made of cloth triangles, and roller bandages for holding dressings in place.

Strips of sheets, pillowcases, clean shirts or other clothing may be torn and used as a roller bandage.

A **triangular bandage** is commonly used to form a sling for a broken arm or hand. **Slings** can be made by folding up or cutting a large square of cloth diagonally to form a triangle. To make a strong support for an arm or hand, fold over one point of the triangle toward the base. The folds can be of any desired width, depending on the part of the body that must be bandaged.

The **tailed bandage** usually consists of a piece of cloth cut or torn into two strips from the ends toward the center, leaving a large center area. The center of the tailed bandage is placed over a dressed wound, and the ends are tied together to fasten a dressing.

Whatever type of bandage is used, it is important to remember that in all cases of open wounds a dressing should cover the wound. A bandage is merely used to cover the dressing. Notice when you buy first-aid supplies that dressings are sterile, but bandages are not.

No one can be equipped for every possible type of emergency. But there are some basic first-aid supplies that will help you in many emergencies that can occur at home and away from home. These supplies are listed in Appendix B.

SELF CHECK

1. What are the characteristics of first-, second-, and third-degree burns?

2. What are some health problems that can be caused by excessive heat or cold?

3. What is the difference between a closed and an open fracture?

4. What is the difference between a strain and a sprain?

5. What are some of the uses of bandages?

Chapter Summary

Knowing what to do and keeping a clear mind in order to do it effectively are the first rules of first aid. The next rule to follow in an emergency is to get a doctor or an ambulance quickly so that your first, life-saving measures may be followed as fast as possible by professional medical treatment.

Most life-threatening emergencies can be handled by relatively simple measures. A shock victim should be kept warm, lying down, and reassured if possible. Severe bleeding must be stopped within five minutes by pressure at the place of bleeding or at a pressure point, or, if all else fails, by the careful use of a tourniquet. Mouth-to-mouth resuscitation is the simplest and most effective way to help someone who has stopped breathing. Attempts should be made to dislodge an object from the throat or windpipe if the victim cannot cough it up.

If a person has a heart attack, get a doctor or an ambulance. The victim may have medicine for a heart condition, but need help to take it. You may have to treat for shock or begin artificial respiration. Otherwise, have the victim rest.

If a person's heart has stopped, you may be able to save that person by using closed-chest heart massage. In the case of electrical shock, the first thing to do is turn off the electric current.

People may be poisoned by liquids, gases, or overdoses of medicine or drugs. Before you do anything, you must know whether the poison should be left in the victim's stomach and diluted, or whether you should force vomiting. Some insect bites may be poisonous and should be treated as emergencies. Allergic reaction to poisonous plants is not fatal, but it can be very uncomfortable. If someone has been exposed to poison ivy or some other irritating plant, the skin should be washed quickly and thoroughly with hot water and soap.

Burns are among the most painful of injuries. You can relieve the pain of a small first- or second-degree burn by running cold water over it. The victim of a third-degree burn or extensive first- or second-degree burns should be given first-aid treatment for shock. Cover the burned area lightly with clean cloth, but do not apply any household substance or medicine.

Do not try to set a broken bone. First-aid splinting can make the victim more comfortable and prevent further damage until a doctor is available. All open wounds should be carefully cleaned to prevent infection. Large wounds should be medically treated. A clean dressing should be placed on an open wound before it is bandaged. Any bandaging of a wound should be as simple as possible.

Remember that first aid is what must be done *first* to save a life. It may save an accident victim or a victim of sudden illness, but it is not a substitute for the medical help needed for complete recovery.

Chapter Self Check

1. What is first aid? What is the first thing you should do in an emergency?

2. Why can it be dangerous to move an accident victim? Under what circumstances should you move an accident victim?

3. What is shock? How would you treat it?

4. How does going into shock differ from fainting?

5. How should you try to control severe bleeding?

6. What are the dangers associated with the use of a tourniquet?

7. What are two types of artificial respiration? Which is more effective?

8. In what order should these procedures be used to relieve choking: (a) coughing up, (b) abdominal thrust, (c) mouth-to-mouth resuscitation, (d) dislodging an object from the throat?

9. What should you do to restore heartbeat?

10. Why do victims of electrical shock sometimes require a long period of artificial respiration?

11. Name two types of poison and tell how they affect the body.

12. For what emergency should you induce vomiting?

13. When should vomiting *not* be induced to help someone who has swallowed a poison?

14. How would you treat poison in the eye?

15. What are the first-aid procedures for treating a suspected carbon monoxide poisoning victim?

16. How serious are insect bites? What do you do to remove a bee stinger?

17. What is the treatment for snakebite?

18. What should someone who has been in contact with poison ivy do?

19. How should a first-degree burn be treated?

20. What is the difference between heat exhaustion and heat stroke?

21. How can you tell if a bone has been broken?

22. What is a dislocation?

23. When do you apply warmth and cold in the treatment of strains and sprains?

24. How should you treat any wound?

25. What is the difference between a dressing and a bandage?

26. Tell what you should do for a victim with the following injuries: (a) bleeding from an artery in the arm, (b) fracture of the leg, (c) second-degree burns on the face.

Read More About It

American National Red Cross. *Standard First Aid and Personal Safety.* New York: Doubleday & Company, Inc., 1973. Describes emergency first-aid treatment and gives information on accident prevention and personal safety.

Ferazani, Larry. *Rescue Squad.* New York: William Morrow & Company, Inc., 1974. Describes emergency situations including drug reactions and accidents. Includes a capsule guide for emergency action.

Gardner, A. Ward, and Roylance, Peter J. *New Essential First Aid*. Boston: Little, Brown and Company, 1971. Basic first aid. Stresses recognition and treatment of the most urgent conditions.

Hartley, Joel. *New Ways in First Aid*. New York: Hart Publishing Company, Inc., 1971. Emergencies are listed in alphabetical order and illustrations are clear.

Henderson, John. *Emergency Medical Guide, Third Edition*. New York: McGraw-Hill Book Company, Inc., 1973. Detailed instructions for meeting most medical emergencies. New medical knowledge and techniques for saving life. Also covers drug abuse.

Johnson, G. Timothy. *Doctor: What You Should Know About Health Care Before You Call a Physician*. New York: McGraw-Hill Book Company, Inc., 1975. Information on common medical problems including emergencies and recognizing serious symptoms.

16
Getting Health Care

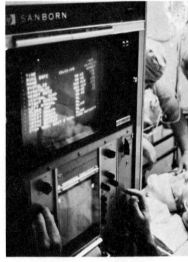

After completing the work in this chapter, you will be able to:

tell when you need medical care and where to go for it.

describe several factors to consider in choosing a doctor.

explain how to choose a hospital.

list at least four rights of hospital patients.

Modern medical equipment can automatically test for many chemicals in the blood (left) or continuously measure blood pressure, temperature, and other vital signs in a patient recovering from surgery (above).

The Person in Charge of Your Health

Staying healthy is easier for some people than others. Some people don't get many infectious diseases. They don't have weight-control problems. They seldom get injured in accidents. And they cope with the difficult times in their lives without developing psychological problems.

Are these unusually healthy people just lucky? Perhaps they are, in part. They may be lucky in their genes and their upbringing. But feelings, attitudes, and behavior are also tremendously important in keeping healthy. That isn't to say that you must lead a timid, overly careful, or "goody-goody" life. Being healthy doesn't require that. It requires mainly that people become sensitive to their mental and physical needs, treat themselves well, and get professional medical care when they need it—all of which is much easier said than done.

Most people often disregard the signs that their minds and bodies need rest or activity. We tend to eat whether we're hungry or not, just because it's time to eat. We keep our discontents bottled up inside us, trying to appear cool and casual when we aren't.

The earlier chapters in this book have explained how the mind and body work and what attitudes and actions will help you stay healthy. This chapter is for those occasional times when you have to take care of yourself by getting medical care.

Everyone needs to see a doctor occasionally, but it's not always easy to know when. How bad should you feel? What kinds of symptoms need medical care? If your family doesn't have a doctor, how do you find one, especially in an emergency? And what should you expect if you have to go to a hospital?

Doctors and Patients

16-1 Serious Symptoms

When something goes wrong in your body, you usually get warning signs or symptoms. A symptom may be minor, such as the pain of a cut finger. You wash it, keep dirt out of the cut, and just let it heal. Symptoms that go on for a long time may mean that something serious is wrong.

Most people have an occasional pain such as a headache, stomachache, or muscle spasm. If the pain lasts, becomes worse, or

seems different from anything you have had before, you should discuss it with a doctor. Pain is one of the most important clues a doctor has in diagnosing an illness.

A fever is another sign of illness. The average body temperature of a healthy person is about 98.6°F (37°C). Some people have slightly higher or lower body temperatures. In addition, women's body temperatures rise when they ovulate. However, if your body temperature goes above 101°F (38.3°C), your body is probably fighting an infection. Many organisms that cause disease cannot reproduce at temperatures much above 98.6°F (37°C). For this reason, many doctors think that fever is one of the body's defenses against infection. A very high fever (over 103°F or 39.4°C) is a sign of a serious illness that needs a doctor's attention.

Severe or unusual bleeding is another warning sign. Blood from the stomach or the upper intestinal tract looks thick and black in the feces. Blood from the kidneys or bladder may turn urine any color from pale pink to dark brown. Severe or unusual bleeding should never be ignored. A doctor has to decide whether the reason is serious.

Anyone who loses a lot of weight and is not on a reducing diet may be sick. Significant weight loss without a decrease in appetite or change in diet means that the body is not using food properly.

A constantly tired feeling and shortness of breath can be caused by obesity and lack of physical activity. And if you suddenly exercise more than you are used to, of course you will get tired. Emotional problems can also cause tiredness. But if you eat right, get enough sleep, and still feel fatigued most of the time, you may be sick.

Other possible indicators of disease include a cough that lasts more than a few weeks, pain during urination or a change in the frequency and amount of urination, or constant and excessive thirst.

There is a big difference between being aware that disease is possible and being afraid of it. Some people worry a lot about illnesses and run to a doctor every time they have a symptom. Other people ignore symptoms and do not get medical help until they are seriously ill. The ideal attitude is to be alert to signs of illness without being constantly worried that you are getting sick. People who know about their bodies and recognize symptoms can usually decide

whether to see a doctor. They know the difference between minor pains and significant symptoms.

● 16-2 When Do You Call a Doctor?

Some people won't go to a doctor unless an emergency forces them to go or to be taken. Other people call or see a doctor for every minor ache or hint of illness. How do you decide if you need medical care?

PROCEDURE

On a separate piece of paper list the numbers 1–16. Then read each of the numbered physical changes or symptoms below. Next to the numbers on your paper, write "yes," "not yet," or "no" to indicate whether you would consult a doctor in each situation described.

1. You notice new acne sores.
2. You have an occasional headache.
3. You feel a burning sensation when you urinate.
4. You often have indigestion after a heavy meal or after eating certain foods.
5. A fingernail becomes dark shortly after you hit it with a hammer.
6. Your urine suddenly becomes much darker than usual.
7. *For women:* Your menstrual periods have been six to ten weeks apart for about a year.
8. *For women:* Your menstrual periods used to occur every four weeks but have stopped for two months.
9. Your nose bleeds without apparent cause.
10. You are tired during the day although you sleep eight to nine hours a night.
11. A large area around a cut becomes swollen and tender.
12. You develop sunburn blisters on your back and shoulders.
13. A cough, without a cold, persists for more than two weeks.
14. You have a cold and a fever of 100°F (37.8°C).
15. You notice a thick, whitish substance discharged from your urinary tract.
16. You notice blood in the toilet after a bowel movement.

DISCUSSION

1. Which symptoms are serious enough to require medical attention?

2. Which symptoms are no cause for alarm right now but deserve careful watching in case they persist or get worse?

3. How should you treat the minor symptoms that you feel don't require a doctor's care?

16-3 Who Needs a Checkup?

By now you know that you shouldn't be running to a doctor every time you feel a minor pain. That's a waste of everyone's time and your money. But sometimes you should go to a doctor when you aren't feeling any pain at all! It's a good idea to have regular checkups (also called "physicals" or "physical exams"). Often a doctor can help keep a person from becoming seriously ill. Or if the doctor finds out about a disease that is just getting started, he or she may be able to keep it from getting worse. Checkups are an important part of what's called **preventive medicine.** By practicing preventive medicine, doctors and other medical professionals try to prevent serious health problems from arising.

How often a person should see a doctor depends on age, general state of health, living conditions, and medical history. The kind of checkup a person gets also depends on those factors. Healthy people your age don't need a checkup every year, but you should be checked every few years and before you start any new, strenuous physical activity, such as taking up a new sport.

Infants and very young children also need preventive medical attention. Parents should know about their young children's

A waiting-room scene. A doctor can advise you and the members of your family on how often to come in for checkups.

diet needs and any special health problems. Immunizations against infectious diseases are necessary during the early years to help ensure a healthy start in life and to prevent more serious forms of diseases in adolescence and adulthood.

Pregnant women sometimes go to a family doctor, but more likely they are cared for by a specialist who watches over the health of the mother before and during birth. Regular prenatal (before birth) checkups are important for the health of the developing baby also.

Middle-aged and elderly people also require regular medical attention. Many diseases begin to show symptoms in middle age. A doctor can often advise patients on how to prevent symptoms from becoming worse.

16-4 Where Should You Go for Health Care?

Whether you have serious disease symptoms or want a checkup, you need a doctor. Many other health problems can be handled by other specially trained people, such as school nurses, psychologists, and physical therapists. Section 16-5 tells how to go about finding a personal or family doctor if you don't have one. Or you may prefer to see a doctor at a clinic or a hospital. Such visits may cost less than private office visits

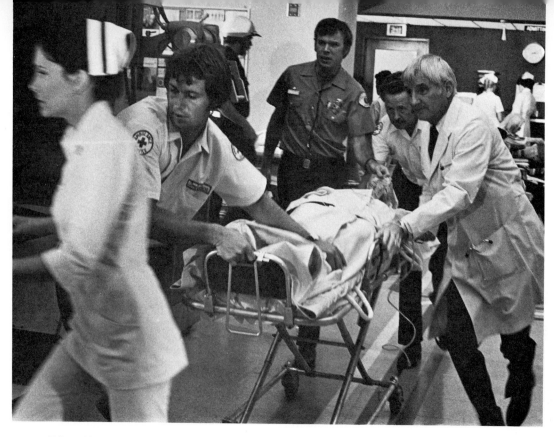

When life is slipping away, the medical team at an emergency ward really moves. It usually knows what to do and how to do it fast.

and usually don't require an appointment in advance.

Many hospitals have **outpatient departments** or **outpatient clinics** where you can walk in during clinic hours and get medical attention. (There may be a long wait, though.) There are also street clinics and free clinics in lots of cities. Some of them are supported by community groups such as the United Fund or United Way and religious organizations. Some clinics specialize in the medical care of pregnant women and newborn babies or other health areas. Some clinics may be free. Others adjust the cost according to ability to pay.

For possibly serious medical problems or situations that need prompt attention, many people are likely to go to the **emergency ward** of a hospital.

What would you see in an emergency ward? First, a sign-in desk where someone asks who you are, what's wrong, and who is going to pay the bill. Patients whose lives are in danger bypass this interview and are taken directly into the examination and treatment area.

Doctors, nurses, technicians, and orderlies staff the emergency ward. The staff has been trained to deal with everything from heart-attack victims to young children who have swallowed cleaning fluid or develop a skin rash after dinner. An emergency ward is like a miniature hospital. Equipment is available to administer electrical shock to a

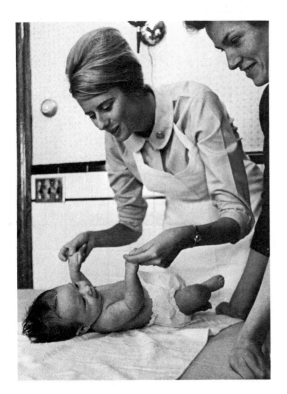

The Visiting Nurse Association brings medical care to people who can't easily get to a doctor.

stopped heart, X-ray a broken leg, give blood transfusions, and make quick analyses of body fluids and tissues. A patient may walk out of an emergency ward to recover at home, or be admitted into the hospital. A patient may need continuing care but may not need to be hospitalized. In that case the doctor may arrange for the Visiting Nurse Association to provide home care.

For other health needs there are many services available. Public health facilities are maintained by local communities, states or provinces, and the federal governments of the United States and Canada. Millions of North Americans get medical care at government-supported facilities. For example, blind, crippled, and mentally retarded peo-

ple may get help from local agencies. Some health departments offer crippled children mechanical devices and therapy for rehabilitation. Large school systems often include special classes and trained teachers for students with physical and emotional disabilities. Tutors may be available to go to the homes of students who cannot go to school.

Disease prevention and control are other important community health services. Local public health departments are responsible for enforcing sanitation laws to remove some causes of infectious diseases. If an epidemic is predicted, mass immunizations are offered. Vaccines are distributed to hospitals, public clinics, and schools. Free tests are offered to detect tuberculosis, high blood pressure, diabetes, and other diseases. Some communities send medically equipped vans throughout a city and suburbs so that more people can be tested.

16-5 How to Find a Doctor

It is useful to have a personal physician to answer your medical questions and to give you regular checkups. This doctor will know your medical history and may therefore be able to give you better treatment than other doctors, especially in an emergency.

If you and your family are new in a community or have not gone to a private doctor for a long time, it may require a large effort to find someone with whom you feel comfortable. A doctor recommended by a friend may not be suitable for you. Your needs may be different from your friend's. Or you may find that the doctor you would like to see is too busy to accept new patients. Then, too, there is such a confusing variety of specialists that the doctor who is right for one family may be wrong for another. The common medical specialties are listed in the table below.

Most adults choose a general or family practitioner or an internist as their regular doctor. These doctors can diagnose and treat many problems and send the patient to a specialist if necessary. Families may also look for a pediatrician for the children.

One good way to start looking for a doctor is to ask the advice of a doctor you already know. Doctors can often recommend doctors in other communities. Another reliable way is to check with an accredited hospital. (See Section 16-9 for a

Medical Specialties

DOCTOR	SPECIALTY AREA
general or family practitioner	medicine in general
internist	diagnosis and treatment of medical conditions of the whole body
obstetrician (ahb stuh TRIHSH uhn)	cares for pregnant women and delivers babies
pediatrician (pee dee uh TRIHSH uhn)	infants and children
surgeon (SUR juhn)	performs operations (may specialize in one part of the body)
gynecologist (gy nuh KAHL uh jihst)	female organs
urologist (yoo RAHL uh jihst)	male and female urinary systems and male genitals
orthopedist (awr thuh PEE dihst)	bones and joints
otolaryngologist (oh toh lar ihng GAHL uh jihst)	ears, throat, sinuses, nose
ophthalmologist (ahf thal MAHL uh jihst)	diseases of eyes (also performs surgery on eyes)
dermatologist (dur muh TAHL uh jihst)	skin, hair, and scalp (often specializes in venereal disease treatment as well)
allergist (AL uhr jihst)	hay fever, asthma, hives, allergies
psychiatrist (sih KY uh trihst)	mental illnesses, neuroses, behavior problems
neurologist (noo RAHL uh jihst)	nerves and the brain
gastroenterologist (gas troh ehn tuh RAHL uh jihst)	stomach and intestines
proctologist (prahk TAHL uh jihst)	colon, rectum, anus
radiologist (ray dee AHL uh jihst)	takes and interprets X rays; uses X rays and radioactive substances to treat diseases such as cancer
pathologist (pa THAHL uh jihst)	examines tissues and body fluids for diseases
anesthesiologist (an ihs thee zee AHL uh jihst)	administers anesthetics for surgery

discussion of what an accredited hospital is.) An inquiry at a local medical school may give you the names of doctors in your community who teach at the school. The county or state medical society will also provide names of doctors but will not recommend individual doctors.

After you have a list of qualified doctors, you and your family can make your own survey. It's best to do this before there is a serious medical problem. A member of your family should call or write the doctor and explain your medical needs. Ask about fees, office hours, house calls (few doctors make house calls), and what hospital the doctor sends patients to. If you have health insurance, make sure the doctor will participate in your insurance plan.

The doctor you select may practice alone or may be a member of a group. In one type of **group practice,** different specialists are available in one location. They may include an internist, an obstetrician, a pediatrician, a surgeon, and, often, a dentist. In a **partnership practice,** two or more family doctors or specialists may work together, arranging their schedules so that a doctor is always available for emergencies.

Don't expect your doctor to perform miracles. Like everyone else, doctors have limited abilities, don't know all the answers, and sometimes make mistakes. If your doctor treats you politely, answers your questions honestly, and generally inspires your trust, you are probably getting good medical care. If you don't think you are, change doctors.

If you live in a rural area, you may not have much of a choice of doctors. Many communities have no doctors at all. Doctors also are in short supply in the poor areas of many large cities. For many people, the family doctor is whoever is on duty in the emergency ward or outpatient clinic of the nearest hospital.

The staff of a general hospital is a community of different specialists.

16-6 **Having a Checkup**

This section will show you what goes on during a typical examination by a family or general practitioner, or an internist. Your checkups may be different. Individual doctors have individual techniques. Also, if you have a special symptom or problem, the doctor will concentrate on that. Special tests may be ordered. You may also have to go to another office for X rays or other examinations.

A doctor will perform most of the examination, but other medically trained men and women may record your medical record, perform tests, and make laboratory analyses that the doctor asks for.

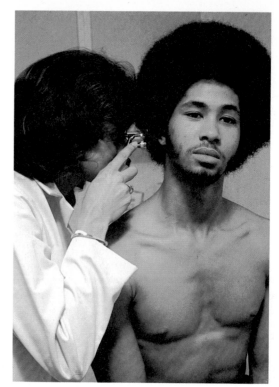

Interview Name? Age? Address? An interview begins with questions such as these and goes on to a discussion of your physical and emotional health. The doctor will ask about any previous illnesses you have had. He or she will also want to know about your family's health, to determine whether there are any possible inherited tendencies toward disease.

What do you eat? How long do you sleep? What are your bowel habits? Do you have any symptoms at all right now? While the doctor is asking such questions, you are being observed carefully. As you read earlier, the appearance of your skin, hair, nails, and teeth, and the way you sit, stand, and walk tell a trained observer a lot about your health.

Ear, Nose, Throat, Eyes A doctor uses an **otoscope** (OHT uh skohp) to look into your ear canal and check your eardrum. Your hearing may also be checked. When you open your mouth and say, "A-a-ah," the doctor is looking at your teeth, tongue, throat, and tonsils. Your eyes will be checked with an **ophthalmoscope** (ahf THAL muh skohp). With this instrument, a doctor can see the blood vessels in the retina, and the optic nerve. If you have an eye disease or vision problem, you will probably be referred to an ophthalmologist or another eye specialist, described in Section 16-7.

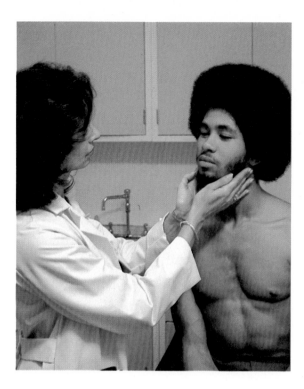

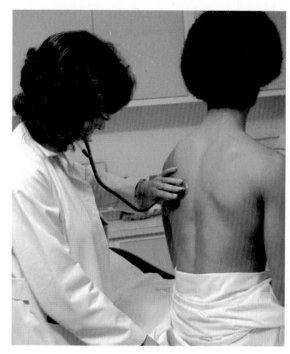

Lymph Nodes Lymph nodes are concentrated in the sides of the neck, behind the ears, in the inner parts of the knees and elbows, in the armpits, and in the groin. (The diagram on page 51 shows the lymphatic system.) Lymph nodes filter out disease-causing organisms from the lymph, and produce lymphocytes, which destroy harmful organisms in the body. If the lymph nodes are swollen or enlarged, it usually tells the doctor that the body is fighting an infection. While examining the lymph nodes in your neck, the doctor also checks the thyroid gland.

Lungs Healthy lungs produce certain sounds when a doctor taps your chest. Scarred or diseased lungs sound different. The doctor also checks your lung capacity by asking you to breathe deeply.

By listening to the lungs through a stethoscope, the doctor can hear any slight wheezing or other noises that may indicate a respiratory problem. The examination sometimes includes a special test of lung capacity, performed by having the patient blow steadily into a tube for as long as possible.

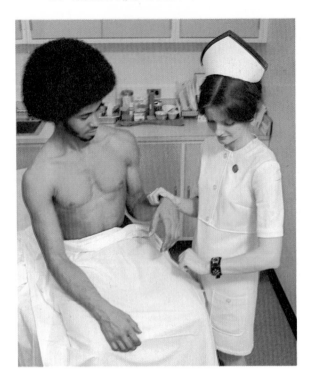

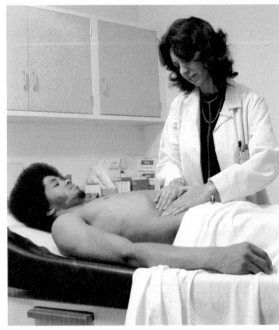

Heart By observing you breathe normally and seeing your chest rise and fall, a doctor gets information about your heart—the rhythm and rate of the heartbeat, and any abnormality in heart size. By placing his or her hands over your heart, a doctor feels the way it beats. Tapping the chest produces sounds that tell still more about the size and location of the heart. A stethoscope magnifies the normal sounds of the heartbeat, as the valves open and close, and any abnormal sounds, such as a heart murmur.

A doctor or nurse will check your pulse while you are quiet and relaxed. You may be asked to run in place for a minute or two and then have your pulse checked again. The doctor may check the time it takes your pulse to return to its resting rate. Your overall physical condition significantly affects these pulse rates and the time needed for the pulse rate to return to normal after you exert yourself.

Abdomen, Genitals, Rectum The position, size, and general condition of several abdominal organs can be felt in all but extremely fat patients. It is important to relax for this part of the examination. A doctor cannot precisely feel the organs through tight muscles. The examination of the abdomen also informs the doctor of any unusual mass or other abnormality. The doctor may ask you to stand up and cough, to determine if you have a hernia.

The male genitals are examined visually and by gentle manipulation. In examining the female genitals, the doctor uses gloved fingers, as well as a **speculum** (SPEHK yuh luhm). This is a cylindrical instrument that is inserted into the vagina, and holds the walls apart. The doctor then can see the cervix, or narrow, lower end of the uterus.

By inserting a gloved finger, the doctor examines the rectum. In this way, he or she can detect irregularities or growths, the condition of nearby glands and organs, and the presence of hemorrhoids (HEHM uh roydz), masses of swollen veins in tissues of the anus.

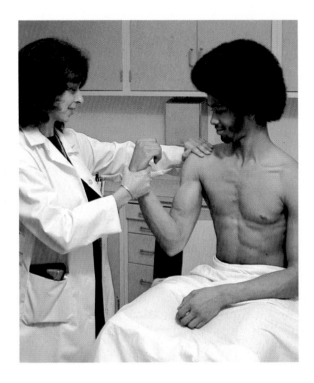

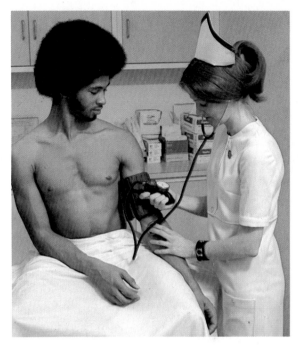

Bones, Joints, Muscles A doctor will examine you while you are lying down and again when you stand up, to determine your muscle tone and the general condition of your bones and joints. You may be asked to flex your arms and legs, rise on your toes, bend at the waist, and perform other movements. By observing you and testing your strength, a doctor will learn a lot about your muscular and skeletal systems. Your height and weight will also be checked and any weight problem noted.

Blood Pressure When the left ventricle of the heart contracts, it pumps blood through the arteries under strong pressure. When the ventricle relaxes, the pressure drops. Each of these blood pressure levels is measured: the **systolic** (sihs TAHL ihk) pressure when the heart contracts, and the **diastolic** (dy uh STAHL ihk) pressure when it relaxes.

The device used to measure blood pressure is, unfortunately, called a **sphygmomanometer** (sfihg moh muh NAHM uh tuhr). A rubber cuff is wrapped around the upper arm. Air is pumped into the cuff to tighten it until it collapses the arteries, and a pulse can no longer be heard with a stethoscope. The systolic pressure isn't great enough to force blood through. Air is slowly released from the cuff until the doctor or nurse can hear the pulse return. At that moment the systolic blood pressure is read on the sphygmomanometer. More air is released from the cuff until even the diastolic pressure forces blood through the squeezed arteries. The diastolic blood pressure is then read. Extremely high or low blood pressure is a danger signal.

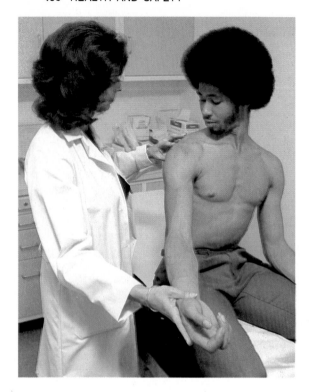

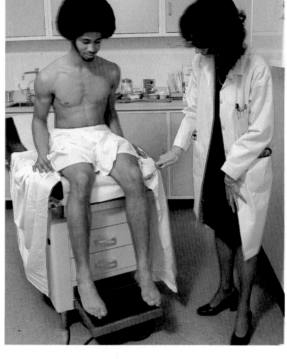

Skin A checkup begins the moment you walk into a doctor's office. The doctor can recognize the symptoms of many diseases of the skin, as well as signs of internal illness that show up on the skin. Whether you are eating right, whether you get enough rest, how clean you are, and even the state of your feelings affect the condition of your skin. The doctor will examine your skin further, particularly if you have acne, a skin rash, or any sign of allergy.

Nervous System A few basic tests can tell a doctor whether the nervous system is in good condition. The most familiar of these is a test of the knee-jerk reflex, performed by tapping lightly with a rubber hammer just below the kneecap. Tests of vision and hearing may be performed separately but they are also part of the observation of the nervous system. A doctor might, for example, test hearing with a tuning fork. The doctor uses observations of reflexes, the condition of the senses, and how the patient moves and responds to questions to make a judgment of the nervous system.

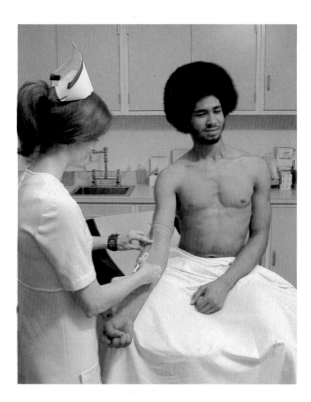

Laboratory Tests Examination of the urine (urinalysis) and of the blood are the tests most commonly associated with a checkup. Sugar, protein, or blood in the urine are symptoms of disease. The red and white cell count of the blood is checked. A doctor may also want to know the sedimentation (sehd uh muhn TAY shuhn) rate of the blood—that is, the time it takes all the solid components of blood to sink, leaving the plasma at the top. The sedimentation rate gives a clue to the possible presence of disease.

An enormous range of other tests is available if the doctor thinks they are necessary. For an individual in good health, they are rarely necessary. The basic urine and blood tests and X rays of the chest generally complete a routine physical examination.

Expect to answer many questions during a complete physical checkup. Some questions may be embarrassing but should still be answered. Other questions may seem unimportant. For example, why does anyone want to know if your grandparents are alive, if they have any illnesses, or what was the cause of their deaths? The answers to these questions might tell a doctor whether there are certain diseases that run in your family. Other questions you will be asked will also help the doctor evaluate your health.

16-7 Getting Your Eyes Checked

Several health specialists take care of eye ailments. An **ophthalmologist,** or oculist (AHK yuh lihst), is a medical doctor who specializes in vision defects and eye diseases. He or she decides if glasses are necessary, prescribes proper corrective lenses, treats eye diseases, and also performs eye surgery.

You read about some vision problems such as being nearsighted or farsighted in Chapter 4. An **optometrist** (ahp TAHM uh trihst) is not a medical doctor, but specializes in correcting such vision defects by means of glasses and eye exercises. An optometrist refers patients to an ophthalmologist for medical treatment or surgery when necessary. An **optician** (ahp TIHSH uhn) specializes in grinding lenses and fitting glasses. Opticians fill prescriptions written by either an ophthalmologist or an optometrist.

Glaucoma and cataracts are two serious threats to the vision of adults. Together, they cause nearly 30 percent of all cases of blindness in the United States.

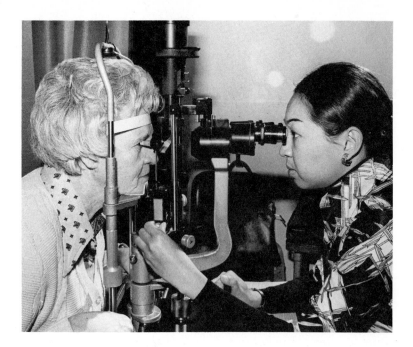

Getting tested for glaucoma.

Glaucoma (glaw KOH muh) results from an abnormal accumulation of fluid in the eye. The high pressure caused by the fluid impairs vision. Glaucoma may strike suddenly, dimming the vision and making the person feel quite ill. Another type of glaucoma develops so slowly that the victim frequently is unaware of any disorder until vision is seriously affected. The pressure inside the eye can be measured simply and painlessly by an ophthalmologist. Ophthalmologists recommend that every person over the age of 40 receive a periodic test for glaucoma.

Cataracts are cloudy areas that develop in the lens of the eye. When they grow large enough, they interfere with vision. Nearly all cataracts can be removed surgically. Afterwards, the individual's vision can be restored to a near-normal condition with glasses. Cataracts usually affect only older people, but they have been known to develop in children.

Many eye ailments can be diagnosed before they become serious. But even a person who has lost his or her sight should periodically review the condition with a doctor. New advances in medicine have been able to help people who would have been considered beyond help only ten years ago.

● 16-8 Investigating Body Temperature

People are warm-blooded creatures. The body has to maintain its temperature at a relatively constant level to stay alive. When you are overheated, you perspire heavily, and the blood carries excess heat to the body surface. In cold weather, perspiration decreases and the surface blood vessels narrow, which helps retain body heat. Temperature readings are an important indication of the state of a person's health. In many medical emergencies it is important to know whether the patient's temperature is much below normal or much above normal.

In this investigation you are going to practice reading a fever thermometer and take your internal and external temperatures.

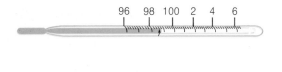

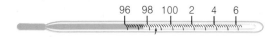

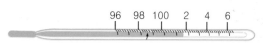

Which thermometers show 97.4°, 101.5°, and 98.6°?

MATERIALS

clean water   fever thermometer
rubbing alcohol or   watch (or wall clock)
   other antiseptic

PROCEDURE FOR READING FEVER THERMOMETER

1. The lowest marking on the fever thermometer is probably 94°F (34.4°C). After your teacher demonstrates the procedure, shake the thermometer vigorously, with the mercury bulb down, until the mercury reads no higher than 94°F (34.4°C). Try to keep your fingers off the bulb. Avoid people and furniture while shaking the thermometer.

2. To read the thermometer, hold it by the stem, not the bulb, in your right hand. The degree markings should be on the upper side and the numbers on the lower side. Keep turning the thermometer until the mercury column is plainly seen. Standing with your back to the light will help. The mercury level may not be exactly opposite a degree mark on the thermometer. In that case, you have to estimate the temperature to the nearest tenth of a degree.

PROCEDURE FOR TAKING TEMPERATURES

1. Copy the table below.

2. Before each person takes his or her temperatures, sterilize the thermometer in alcohol or another antiseptic and rinse it in

NAME	IN MOUTH UNDER TONGUE	IN MOUTH OVER TONGUE	IN CLOSED FIST	IN BENT ELBOW	UNDER TONGUE AFTER RUNNING IN PLACE FOR 2 MINUTES
	Copy This Table on a Piece of Paper				

clean water. Never put a thermometer in hot water.

3. Shake the mercury down to 94°F (34.4°C) before taking your temperature at each location. Leave the thermometer in place for three full minutes before reading your temperature.

4. Take your temperature at each of the locations listed in the table and record your results in the table. Hold the thermometer tightly but try not to break it. Take all temperatures only while sitting down.
CAUTION! Do not run with a thermometer in your mouth.

DISCUSSION

1. At which location of the body do temperatures vary the least between people in the class?

2. Normal body temperature is said to be 98.6°F (37°C). How many people in the class have exactly that temperature? At what locations of the body? How do you think that 98.6°F (37°C) was decided upon for normal body temperature?

3. Why do you think temperatures are most often taken with the thermometer under the tongue?

4. Using everyone's results taken under the tongue, calculate the girls' average temperature and the boys' average temperature for the class. Are there temperature differences between boys and girls?

5. Body temperature doesn't remain constant throughout the day. You might want to take your temperature under the tongue every hour for a day and report your results to your class.

SELF CHECK

1. What are four symptoms of possibly serious disease?

2. How often do you need a medical checkup?

3. What does a doctor examine during a typical checkup?

4. How would you go about finding a family doctor in a town you just moved to?

Hospitalization

16-9 Choosing a Hospital

If you have to go to a hospital, you may have a choice of two or more. Your doctor will be able to advise you, but the final decision is yours as to where you want to be hospitalized. In fact, your doctor may not treat patients at the hospital that you espe-cially want to go to. In that case, you may have to consider changing doctors.

Most of the hospitals in the United States and Canada are accredited. To be accredited, a hospital has to meet certain standards in the way it is run and delivers health care. Special agencies inspect hospitals to see whether they deserve being accredited. It's easy to find out whether a hospital you are thinking of being admitted to is accredited. Ask the hospital administrator or see if a certificate of accreditation is hanging in the lobby. The quality of medical care varies from one accredited hospital to another, but it is generally far better than the care you would get at a hospital that is not accredited. You should avoid the unaccredited hospitals.

There are many different kinds of hospitals. **General hospitals** take care of all types of illness, accidents, and surgery. **Specialized hospitals** are limited to one type of medical problem, such as tuberculosis, mental illness, cancer, maternity, or children's diseases. Large **medical centers** have specialized hospitals grouped near a general hospital.

Government hospitals, such as those operated by the Veterans' Administration, are staffed and financed by the federal government. Many large **city** or **county hospitals** are supported by municipal governments.

Some of these types of hospitals are open to people who cannot pay for hospitalization. Some of them treat only special groups such as veterans or government employees.

Your doctor may be associated with two or more accredited hospitals. In that case, you and your family should discuss with the doctor which hospital is the most convenient and which one has the best facilities and has the highest standards of medical care.

16-10 Having an Operation

If a patient is lucky, a physical problem is discovered during a routine examination, before the problem becomes an emergency. The doctor can then arrange for treatment. That is what happened in the imaginary case history described here.

When Ted Kerr went to his family doctor for his pre-football-season physical, the doctor heard in his chest something different from a healthy heart sound. She recognized the meaning of the sound and sent Ted to the cardiac clinic of a large hospital for tests and diagnosis.

Ted had two **electrocardiograms** (ih lehk troh KAHR dee uh gramz), pictures of the electrical activity of his heart. One was taken while he lay quietly on the examining table. The second was taken while he walked faster and faster on a treadmill. The purpose of the second electrocardiogram (EKG) was to find out how his heart behaved under stress. Then, Ted's heart was X-rayed to determine its position in his chest and its size. Finally, a thin tube was inserted into a vein in his arm, threaded to his heart, and pressure in the vessels recorded at various points. This study confirmed what his doctor had originally thought.

A portion of Ted's aorta, just above the heart, was narrowed as shown on page 442. The condition had to be corrected surgically. Otherwise, Ted might suffer a sudden, fatal bursting of the aorta. Or he would develop high blood pressure that could result in a stroke, perhaps when he was only in his twenties.

Ted was admitted to the hospital. He brought toilet articles, pajamas, slippers, a robe, and a few magazines with him. Since he felt well, he answered the admitting clerk's questions himself and walked to his room, where there was one other patient. A nurse showed him his table, chest of drawers, closet, and a buzzer to press if he needed help. Ted also explored the lounge on his floor and learned about the hospital's circulating library. His parents were told about visiting hours and were shown where they could wait for word from the surgeon after the operation.

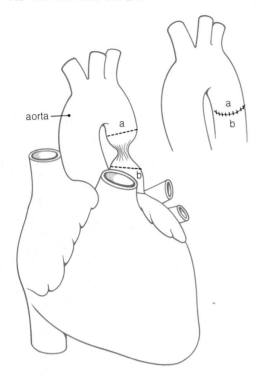

The narrow part of the aorta between *a* and *b* has to be removed and the ends sewn together.

For several days, Ted was prepared physically and mentally for the operation. His blood was tested for type and clotting ability. His doctors made sure that he did not have any infection. That would be a reason to delay the surgery. A detailed medical history was recorded to rule out any other condition that might change or delay the operation. For several days Ted's blood pressure, pulse rate, respiration, and temperature were checked. Except for the narrowing in his artery, he was in good physical condition.

Ted's surgeon visited him to discuss the operation in detail. He explained not only the procedure itself but what Ted should expect when he woke up. The night before the operation, the anesthesiologist also visited Ted, to examine him and to discuss exactly what he would do the next day.

When Ted was wheeled into the **operating room,** he was feeling relaxed from the medication he had received that morning. He saw a team of doctors, nurses, and technicians. Within three seconds after the anesthetic was injected into his arm, he was asleep.

During the four-hour procedure, the anesthesiologist constantly checked Ted's pulse, blood pressure, and respiration. A general surgeon opened his chest, then the cardiac surgeon took over. He cut away the narrowed area of the aorta and then sewed together the two normal ends. While this was going on, other specialists connected a heart-lung machine to a major artery and vein. This machine took over the heart's pumping action for Ted. His heartbeat was stopped while the doctor worked on the aorta.

When the surgery was finished, the heart-lung machine was disconnected. Ted's normal heartbeat was restored. The cut chest muscles were sewn back together. The stitches would later be absorbed into his body. Finally, the skin was sewed up. The outside stitches would be removed within a few days. Ted was wheeled into the **recovery room,** still unconscious.

To help him through the difficult postoperative period, a needle was inserted into a vein of his arm. He would receive liquid nourishment for several days from a bottle connected by a tube to this needle. Ted's blood pressure and pulse were constantly checked to see whether normal blood pressure was being maintained.

When his doctors were certain that his condition was stable, Ted was taken back to his own room. In about 24 hours most of the effects of the anesthetic had worn off. Ted felt weak and his chest hurt, but medications relieved the pain.

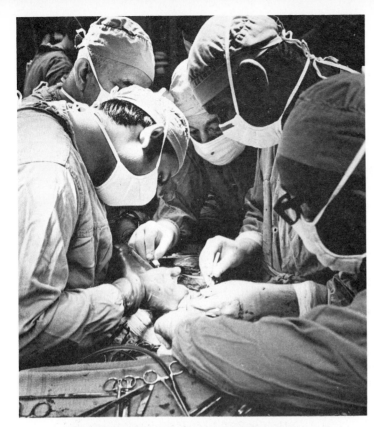

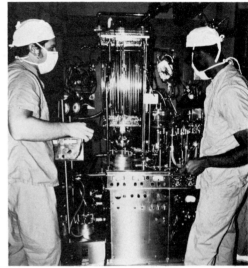

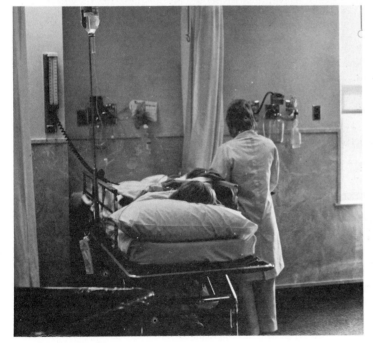

It takes knowledge, skill, teamwork, and complex equipment to perform major surgery. *Top left:* Surgeons operating inside the chest. *Top right:* A heart-lung machine supplies oxygen to the patient's blood and circulates it throughout the body. *Left:* In the recovery room, the patient's condition is constantly checked to see how well he is recovering from the operation.

Ted's doctors checked him every day. The nurses constantly checked his body functions to make sure that he was recovering normally.

The second morning after the operation, he was helped to sit up in bed. The next day, his nurses helped him stand beside the bed and take a few steps in his room. In a week, with help, he began to walk slowly for a short distance. Getting out of bed as soon as possible helps surgical patients recover faster. It also helps prevent blood clots.

Three weeks after he was admitted to the hospital, Ted was home again. He stayed in his room for a week, then gradually became more active. He was first allowed to walk up and down stairs, and later to go outdoors. Two months after his doctor had first heard the peculiar heart sounds, Ted was back in school. His circulation and blood pressure were normal. He could now participate in sports. He could lead a normal life.

16-11 Patients' Rights

Hospitals exist to provide expert medical care. But millions of people admitted to hospitals every year are not completely satisfied with the care they get. Many people feel that hospitals are impersonal. They feel they are sometimes treated as objects instead of people. Patients complain that hospitals are organized and operated for the convenience of the medical staff. They worry about having errors in their treatment caused by unqualified or overworked employees. Patients become furious at having to wait a long time for doctors and nurses to come. Another common complaint is that patients often can't seem to get their questions answered.

Consumer organizations today claim that hospital patients have legal rights and legitimate interests. The rights include the following items.

Patients are entitled to:

have their questions answered concerning their condition and treatment.

participate in decisions involving their health care.

be told whether research or experimental procedures are being used on them.

be insured of privacy regarding their condition, treatment, and their ability to pay.

have access to their medical records and X rays.

be free to leave the hospital against medical advice.

be free to refuse any drug or test.

have their questions answered concerning the identity and qualifications of anyone involved in their care.

Since you may feel uncomfortable, anxious, and bored during a hospital stay, you can easily become overly critical of the services you receive. Try to be objective and understand that other peoples' needs must be met as well as your own. Then if you still feel that the service is poor, complain to someone in charge and try to get things changed.

Self Check

1. What factors should you discuss with your doctor in choosing a hospital if you need an operation?

2. If you had to be operated on to reset a broken bone, what procedures would probably be followed at the hospital?

3. What does a doctor or nurse check after an operation to make sure that the patient is recovering properly?

4. What are some important patients' rights during a hospital stay?

Health Frontier

Paying Medical Bills

Everybody talks about the high cost of medical care, and some people are trying to do something about it. High costs result because hospitals use expensive equipment and employ highly paid professionals. Some hospitals may have more employees than patients. But medical care costs have been rising at about twice the rate that the cost of living has been rising.

Health economists are looking for ways to hold down the rise in hospital costs. One way is to organize certain hospitals in a community as centers for specialized treatment. This practice is more economical than having each hospital purchase all the same modern and expensive equipment. There are other, less complicated ways to hold down costs. But sometimes the quality of the care goes down, as for example, when the nursing staff is cut back.

Insurance is used by most people to help pay hospital charges. They buy insurance that pays part of their hospital bills and doctors' fees. People may also belong to a pre-payment plan, sometimes called a Health Maintenance Organization. So long as they get their health care at the organization's medical facilities or from organization doctors, they have all their medical expenses paid for, regardless of how much they are.

Health insurance is expensive. Changes in insurance plans may help reduce costs. For example, certain tests and medical treatments performed outside a hospital are only partially covered by insurance. In a hospital, they are usually totally covered. So, many patients ask their doctors to hospitalize them to have the tests or treatment done "free." That of course greatly adds to the overall costs the insurance company is paying for. The companies then raise their insurance rates. Insurance coverage for more outpatient services, already announced by some insurance companies, would cut costs.

The United States government already pays for much of the medical care for older people through the Medicare program. It seems likely that during the next few years the government will offer a national health insurance program. Such a program would not be free, but would be paid for by taxes.

Since hospitals cost so much ($200 a day and more for a bed in a semi-private room in some cities), there is a trend to provide more care without hospitalizing patients. Minor surgery is performed in some local walk-in surgical centers. The centers are equipped to perform surgery too demanding for a doctor's office but not so major as to require hospitalization. Procedures may include simple ear, eye, or hand surgery, removal of tonsils and adenoids, and skin grafts. Patients do not stay in the centers overnight.

Chapter Summary

Anyone who experiences serious symptoms of illness or notices a long-lasting physical or emotional change should see a doctor. Healthy high school students should get physical checkups, but not every year. Infants and young children, pregnant women, people who have chronic illnesses, and middle-aged and elderly persons should have checkups regularly. Don't ignore serious symptoms or regard every minor pain with alarm.

Sources of health care include facilities supported by governments at all levels, in addition to private doctors. Many private organizations and hospital clinics also offer special medical attention and assistance. A family that wants its own private doctor should look for a family physician or internist. People should choose their family doctors carefully and question the doctor openly about all matters of concern, including fees and the hospitals the doctor sends patients to.

A complete physical checkup includes an interview and an examination of all the body systems and major organs. The doctor can decide after such a checkup whether additional tests are needed. The doctor may find a health problem that so far has not given the patient noticeable symptoms. Early diagnosis made during a checkup may save a patient's life or protect him or her from a long illness. Eye examinations by ophthalmologists or optometrists can lead to the correction of vision problems and the prevention or control of serious eye diseases.

A family may need to choose a hospital. Important factors to consider in making the choice are whether the hospital is accredited and whether it has the best staff and facilities for the medical problem that needs to be treated. Doctors attend patients only in certain hospitals, so the choice of doctor may limit choices of hospitals.

High medical costs make it necessary for families to examine carefully the various insurance and pre-payment plans for paying their medical bills.

Chapter Self Check

1. If your temperature is 103°F (39.4°C), should you take a couple of aspirins and go to bed or call a doctor?

2. What should you do if you notice blood in your bowel movements or urine?

3. What people should get regular medical checkups?

4. What is preventive medicine?

5. Where can you go to see a doctor in a medical emergency if you don't have a personal physician or if your doctor is unavailable?

6. Name six different medical specialties.

7. What health services does the government provide?

8. What questions should you ask a doctor when you are looking for a family physician?

9. What are some of the instruments a doctor uses to conduct a checkup?

10. What serious diseases can an eye exam detect?

11. What is an accredited hospital?

12. Why might you want to be admitted to one hospital rather than to another if you needed an operation?

13. What is the medical specialist who gives patients anesthetics before and sometimes during an operation?

14. What things should a person who needs an operation bring to the hospital?

15. Why are patients put in recovery rooms after operations?

16. Should you always follow all the orders of the medical staff at a hospital you are in?

17. What point is there in discussing an operation and post-operative care with a doctor when you don't know much about surgery?

18. What can you do to keep your medical expenses down?

Read More About It

Annas, George J. *The Rights of Hospital Patients* (An American Civil Liberties Union Handbook). New York: Avon Books, 1975. A guidebook to the consumer of hospital services. Encourages patients to understand and exercise their rights.

Crichton, Michael. *Five Patients: The Hospital Explained.* New York: Alfred A. Knopf, Inc., 1970. A description of what happened to five patients.

Miller, Benjamin F. and Galton, Lawrence. *The Family Book of Preventive Medicine.* New York: Simon and Schuster, 1971. How everyone can practice preventive medicine in everyday life. Also discusses prevention of emotional and family difficulties.

Nolen, William A. *A Surgeon Under the Knife.* New York: Coward, McCann & Geoghegan, Inc., 1976. A doctor undergoes extensive, difficult surgery. A frank account that includes mistakes made by medical personnel and the importance of a patient's participating in his or her hospital care.

Ribicoff, Abraham (with Paul Danaceau). *The American Medical Machine.* New York: Harper & Row, 1973. A patient-oriented book about the problems of Americans in getting high-quality medical care that they can afford.

The Medicine Show, Revised Edition. The editors of Consumer Reports. New York: Pantheon Books, Inc., 1974. Facts about the effectiveness and safety of home-use health-care products. Advice on the choice of a family doctor, judging a hospital, and the use of antibiotics.

Young, James Harvey. *The Medical Messiahs; A Social History of Health Quakery in Twentieth-Century America.* Princeton University Press, 1968. Discusses quacks, health frauds, self-medication, and government regulatory agencies.

Appendix A   CALORIE TABLE

FOOD	AMOUNT	APPROXIMATE CALORIES
Beverages		
Beer, lager,		
American	1 bottle	170
Chocolate milk	1 glass	185
Coffee, black, without		
sugar	1 cup	0
Cola or root beer	1 glass	100
diet	1 glass	1–10
Tea, prepared iced,		
with sugar	1 glass	60
Breads, Cereals,		
and Pasta		
Bread, white	1 slice	65
whole wheat	1 slice	55
Cereal, cornflakes,		
plain	1 cup	80
sugar-coated	1 cup	145
Oatmeal, cooked	1 cup	135
Crackers, saltines	2	25
Danish pastry	1 small	140
Doughnut, plain	1 medium	130
Grits, corn	1 cup	125
Pancakes	1 medium	65
Macaroni with		
cheese	1 cup	400
Pizza, with cheese	1 medium	
and tomato	slice	200
Spaghetti, plain	1 cup	150
with meat sauce	1 cup	260
Rice, white, cooked	1 cup	180
Roll, white	1 medium	120
Dairy Products		
Cheese, processed,		
American	1 slice	100
cottage	$\frac{1}{2}$ cup	100
cream	1 tablespoon	105
Cream, heavy	1 tbsp.	50
Egg, boiled	1	80
fried or scrambled	1	110
Milk, buttermilk	1 glass	85
skimmed	1 glass	90
whole	1 glass	160
Yogurt, plain	1 cup	125
Desserts		
Brownie, chocolate	1 small	140

FOOD	AMOUNT	APPROXIMATE CALORIES
Desserts (cont.)		
Cake,		
chocolate layer	1 small slice	350
sponge	1 small slice	115
Custard	1 custard	
	cup	150
Gelatin, any flavor	$\frac{1}{2}$ cup	85
Ice cream, vanilla	$\frac{1}{2}$ cup	165
Ice milk, vanilla	$\frac{1}{2}$ cup	135
Pie, apple	$\frac{1}{6}$ of pie	350
lemon meringue	$\frac{1}{6}$ of pie	280
Pudding, vanilla	$\frac{1}{2}$ cup	140
Sherbet, fruit	$\frac{1}{2}$ cup	145
Fish		
Fish sticks, breaded	5	200
Haddock, broiled	1 medium	
	serving	160
Mackerel, broiled	1 medium	
	serving	190
Sardines, canned,		
in oil	6	175
Tuna, canned		
oil-packed	$\frac{1}{2}$ cup	170
water-packed	$\frac{1}{2}$ cup	125
Fruits		
Apple, raw	1 medium	80
Applesauce, canned		
sweetened	$\frac{1}{2}$ cup	95
unsweetened	$\frac{1}{2}$ cup	50
Apricots, canned		
in syrup	4 halves	95
Banana	1 medium	85
Cantaloupe	$\frac{1}{2}$ medium	35
Cherries, canned,		
in syrup	$\frac{1}{2}$ cup	105
fresh, sweet	15 large	60
Grapefruit, fresh	$\frac{1}{2}$ medium	55
Oranges, fresh	1 medium	70
Peaches, fresh	1 medium	45
canned, in syrup	2 halves	70
Plums, fresh	1 medium	35
Raisins	$\frac{1}{2}$ cup	215
Watermelon	$\frac{1}{2}$ slice	45
Juices		
Apple, or cider	$\frac{1}{2}$ cup	65
Grapefruit, un-		
sweetened	$\frac{1}{2}$ cup	50

FOOD	AMOUNT	APPROXIMATE CALORIES
Juices (cont.)		
Orange juice, fresh	½ cup	60
frozen, diluted	½ cup	55
Tomato, canned	½ cup	25
Meats and Poultry		
Bacon, fried	2 strips	100
Beef, liver, broiled	1 small slice	221
patty, lean	1 small	180
pot roast	1 small slice	95
roasted, lean	1 small slice	180
steak, sirloin	1 small piece	330
Bologna	2 slices, small	80
Chicken, fried, leg and thigh	1	210
Ham, baked	1 small slice	250
Lamb, chop, broiled	1 thick	140
roasted, leg	2 slices	230
Pork, chop, broiled	1 thick	200
sausage	1 patty	270
Turkey	2 slices	160
Relishes		
Catsup or chili sauce	1 tbsp.	18
Mustard	1 tbsp.	10
Pickles, dill	1 medium	10
Relish, sweet	1 tbsp.	20
Sandwiches (on 2 slices white bread)		
Bacon, lettuce, and tomato	1	350
Grilled cheese	1	230
Ham, sliced	1	390
Hamburger, on bun	1	300
Hot dog, on bun	1	250
Peanut butter and jelly	1	285
Tuna salad	1	405
Sauces and Dressings		
Brown gravy	½ cup	60
Cheese sauce	½ cup	180
Chocolate fudge sauce	1 tbsp.	125
French dressing	1 tbsp.	65
Mayonnaise	1 tbsp.	100
Oil, corn or salad	1 tbsp.	125
Soy sauce	1 tbsp.	6

FOOD	AMOUNT	APPROXIMATE CALORIES
Snacks		
Candy, bar, milk chocolate	1 medium	150
hard, fruit flavored	1 piece	20
Popcorn, buttered	1 cup	100
Potato chips	10 medium	115
Salted peanuts	½ cup	420
Soups		
Beef broth, instant	1 cube	5
consomme	1 cup	30
Chicken noodle	1 cup	65
Cream of tomato	1 cup	145
Split pea	1 cup	145
Vegetable-beef	1 cup	75
Spreads		
Butter	1 tbsp.	100
Honey	1 tbsp.	65
Jam or jelly	1 tbsp.	55
Margarine	1 tbsp.	100
Vegetables		
Asparagus	6–7 stalks	20
Beans, green,	½ cup	20
baked, canned	½ cup	140
sprouts	½ cup	10
Beets	½ cup	35
Broccoli	1 large stalk	30
Cabbage, cooked	½ cup	20
Carrots, cooked	½ cup	25
Celery, raw	1 large stalk	5
Corn, fresh	1 ear	70
Cucumber	½ medium	5
Eggplant, fried	2 slices	25
Lettuce	3 leaves	5
Okra, cooked	10 pods	11
Onions, cooked	3 small	10
Peas, green, cooked	½ cup	55
black-eyed	½ cup	90
Pepper, green, sweet	1 medium	15
Potato, sweet or yams, baked	1 medium	155
white, baked	1 medium	100
French fried	5 pieces	80
salad	½ cup	200
Spinach, cooked	½ cup	25
Tomatoes, canned or cooked	½ cup	25
raw	1 medium	30

Appendix B FIRST-AID SUPPLIES

Keep all first-aid equipment and medicines in one place where you can get to them easily and quickly. At home, keep them in an unlocked container or cabinet or on a separate shelf of the kitchen or bathroom. In a car, they should be stored in a closed, unlocked container. When you go camping, keep first-aid supplies with you in your tent or cabin. Observe the following additional precautions:

1. Keep all medicines and sharp instruments out of the reach of children.
2. Label all medicines, indicating what they are, what they are to be used for, and how much to use.
3. Ask a druggist or doctor how long medicines may be kept. Date them, and replace them before they go bad or lose their strength.

In the Home

SUPPLIES
Absorbent cotton, sterile
Adhesive-strip bandages, assorted sizes
Adhesive tape, roll, $\frac{1}{2}$" wide (about one centimeter wide)
Alcohol, rubbing
Antiseptic
Aromatic spirits of ammonia, for faintness
Cotton-tipped applicators
Elastic bandage for wrist or ankle
Fever thermometer
Flashlight
Gauze bandage, roll, 1" wide (about three centimeters wide)
Gauze pads, sterile, 2" × 2" (about five centimeters square)
Hot-water bag or bottle and ice bag
Needles, to remove splinters
Safety matches
Safety pins
Sharp scissors
Tweezers

MEDICINES
Aspirin or substitute (stays good for about two years)
Ipecac, syrup of, to induce vomiting (stays good about two years)

Lotion for relief of itching (stays good about two years)
Ointment for insect bites

Optional: bath towels or sheets for large dressings; tourniquet; eye drops and nose drops; antibiotic, as prescribed by a physician, if you live where medical care is not available.

In the Car

SUPPLIES
Adhesive-strip bandages, assorted sizes
Adhesive tape, $\frac{1}{2}$" wide (about one centimeter wide)
Antiseptic
Flashlight
Gauze bandage, roll, 1" wide (about three centimeters wide)
Gauze pads, sterile, 2" × 2" (about five centimeters square)
Matches
Needle and tweezers for splinters
Sharp scissors
Toilet soap
Tongue depressors, for splints

MEDICINES
Aspirin or substitute
Ointment for insect bites

Optional: airway for resuscitation; medication for motion sickness if a member of the family needs it; antibiotic, as prescribed by a physician.

On a Camping Trip

First-aid equipment ordinarily carried in a car should be available, with these extras:

Insect repellent
Snakebite kit, consisting of suction cups, a small, sharp knife, and a medicated ointment
Sunburn lotion
Throat lozenges
Water purification tablets

Appendix C CHOOSING AN OCCUPATION

Have you decided what you want to do when you finish school? Some people decide when they are very young, but many high school students have only a general idea or no idea at all about the occupations they will choose.

It is useful to have an organized way of thinking about occupations that you might want to take up. This activity will deal with ways of investigating health-related occupations. The procedures you will learn can be used when considering any other kind of occupation as well.

WHAT INTERESTS YOU?

One way to start thinking about a possible future job is to determine what interests you. Make a table like the one below on a separate piece of paper.

List in the first column of your table specific subjects or activities that interest you. Some may be school subjects such as biology or bookkeeping. Others may be hobbies or activities. You may include items you know little about if they sound fascinating to you. Here are some ideas to get you started:

art	music
business	computers
electronics	crafts
journalism	history
medical research	plumbing
cooking	stenography
driving	working with tools
sports	teaching

WHAT ARE YOUR WORK PREFERENCES?

In the second column of your table, write the following kinds of work and working conditions that you prefer most of the time:

Work	*Working Conditions*
working as part of a team	sitting down
working alone	moving around
working in quiet surroundings	being indoors
working with a lot going on	being outdoors
doing routine duties	helping others
doing tasks that vary	having individuals depend on me
working with my hands	having responsibility
solving problems	following directions
directing my own activities	organizing my own work
putting things in order	speaking to audiences
working with machines or tools	writing
working under pressure	
working slowly and methodically	

You may want to add other preferences not on the list.

Now you have some ideas to start with. Next, you will match up your personal interests and work preferences with some actual occupations.

POSSIBLE OCCUPATIONS

PERSONAL INTERESTS	WORK PREFERENCES	JOB TITLES THAT INTEREST ME	QUESTIONS ABOUT JOBS

Copy This Table on a Piece of Paper

CAREERS IN HEALTH

In the Health-Related Occupations chart at the end of this appendix you see some interest areas listed on the left. A health-related career that matches each interest is described in the next column. At the right is a brief list of additional opportunities that relate to each interest. Each occupation is listed with its classification number according to the United States *Dictionary of Occupational Titles*. The numbers will help you if you want to look up job descriptions in this useful reference.

Read the information in this chart carefully. You will see that the health field is very broad. It includes occupations that call for various interests and kinds of training. In fact, the health field is one that people with almost *any* career interest can work in.

Which job or jobs in the chart seem as if they fit best the personal interests and work preferences you have listed in your Possible Occupations table? In the third column of your table, write three job titles from the Health-Related Occupations chart that best fit your own interests and work preferences. (Leave some space between jobs in your own table. You may choose *any* job titles from column 2, or any other health-related occupations that you are familiar with. You are not limited to choosing jobs described in the chart.)

QUESTIONS ABOUT JOBS

Now write down in the fourth column of your own table some specific questions you have about the possible health-related occupations you have listed. For instance, you may be interested in *medical illustration* because you like art and like working with your hands, and because you like working alone in quiet surroundings. After reading the brief description of the job in the chart, you might want to find out answers to these questions:

Is a medical illustrator expected to be extremely neat and careful?
Is medical illustration more like creative artwork or more like mechanical drawing?
Do some medical illustrators work at home?

A medical photographer shooting a surgical procedure.

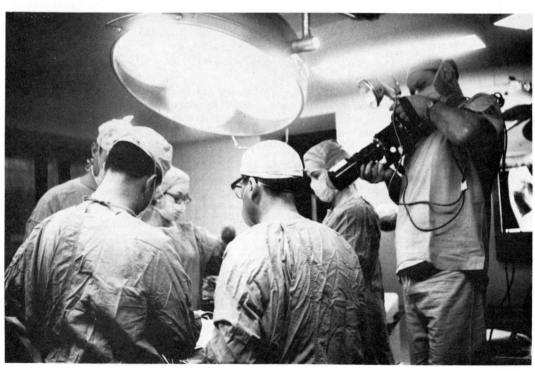

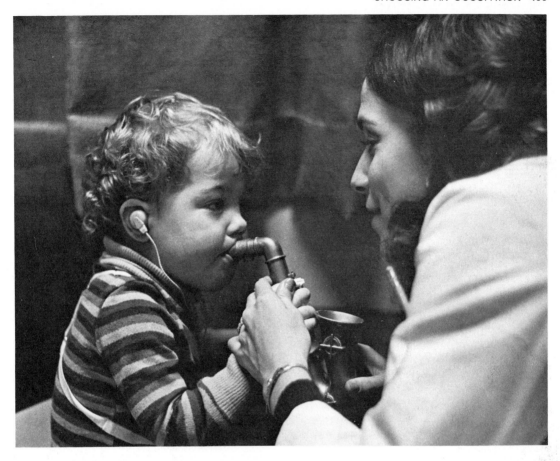

A hearing therapist working with a partly deaf child.

Must medical illustrators often work to meet a deadline?

What specific schools offer training in medical illustration?

How much money can someone in this field hope to earn?

Now, what are some important questions you have about the occupations *you* listed in your table?

HOW TO LEARN MORE

Accurate information is necessary for anyone making career decisions. You might begin by asking your school counselor or advisor for help. School and public libraries usually have books such as the *Dictionary of Occupational Titles* and the *Occupational Outlook Handbook,* which is published annually by the United States Department of Labor, as well as pamphlets and leaflets about particular jobs. In many of these you will find the names and addresses of organizations to write to for more specific information. You can also check local and state agencies.

People who work in the occupations you are interested in may be your best source of information. They can tell you firsthand what their work is like and how they prepared themselves for the jobs they do. You or someone you know may be acquainted with such people. People you contact can sometimes arrange for you to visit them at work so that you can form your own impressions.

INTEREST	CAREER IN BRIEF	RELATED OPPORTUNITIES
Art and Photography	**Medical Illustrator 141.081** Makes drawings and models to illustrate parts of the body, medical procedures, and equipment for use in publications, exhibits, or teaching. Usually works in a hospital or research laboratory. Must have artistic talent and good background in biology. Requires 5 to 7 years of training beyond high school, including art and science courses.	Medical Photographer 143.382 X-ray Technologist 078.368
Business and Administration	**Medical Assistant 079.368** Assists physician by managing office. May purchase supplies, handle billing, and plan schedules. May interview patients, and make simple laboratory tests. Generally requires completion of a 2-year associate degree with courses in sciences and business skills. On-the-job training may be combined with part-time course work.	Public Health Administration Officer 187.118 Hospital Administrator 187.118
Clerical Skills	**Ward Clerk 219.388** Keeps files of office and personnel records and patient medical records in a hospital nursing unit; copies information onto medical records; orders supplies requested by nursing staff; answers telephone; directs visitors; distributes mail and gifts to patients. Requires on-the-job training.	Medical Secretary 201.368 Hospital-admitting Clerk 237.368
Education	**Teacher of Handicapped Children 094.228** Teaches handicapped students in elementary or secondary grades, taking into account students' abilities and physical limitations; plans studies and extra-curricular activities to meet individual needs. Works in students' homes, in a hospital, or in a classroom. Must be patient and enjoy children. Requires state certification. A college degree in special education is the best preparation.	School Health Educator 091.228 Public Health Educator 079.118 Teacher of Physical Education 153.228
Electronics and Industrial Arts	**Prosthetist-Orthotist 078.368** Writes specifications, following a physician's prescription, for construction of artificial limbs and orthopedic appliances to correct body deformities or disorders; fits and adjusts finished devices on patients. Usually works in a hospital. Requires an associate degree and 4 years of on-the-job experience for certification.	Manual-arts Therapist 079.128 Maintenance Engineer 950.782 Optician (lens grinder) 713.381
English and Journalism (Communications)	**Medical Record Librarian 100.382** Prepares, analyzes, stores, and retrieves records, statistics, and reports on patients in hospitals and clinics. May supervise medical record department. Usually works in a hospital or medical research center. Requires a special	Medical Writer 139.288 Medical Record Clerk 249.388

INTEREST	CAREER IN BRIEF	RELATED OPPORTUNITIES
	4-year college program or a 1-year certificate program beyond a college degree in biological sciences or management.	
Home Economics	**Dietician 077.168** In a hospital or other health-care institution, plans menus for patients, instructs patients on their nutrition needs; may manage hospital food service. Requires a college degree in dietetics plus an internship. Graduate degree programs are available.	Research Nutritionist 077.081 Hospital Housekeeper 321.138 Diet Clerk 079.588
Mathematics	**Public Health Statistician 020.188** Plans systems for recording data on diseases and other matters of public health. Works in a government office. Must be good in mathematics and well organized. Requires minimum of a college degree in statistics.	Medical Statistician 020.188
Medicine and Dentistry	**Nurse-Midwife 075.378** Works with obstetrical team in delivering babies. Cares for expectant mothers and newborns. Works in a hospital or a clinic. In some areas, may deliver a baby independently in the mother's home. Must be a registered nurse in order to begin special advanced training; training and certification programs vary from 8 to 24 months.	Physician 070.108 Physician's Assistant (paramedic) 079.378 Dentist 072.108 Dental Assistant 079.378 Registered Nurse 075.378 Emergency Medical Technician (ambulance driver) 355.878 Surgical Technician 079.378 Licensed Practical Nurse 079.378 Nurse Practitioner 075.378 Nurse's Aid 355.878 Orderly 355.878
Music	**Music Therapist 079.128** Devises programs using music to help change behavior and increase self-understanding in patients who have emotional or physical handicaps. Works in a hospital, psychiatric hospital, clinic, nursing home, or other institution. Must have musical skill and ability, patience, and imagination. Requires a college degree in music therapy and an internship.	
Physical Education	**Occupational Therapy Assistant (or Aid) 079.368** Assists Occupational Therapist, who plans and directs activities designed to help mentally and physically disabled patients become self-sufficient. Works with patients and maintains equipment. Works in a hospital, nursing home, clinic,	Occupational Therapist 079.128 Physical Therapist 079.378 Recreation Therapist 079.128 Speech and Hearing Therapist 079.108

INTEREST	CAREER IN BRIEF	RELATED OPPORTUNITIES
	or other institution. Certification requires a 2-year college program, a one-year special program, or 20 to 25 weeks of training by a hospital or community agency. (Certified O.T. Assistants with approved work experience are eligible to take examinations to become registered occupational therapists.)	
Psychology	**Clinical Psychologist 045.108** Interviews patients who have emotional or mental disorders. Treats them in therapy or counseling sessions. May devise and use psychological tests. Works in a hospital, mental health clinic, or private office. Must listen and communicate well with people. Requires graduate work (often a doctoral degree).	Psychiatrist 070.108 Psychiatric Social Worker 195.108 Psychiatric Aid 355.878 Child Psychologist 045.088 Drug Counselor 045.108
Public Health and Safety	**Meat and Poultry Inspector 168.287** Visits establishments where meat and poultry are being processed. Inspects for wholesomeness and sanitation. Works for federal or state government. Requires a college degree, including science courses. The Food and Drug Administration provides further on-the-job training for its employees.	Hospital Inspector 168.168 Fire Inspector 373.168 Field Health Officer 168.168 Water-Treatment Plant Operator 551.885
Science and Engineering	**Biomedical Engineer 729.281** Uses knowledge of biology and technology to improve health care. May develop new equipment or research techniques. Often is employed in a hospital to advise medical staff on acquisition and use of equipment. Makes sure equipment is working properly. Requires a college degree with both biology and engineering courses.	Sanitary Engineer 005.081 Pharmacist 074.181 Pharmacy Helper 074.387 Bacteriologist 041.801 Food and Drug Inspector 168.287 Optometrist 079.108 Industrial Hygienist 079.188 Electrocardiograph Technician 078.368 (Biologists, chemists, biochemists, physicists, and engineers may play a part in research in medicine, nutrition, public health, and related fields. A college degree in any of these sciences is the minimum educational requirement.)

GLOSSARY

abcess a painful, pus-filled sore, at the root of an infected tooth or elsewhere in the body.

abdominal thrust also called the Heimlich maneuver; a method of helping someone who is choking by squeezing the abdomen upward to compress the lungs quickly and force the object up from the throat.

abrasion a scrape damaging the outer layers of skin.

accredited hospital a hospital that meets certain standards in the way it is run and delivers health care; gives better medical care than an unaccredited hospital.

acne a skin condition caused by infection of sebaceous glands by bacteria.

acquired immunity immunity to a disease, that develops after antigens have entered the body.

acute describing a severe illness that arises suddenly, lasts a short time, and requires immediate attention.

addiction a physical dependence on a drug.

additives chemicals added to food to prevent spoilage and to improve color, flavor, nutrition, or other food characteristics. Also, chemicals added to soaps and shampoos for various reasons.

adrenal glands a pair of endocrine glands, one located on top of each kidney, that produce hormones that help the whole body respond quickly to danger, excitement, or stress.

allergen any substance that sets off an allergic reaction.

allergy an extra-sensitivity to certain substances.

alveoli the tiny, thin-walled air sacs in the lungs where oxygen passes from the air into the blood and carbon dioxide passes from the blood into the air.

amino acids the chemical building blocks of proteins.

anemia any condition in which the blood does not carry as much oxygen as it should.

anesthetic a medicine used to reduce or eliminate pain.

angina pectoris pain over and around the heart that is a symptom of arteriosclerosis affecting the arteries of the heart.

antibiotic a medicine that will kill certain disease-causing organisms.

antibody a substance produced by the body to fight a specific pathogen.

antidote a substance that counteracts the effects of a poison.

antigen any substance that can stimulate the production of antibodies after entering the body.

antihistamine a medicine for relieving the symptoms of an allergy or cold.

antiseptic a substance that kills disease-causing organisms.

anus the opening of the rectum at the end of the digestive tract.

anxiety a state of uneasiness or worry.

anxiety neurosis the condition of feeling worried without knowing why.

aorta the body's largest artery, which carries oxygen-rich blood from the left ventricle, away from the heart to the rest of the body except the lungs.

appendicitis inflammation of the appendix.

appendix a small, hollow, fingerlike organ that extends down from the large intestine and has no known function; can become inflamed and cause illness called appendicitis.

appetite the psychological need to eat.

arteriosclerosis hardening of the arteries, due to the depositing of fat and other minerals on the lining of the arteries.

artery a vessel that carries blood away from the heart to the rest of the body.

artificial respiration methods of stimulating breathing in someone temporarily unable to breathe.

asphyxiation see **suffocation**

asthma a respiratory disease in which there is sudden contraction of the bronchial tubes.

athlete's foot a contagious skin disease caused by a fungus that grows between the toes.

ATP a high-energy phosphorus compound that muscle and other body cells use as an energy source.

atrium one of the two upper chambers of the heart, where blood is received through veins from the lungs or from the rest of the body.

auditory nerve the nerve that carries impulses from the inner ear to the brain.

autonomic nervous system the part of the nervous system that controls organs, smooth and cardiac muscle, and blood vessels, and that works without conscious control.

bacteria single-celled organisms that reproduce by dividing; some types can cause infection and disease in human beings.

bandage a cloth or gauze used to hold a dressing in place.

basal metabolic rate the minimum rate at which the body uses energy for essential life processes.

benign tumor a tumor enclosed by a wall; does not spread to other parts of the body.

beriberi a disease caused by a deficiency of one of the B-complex vitamins, resulting in partial paralysis of limbs, anemia, and wasting away.

bile a chemical produced by the liver that helps digestion by breaking up large fat particles.

birthmark an abnormal network of capillaries in the skin, sometimes combined with rough, bumpy, or raised epidermis; abnormal pigmentation of an area of skin.

blackhead a plug of oil and epidermal cells in a sebaceous gland.

bladder the sac where urine collects before it is released from the body.

blood pressure the force with which blood presses against the artery walls as it is pumped through the arteries by the heart.

blood sugar the glucose in the bloodstream that the body uses for energy.

blood type one of the four kinds of blood a person may have, depending on whether or not two substances (called "A" and "B") are present in the blood.

boil a hard, inflamed swelling in the skin caused by bacterial infection.

botulism a dangerous food poisoning caused by certain bacteria in improperly canned food.

brain the portion of the central nervous system located in the skull, that coordinates everything that happens in the body.

bronchi two tubes, each leading from the trachea to one lung.

Calorie the energy required to heat one kilogram (about a quart) of water one Celsius degree (about two Fahrenheit degrees); used as a measure of the energy content of foods. A kilocalorie.

cancer a malignant tumor; or the condition of having an uncontrolled growth of cells in the body.

capillaries thin-walled blood vessels throughout the body that connect arteries to veins and permit transfer of substances between body cells and the bloodstream.

carbohydrates starches and sugars; the nutrients containing only carbon, hydrogen, and oxygen that supply the body with energy.

carbon monoxide a colorless, odorless, tasteless gas that combines with hemoglobin when inhaled and prevents red blood cells from carrying oxygen to body cells.

carcinogen a substance that can cause cancer.

carcinoma a cancer beginning in tissues that cover or line organs, such as the skin or the linings of the lungs, uterus, breast, or intestines.

cardiac muscle a network of smooth and striated fibers bound together by connective tissue; found only in the walls of the heart.

cardiovascular diseases diseases of the heart and blood vessels.

carotene the yellowish pigment in skin.

cartilage a tough, flexible tissue that forms part of the skeleton.

cataract cloudiness in the lens of the eye; when large, cataracts interfere with vision.

cavity tooth decay; a hole in tooth enamel or penetrating into the dentin or pulp, that is caused by acid produced by bacteria in the mouth.

cell the basic structural unit of all living things, which carries out basic life functions such as taking in and utilizing food; different cells have different functions in the body.

cellulose a carbohydrate found in plants that the human body cannot digest but that the intestines need to function properly.

central nervous system the brain and spinal cord.

cerebellum the part of the brain that coordinates muscular activities.

cerebral cortex the outer layer of the cerebrum; the brain's center for speech, reasoning, memory, and creativity.

cerebral hemisphere either half of the cerebrum, which is divided from front to back.

cerebral palsy partial paralysis and lack of muscle coordination due to brain damage.

cerebrum the main part of the brain, controlling thinking, feeling, and voluntary activities.

chemotherapy treatment of cancer by use of powerful chemicals.

cholesterol a fatty substance produced by the body and absorbed from food; excess cholesterol may be stored in clumps deposited on the lining of artery walls.

chromosome a structure within the cell nucleus that is made up of genes. Chromosomes provide the directions for cell growth and activity.

chronic describing a prolonged, lingering, or frequently recurring illness that progresses slowly in seriousness.

cilia tiny, protective hairs on the surface of the mucous membrane in the nasal passages and trachea.

circulatory system the group of structures by which blood and lymph circulate throughout the body.

closed fracture (simple fracture) a broken bone with surrounding skin not broken.

cochlea also called the inner ear; a liquid-filled organ resembling a snail shell, containing sound-receptor cells, which send impulses to the brain by way of the auditory nerve.

colon the large intestine.

compensation a defense mechanism; making up for dissatisfaction in one area of life by excelling in another.

complementary proteins proteins from different

foods that, when eaten together, supply the body with the right combination of needed amino acids.

compound fracture see **open fracture**

cones cells in the retina that enable us to see colors and to see in bright light.

congenital defect a defect that exists at birth.

contact dermatitis an allergic reaction of the skin to certain substances.

contagious disease a disease that can spread among people or between people and other animals.

contraction the shortening, and often thickening, of muscle.

coping managing a problem with some degree of effectiveness without outright success or failure.

cornea the transparent cover in the front of the eyeball.

coronary artery the vessel that carries oxygen-rich blood from the aorta back to the heart for use by the heart cells.

coronary thrombosis see **heart attack**

dandruff flaking of the scalp caused either by excessive dryness or by excessive sebum.

decongestant a medication that drys the nose and promotes sinus drainage and easier breathing.

defense mechanism any tactic used to avoid coping with problems directly.

delirium tremens mental confusion with anxiety, tremors, and hallucinations.

dentin the bonelike material, underneath the enamel, that most of a tooth is made of.

depilatory a chemical hair remover.

depressant a psychoactive drug that slows down the activities of both the body and the mind.

depression a feeling of helplessness and hopelessness.

depth perception ability to determine how far something is from you by eyesight.

dermis the thick, middle layer of skin, which contains nerve endings, sweat glands, capillaries, hair follicles, and sebaceous glands.

diabetes a disease caused by insufficient production of the hormone insulin; the body of a diabetic person does not use sugar properly.

diagnosis the act of trying to identify a disease, or the identification.

diaphragm a large muscle below the lungs, at the bottom of the chest cavity. By contracting and relaxing, it changes the air pressure in the chest cavity, which forces air in and out of the lungs.

diarrhea frequent, watery bowel movements.

digestion the process by which the body changes food into forms the cells can use.

digestive system the group of organs and structures that break down foods into materials the cells can use, and remove unusable parts of food.

digestive tract the long, coiled tube where digestion takes place; runs from the mouth to the anus.

disease a condition in which the body does not function normally, which may affect one organ or the entire body.

disk a broad, flat pad of cartilage separating two vertebrae; can slip out of position, causing pain or numbness.

dislocation an injury in which a bone is moved from its normal position at a joint.

displacement a defense mechanism in which a person directs a powerful emotion to a safe place.

DNA the chemical that genes are made of (deoxyribonucleic acid).

dressing a clean material placed directly on a wound.

drug a substance that people put into their bodies to change the way they feel, perceive things, or behave.

duodenum the first part of the small intestine.

dwarfism insufficient growth of the body, usually caused by insufficient production of growth hormone.

dysentery infection of the lower intestinal tract, caused by bacteria, protozoa, or viruses, and spread by poor sanitation.

eardrum a thin membrane stretched across the inside of the ear canal, that vibrates when hit by air waves.

eczema an allergic skin rash.

EEG see **electroencephalogram**

ego according to psychoanalytic theory, the part of the mind that leads a person to act on the basis of thought and experience.

EKG see **electrocardiogram**

electrical shock electric current passing through the body, which can result in stoppage of heartbeat and breathing.

electrocardiogram (EKG) a graph, made by a machine, of the electrical activity of the heart.

electroencephalogram (EEG) a graph, made by a machine, of the electrical activity of the brain.

electrolysis use of an electric needle to permanently remove unwanted hair.

emergency ward the part of a hospital where patients can get treatment for possibly serious medical problems or problems that need prompt attention.

emetic a substance that causes vomiting.

enamel the hard material that forms the outside layer of teeth and protects them.

encephalitis also called sleeping sickness; a viral disease that causes inflammation of the brain.

endocrine glands glands that send chemicals called hormones directly into the bloodstream.

enema insertion of a fluid into the rectum for cleansing or as a laxative.

enzymes chemicals produced by the tissues of the digestive system that speed the breakdown of food.

epidemic a disease spreading rapidly and affecting many people.

epidermis the thin, outside layer of skin.

epiglottis a flap of tissue attached to the base of the tongue that prevents food and water from entering the trachea during swallowing.

epilepsy a disorder characterized by seizures involving the nervous system, often accompanied by loss of consciousness when severe.

esophagus the food tube connecting the mouth and the stomach.

euphoric feeling very happy and blissful.

Eustachian tube the tube connecting the middle ear and the throat; maintains equal air pressure on both sides of the eardrum.

fainting a temporary loss of consciousness.

fat a concentrated source of energy in food. Fats can be stored in the body.

feces the soft, solid food wastes in the rectum that are periodically expelled from the body through the anus.

fever body temperature much above 98.6°F (37°C), that indicates the body is fighting an infection.

fibers the structures that make up muscles; occur in bundles.

fitness physical and emotional health that enables a person to meet the demands of everyday life.

flu see **influenza**

fluoride a chemical that strengthens teeth and helps them resist decay.

follicle the pocket in the dermis out of which a hair grows.

food poisoning illness caused by certain bacteria in spoiled food.

frostbite freezing of the skin.

fungi microscopic plants, some of which cause highly contagious diseases that spread rapidly over the body.

gall bladder a small sac near the liver where bile is stored.

gamma globulin a protein in the blood from which antibodies are made.

gangrene destruction of tissue due to complete, prolonged loss of circulation.

general hospital a hospital that takes care of all types of illness, accidents, and surgery.

genes tiny bits of material made of DNA, in chromosomes, that carry the directions for all inherited traits.

gigantism too much growth, caused by overproduction of growth hormone.

gland any organ that produces a substance and releases it to another part of the body.

glaucoma increased pressure within the eye caused by abnormal accumulation of fluid, damaging the retina and the optic nerve; impairs vision and may lead to blindness.

glucagon a hormone produced by the pancreas that stimulates the liver to change glycogen back to glucose and to release it into the bloodstream.

glucose a simple sugar, which results when digestion causes breakdown of carbohydrates; provides energy for the body.

glycogen a form of glucose stored in the liver and in muscles.

goiter a disease of the thyroid gland caused by iodine deficiency, resulting in enlargement of the thyroid gland visible as a swelling in the front of the neck.

gonorrhea a highly contagious, common, venereal disease.

grounding device a special plug used with a special outlet, that electrically connects an appliance to the ground and protects users from electrical shock.

habituation a psychological dependence on a drug.

halitosis unpleasant-smelling breath.

hallucinations seemingly real events and objects that actually exist only in the mind.

hallucinogen a psychoactive drug that changes sensory perceptions.

hay fever unpleasant reactions in the nasal passages, that are set off by an allergen.

heart the muscle that pumps blood throughout the body.

heart attack also called coronary thrombosis; sudden blocking of the flow of blood to the heart by a blood clot.

heartbeat a single contraction and relaxation of the heart.

heart-lung machine a machine used to take over the pumping action of a patient's heart during surgery.

heart massage squeezing the heart between the rib cage and spine in order to restore heartbeat.

heart murmur a sound made by the heart, sometimes indicating that a heart valve does not work properly.

heat exhaustion a condition resulting from the body's loss of fluids and salt when strenuous activity is combined with excessive exposure to intense heat.

heat stroke sudden collapse, with high body temperature, rapid pulse, and other symptoms, resulting from being in a place that is too hot.

Heimlich maneuver see **abdominal thrust**

hemisphere see **cerebral hemisphere**

hemoglobin an iron-containing chemical in red blood cells that carries oxygen to body cells.

hepatitis a contagious viral disease that may affect several organs, especially the liver; often accompanied by jaundice.

hernia a loop of intestine bulging through a weak spot in the muscle tissue of the abdomen.

high blood pressure also called hypertension; a disease in which the blood presses too hard against the artery walls as it is pumped through the arteries.

histamine a chemical produced in the body that causes the symptoms of allergy.

hives itchy swellings on the skin.

hormone a chemical, produced by an endocrine gland, that affects various organs.

hunger the body's physical need for food.

hydrochloric acid a strong acid produced in the stomach that aids digestion of protein.

hypertension see **high blood pressure**

hyperthyroidism production of too much thyroid hormone.

hypothalamus the tiny part of the brain where most of the control of the autonomic nervous system is carried out.

hypothyroidism production of too little thyroid hormone.

hysteria a neurosis in which there are physical symptoms having no physical cause.

id according to psychoanalytic theory, the part of the mind consisting of basic biological needs.

immunity protection from a disease caused by pathogens.

immunization getting protection from a disease, usually by use of a vaccine.

impotence a male's inability to respond sexually.

incision a smooth cut.

infection invasion of body tissue by pathogens.

infectious disease a disease caused by pathogens.

infectious mononucleosis also called mono; a contagious, but not well understood disease that usually causes extreme fatigue and characteristic changes in the white blood cells.

inflammation heat, redness, swelling, and pain in a part of the body, resulting from infection, injury, or irritation.

influenza also called flu; a viral respiratory disease resembling the common cold but more serious.

inner ear see **cochlea**

insomnia having difficulty sleeping.

insulin a hormone produced by the pancreas that regulates the amount of glucose that gets into the cells, and stimulates the liver to store glucose in the form of glycogen; helps control the amount of blood sugar.

involuntary muscle see **smooth muscle**

iris the colored part of the eye that surrounds the pupil.

jaundice yellowing of the skin and the whites of the eyes caused by a disturbance in the body's processing of bile; associated with hepatitis.

joint a place where two or more bones come together.

kidneys a pair of organs that clean the blood and control the amount of water in the blood; they release wastes and water together in the form of urine.

laceration an uneven cut in which the skin is torn.

lacteal a tiny lymphatic capillary that absorbs fat particles from the small intestine into the lymph, which delivers them to the bloodstream.

large intestine the part of the digestive tract following the small intestine, where water is removed from food wastes before they enter the rectum.

larynx the voice box, located in the upper part of the trachea.

lead poisoning damage to the stomach, brain, and nervous system caused by absorption of lead into the body.

leukemia cancer of the blood-forming tissues in the bone marrow, spleen, and lymph nodes, which results in uncontrolled production of defective white blood cells.

lice small insects that live in animals' hair and feed on their blood.

ligaments strands of tough tissue that holds bones together at a joint.

liver a large organ that carries out many chemical reactions, including production of bile.

lung capacity the amount of air the lungs can hold.

lungs a pair of spongy organs where oxygen is taken in from the air and carbon dioxide is released into the air.

lymph a clear, watery fluid that circulates throughout the body in lymphatic vessels, helping to protect the body against disease-causing organisms and transporting certain substances throughout the body.

lymphatic system the group of vessels and nodes through which lymph circulates.

lymph nodes specific areas in the lymphatic system where lymph is filltered and lymphocytes are produced.

lymphocyte a kind of white blood cell, produced in the lymph nodes, that destroys harmful organisms.

lymphoma cancer of the lymphatic system.

malaria a disease caused by protozoa and spread by mosquitoes; found in hot climates.

malignant tumor a tumor that is not confined, from which fragments break off and travel elsewhere in the body; a cancer.

marrow the spongy substance in the core of bones that produces red and white blood cells.

medical center specialized hospitals grouped near a general hospital.

melanin the dark-colored pigment in skin.

membrane a thin layer of tissue.

mental retardation having less than normal learning ability.

metabolism all the activities of cells: breaking down foods, using energy, building tissue, and so on; occurs at a rate that varies from one person to another.

microbes living things too small to be seen without a microscope.

middle ear an air-filled cavity within the ear, containing three small bones that increase the strength of the vibrations of the eardrum and send the vibrations to the inner ear.

migraine headache a severe headache that recurs periodically in certain people, probably having both physical and emotional causes; often accompanied by nausea.

minerals inorganic substances that are components of body tissue.

mole a small, pigmented spot on the skin, sometimes raised or having hair growing from it.

mononucleosis (mono) see **infectious mononucleosis**

MS see **multiple sclerosis**

mucous membrane a special form of skin that lines body openings such as the nose and mouth and body parts such as the esophagus and trachea; produces protective, cleansing, and lubricating fluids.

mucus a protective, lubricating substance produced by glands in mucous membrane.

multiple sclerois (MS) a disease affecting young adults, in which the covering of the axons in the central nervous system is damaged.

muscle body tissue that can contract (shorten) and relax (lengthen). Muscles can move themselves and move other tissues and organs.

muscular system all the muscles and connective tissue of the body.

mutation a change in the DNA in a cell nucleus that produces a cell that behaves differently from its parent cell.

natural immunity inherited immunity to a disease.

nephrons tiny blood-filtering units in the kidneys.

nerve endings sensory receptors in the skin, each one specializing in one sensation.

nerve impulses electrochemical impulses that travel across nerve pathways and carry messages to and from parts of the body.

nerve pathway the many neurons that carry a nerve impulse from beginning to end.

nervous system the brain, spinal cord, and all the nerves in the body.

neuron a nerve cell, composed of three parts: cell body, dendrite, and axon.

neurosis the condition of having unconscious conflicts and anxiety.

neurotic behavior some kinds of constant, ineffective behavior involving unconscious conflicts and, usually, anxiety.

nucleus the central part of a cell, which controls cell activity.

nutrients the components of food that enable the body to survive and maintain health.

obesity weight that exceeds desirable weight by more than 15 or 20 percent.

obsessive-compulsive having repeated, anxious thoughts much of the time and feeling the need to keep doing certain things over and over.

open fracture (compound fracture) a broken bone that punctures the skin.

ophthalmoscope an instrument used for examining the inside of the eye.

optician a person who specializes in grinding lenses and fitting glasses, according to the prescription written by an ophthalmologist or optometrist.

optic nerve the bundle of nerve fibers that carries impulses from the retina to the brain.

optometrist a person who specializes in correcting vision defects by means of glasses and eye exercises; not a medical doctor—refers patients to an ophthalmologist for medical treatment when necessary.

organ an organized group of different tissues that performs a particular function.

orthodontia special dental work that changes teeth positions.

osteoarthritis wearing away of the cartilage in much-used joints of the body.

otoscope an instrument used for examining the ear canal and eardrum.

outpatient clinic or department the part of a hospital where patients can walk in during clinic hours and get medical attention.

ovaries the female endocrine glands, which produce sex cells and sex hormones.

over-the-counter drugs products sold without a doctor's prescription that are supposed to cure or relieve ailments.

oxygen debt the muscles' need for oxygen, which builds up quickly during strenuous exercises.

pacemaker a special nerve and muscle tissue in the heart that triggers each heartbeat and controls the rhythm of the heart's contractions.

pancreas an organ that produces hormones, including insulin, and enzymes.

Pap test a routine medical test that can detect cancer of the uterus by examining cells from the narrow, lower end of the uterus.

paranoid having an exaggerated sense of self-importance and also feeling persecuted by the rest of the world.

parasitic worms worms varying in size that live part of their life cycle within other animals.

Parkinson's disease a disease that slowly damages parts of the brain, causing physical shaking, but not loss of intelligence; does not usually strike people under 40.

pathogens microbes that can cause disease.

pellagra a disease caused by a deficiency of one of the B-complex vitamins, resulting in skin problems, upsets in the digestive and nervous systems, and eventual mental deterioration.

periodontal having to do with the gums.

peripheral vision the distance you can see all around you when you are directing your gaze straight ahead.

peristalis the muscle action that pushes food through the digestive tract.

peritonitis a serious infection throughout the abdominal area; can be caused by the bursting of an inflamed, infected appendix.

pernicious anemia anemia caused by a breakdown in the mechanisms by which vitamin B_{12} is absorbed in the body.

personality the behavior, attitudes, and feelings that make each person an individual.

phobia a strong fear resulting from focusing anxious feelings on an object or situation.

pineal gland a small gland connected to the optic nerve that seems to affect the rate at which the sex hormones work.

pituitary gland called the "master endocrine gland" because it releases several different hormones that trigger the activities of other endocrine glands; also controls body growth. Located in the brain.

plaque a sticky mucus containing bacteria, food particles, and dead tissue that can accumulate on teeth.

plasma the watery part of the blood.

platelets cell fragments carried in blood plasma that have an important part in the clotting of blood.

pneumonia one of several infectious lung diseases, caused by bacteria or viruses.

poison any harmful substance that enters or contacts the body by way of the mouth, lungs, or skin.

pollutant a substance, often waste material, that dirties air, water, or soil; is often dangerous to living things.

pollution materials, often wastes, in the wrong place; the dirtying of air, water, or soil.

pores tiny openings in the epidermis that lead to sweat glands and oil glands in the dermis.

pressure points areas where arteries may be pressed against underlying bone to reduce bleeding.

preventive medicine a type of medical practice in which medical professionals try to prevent serious health problems from arising by giving patients regular checkups and health information.

processed food food prepared in a factory by a special process or treatment.

projection a defense mechanism; denying an unwanted trait by repressing it from the conscious mind and assigning it to someone else.

proteins substances, made up of amino acids, that are used to build and repair body cells.

protozoa certain single-celled organisms, some of which can cause disease.

psittacosis also called parrot fever; a viral form of pneumonia that is spread in the feces of birds.

psychoactive drug a substance that alters mood by affecting the central nervous system.

psychoanalytic theory the belief that the human personality consists of id, ego, and superego.

psychosis any severe emotional and behavioral difficulty that makes a person lose touch with reality.

psychosomatic illness physical illness brought on by emotions.

psychotherapy treatment for emotional and behavioral difficulties by a qualified therapist.

pulp the soft, sensitive tissue at the center of the tooth.

pulse the heartbeat, as felt and counted where an artery near the skin is also close to bone or firm tissue, as at the inner side of the wrist on the thumb side.

puncture a deep hole through the skin produced by a sharp object.

pupil the opening in the eye that lets light in.

pus a thick fluid, containing leukocytes and cell materials, that forms in infected tissue.

rabies a disease of warm-blooded animals that affects the brain and nervous system; transmitted to humans by the bite of an infected animal.

radiation therapy various treatments for cancer that alter the nucleus of the abnormal cells.

rationalization a defense mechanism; finding reasons to justify certain behavior.

reaction time the amount of time between the instant you sense something and the instant you do something about it.

receptors parts of the nervous system that respond to different sensory stimuli and provide information about what is happening inside and outside the body.

recovery room the room in a hospital where a patient is taken after surgery to be checked by medical staff until they are sure the patient's condition is stable and the patient can be returned to his or her room.

rectum the last section of the digestive tract, where solid waste materials collect before leaving the body.

red blood cells circular cells with no nucleus that transport oxygen by way of the blood to cells.

reflex arc a nerve pathway to and from the spinal cord that bypasses the brain.

REM sleep a 10- to 15-minute stage of the sleep cycle during which the sleeper's closed eyes show rapid eye movement.

repression a defense mechanism in which the conscious mind pushes aside upsetting thoughts and feelings by allowing them to be forgotten.

respiratory system the group of organs and structures that enable oxygen and carbon dioxide to move between the blood and the air.

retina the inner coating of the eyeball, formed of light-receptor cells.

rheumatic fever a disease of the heart caused by streptococcus bacteria.

rheumatoid arthritis a serious arthritic disease causing inflammation of the lining inside joints.

Rh factor a substance found on the surface of red blood cells in many, but not all, human beings.

rickets a disease caused by a deficiency of vitamin D, resulting in defective bone growth; mostly occurs in children.

rickettsiae certain pathogens carried by insects and ticks that grow only inside a living cell.

ringworm a highly contagious skin disease caused by a fungus.

Rocky Mountain spotted fever an infectious disease transmitted from rodents to people by ticks.

rods cells in the retina that respond to white and shades of gray; enable us to see in dim light.

roots the parts of a tooth anchoring it in a socket in the jawbone.

roundworms certain parasitic worms that may be transmitted from dogs to humans.

saliva the fluid produced by salivary glands and sent into the mouth; moistens food and contains an enzyme that begins the breakdown of starch to sugar.

salivary glands structures located near the mouth that produce saliva, which begins digestion in the mouth.

sarcoma a cancer beginning in supporting tissue such as bone or muscle.

schizophrenia a psychosis in which a person withdraws from contact with other people and the rest of the world.

scurvy a disease caused by a deficiency of vitamin C, resulting in soft and bleeding gums, bleeding under the skin, and overall weakness.

sebaceous glands tiny glands located throughout the dermis that produce sebum and release it onto the surface of the skin.

sebum an oily material that is sent to the surface of the skin by sebaceous glands in the dermis.

semicircular canals structures in the inner ear that help control balance.

senility the gradual mental and emotional deterioration that affects many elderly people.

shock a serious slowing down of the circulatory and nervous systems.

sickle-cell anemia anemia in which an abnormal type of hemoglobin makes red blood cells crescent shaped and prevents them from transporting oxygen.

side effects unwanted effects produced by drugs.

simple fracture see **closed fracture**

sinuses four pairs of hollow bones in the skull lined with protective mucous membrane.

skeletal muscle see **striated muscle**

skeletal system the bony, supporting framework of the body.

skin the organ that covers the exterior of the body.

sleeping sickness see **encephalitis**

small intestine the part of the digestive tract following the stomach.

smooth muscle   also called involuntary muscle; controls internal organs; smooth in appearance.

snoring   various harsh sounds made by a sleeping person; caused by congested or narrow breathing passages and vibrations of tissue around the throat.

sociopath   a person who seems to have no conscience and seems to look at and use other people as objects.

spasm   a sudden contraction of a muscle.

sphygmomanometer   an instrument used for measuring blood pressure.

spinal column   also called the spine; the backbone, which encloses the spinal cord and supports the body.

spinal cord   the part of the central nervous system that extends from the brain to the base of the spine within the spinal column.

spine   see **spinal column**

spleen   an organ that stores blood, destroys some disease-causing organisms, and destroys and produces red blood cells.

splint   a long, stiff object used to support a fracture.

sprain   an injury that occurs when a ligament or tendon around a joint is torn.

sputum   material that is coughed up.

stethoscope   an instrument used for listening to sounds produced within the body.

stimulant   a psychoactive drug that speeds up the activities of both the body and the mind.

stimulus   anything that produces a reaction in or by the body.

stomach   the widest and most muscular part of the digestive tract.

strain   injury of muscle due to overstretching and tearing.

strep throat   a severe throat infection caused by streptococcus bacteria.

streptococcus   the kind of bacteria that causes strep throat and rheumatic fever.

striated muscle   also called skeletal or voluntary muscle; striped in appearance.

stroke   the cutting off of part of the brain's blood supply.

stupor   confusion, being in a daze.

subcutaneous layer   the elastic, fatty layer of skin beneath the dermis.

suffocation   also called asphyxiation; inability to get enough oxygen; can be caused by choking, carbon-monoxide poisoning, or electrical shock.

superego   according to psychoanalytic theory, the part of the personality that consists of conscience and ideals to be lived up to.

sweat glands   tiny glands located in the dermis throughout the body that send moisture to the surface of the skin, where it is released into the air in perspiration.

symptom   a change in appearance or function of the body, or in how a person feels, that usually indicates the presence of disease.

synapse   the microscopic gap between neurons across which electrochemical impulses must pass.

synovial tissue   the tissue that lines the tissues in freely movable joints and produces synovial fluid.

syphilis   a serious venereal disease that can affect any part of the body.

system   a group of organs and tissues working together to carry out a body function.

tartar   a hard, mineral substance that builds up on teeth at the gum line.

taste buds   receptors for taste located mostly in the tongue.

TB   see **tuberculosis**

tendons   tough, inelastic bands of connective tissue that attach skeletal muscles to bones.

testicles   the male endocrine glands, which produce sex cells and sex hormones.

tetanus   a serious bacterial disease that affects the central nervous system.

thalamus   the part of the brain where sensations are received and organized.

thymus gland   a gland in the chest that may help the body fight disease-causing organisms.

thyroid gland   an endocrine gland located in the front of the neck; affects the rate of metabolism.

tissue   a group of cells that are similar in form and do the same kind of work.

tolerance   an inability to be affected by a certain quantity of a drug.

tourniquet   an extremely tight bandage placed around an arm or a leg to stop the flow of blood into the limb.

toxin   a poison produced by living organisms.

trachea   the windpipe, which connects the mouth and lungs.

trichinosis   a disease caused by a parasitic worm in pork not fully cooked.

tuberculosis (TB)   a bacterial disease that affects the lungs and other tissues.

tumor   a mass of cells forming a lump.

typhoid fever   an infectious disease that is spread in improperly treated food and water.

typhus   a group of infectious diseases caused by rickettsiae and transmitted to people from infected rats and mice by way of insects.

ulcer an open sore, often developing on the lining of the stomach or duodenum.

ulcerative colitis ulcers in the lining of the colon.

unconscious a theoretical part of the mind where memories and feelings are stored and forgotten by the conscious mind.

ureters the tubes from the kidneys to the bladder.

urethra the narrow passageway through which urine passes from the bladder out of the body.

urinalysis a laboratory test of urine that can reveal whether certain organs of the body are functioning properly.

urinary system the group of organs and structures that rids the body of wastes and excess water.

urine a yellowish fluid containing waste material that is produced by the kidneys and leaves the body by way of the urethra.

vaccine weakened or killed viruses injected or taken orally to stimulate the body to produce antibodies against that kind of virus.

valve a tissue lying across a passageway in the circulatory system that opens and shuts and allows fluids to flow in only one direction.

VD see **venereal diseases**

vein a vessel that carries blood from all parts of the body back to the heart.

vena cava one of two large veins bringing oxygen-poor blood into the right atrium.

venereal diseases (VD) certain infectious diseases spread by sexual contact.

ventricle one of the two lower chambers of the heart, from which blood is pumped through arteries to the lungs or to the rest of the body.

vertebra one of the bones of the backbone.

villi tiny projections on the lining of the small intestine, through which digested food passes into the blood.

viruses the smallest pathogens, which reproduce by invading living cells and changing the cell protein into more viruses.

vital organs organs that are necessary for life to continue.

vitamins chemical substances that help transform digested food into tissue and help regulate body functions.

vitiligo lack of normal pigment in certain areas of the skin.

vocal cords a pair of folds of tissue in the larynx that produce sounds when they vibrate.

voluntary muscle see **striated muscle**

voluntary nervous system the part of the nervous system that activates those muscles over which the cerebrum has conscious control.

wart an overgrowth of epidermal cells that has a large supply of capillaries and that may be darkened with melanin; caused by a virus.

white blood cells cells in the blood that destroy certain kinds of disease-causing organisms.

withdrawal symptoms physical discomfort or pain resulting from a physical dependence (addiction) on a drug that is taken away (withdrawn).

X ray a photograph that reveals structures inside the body.

yellow fever a viral disease, spread by mosquitoes, that causes malfunction of the liver.

zygote the cell formed when an egg cell and a sperm cell join; the first cell of a human life.

CREDITS

Illustrations by Charles H. Boyter, D. Patrick Russell, and Marcia Williams of The Boston University Educational Media Support Center under the direction of Jerome Glickman, Boston University School of Medicine.

Cartoons by Bob Dole/Bookmakers, Inc.

viii., 1 Peter Vandermark/Stock, Boston
4 Ken Heyman
6 (*top left*) Reuven Miller
7 from *Photographic Anatomy of the Human Body* by Dr. Chihiro Yokochi
11 Wide World
12 (*top left*) Paul Fusco/Magnum (*top right, bottom left and right*) Fredrik D. Bodin
14 Dr. Joseph Gennaro
15 Runk/Schoenberger/Grant Heilman
19 Robert Halmi, *Life Magazine*, © Time, Inc.
21 (*left*) Fredrik D. Bodin/Stock, Boston (*middle*) Michael Hayman/Black Star (*right*) Jean-Claude Lejeune/Stock, Boston
22 Fredrik D. Bodin
23 Frank Siteman/Stock, Boston
26, 27 from *Photographic Anatomy of the Human Body* by Dr. Chihiro Yokochi
30 Peter Southwick/Stock, Boston
36 courtesy of Abbott Laboratories
40 Martin M. Rotker/Taurus Photos
56 Ed Lettau/Photo Researchers
60, 61 Tim Carlson/Stock, Boston
63 from *Photographic Anatomy of the Human Body* by Dr. Chihiro Yokochi
64 Jerry Schrader/Stock, Boston
66 Andreas Feininger, *Life Magazine*, © Time, Inc.
68 Mayer Spivack
71 NASA
74 (*top*) Alex Borodulin/Peter Arnold (*bottom*) Peter Southwick/Stock, Boston
75 (*top*) Daniel S. Brody/Stock, Boston (*bottom*) George Silk, *Life Magazine*, © Time, Inc.
76 Alex Borodulin/Leo deWys, Inc.
78 UPI
80 Gerry Cranham/Rapho/Photo Researchers
83, 85 Fredrik D. Bodin
88 courtesy of Geometrics, Inc., Cambridge, Massachusetts
90 George Bellerose/Stock, Boston
95 Ken Heyman
97 (*both*) Ken Heyman
101, 103 Mayer Spivack
106 (*left*) Harry Callahan (*right*) Dr. Hillier L. Baker/Mayo Clinic

107 Dr. I. Kaufman Arenberg
110 (*both*) Fredrik D. Bodin
111 Cary Wolinksy/Stock, Boston
112, 113 (*all*) Alex Borodulin/Leo deWys, Inc.
115 Peter Southwick/Stock, Boston
117 Tom Rothschild/Stock, Boston
120, 121 Vanucci Foto-Services/FPG
124 (*left*) Rene Burri/Magnum (*right*) Michael Dobo/Stock, Boston
126 (*top*) Andy Mercado/Jeroboam (*bottom*) Kent Reno/Jeroboam
128 (*top*) Per-Olaf Odman/Editorial Photocolor Archives (*bottom*) Ken Heyman
129 (*top*) Fredrik D. Bodin (*bottom*) Arthur Grace/Stock, Boston
130 Suzanne Szasz
131 (*all*) courtesy of the American Heart Association
132 (*left*) Ken Heyman (*right*) Ira Kirschenbaum/Stock, Boston
134 Ellis Herwig/Stock, Boston
135 Peter Southwick/Stock, Boston
137, 138, 139 Ken Heyman
142 Silvester/Rapho/Photo Researchers
146, 147 Cornell Capa/Magnum
148 Inger McCabe/Rapho/Photo Researchers
151 Grant Heilman
152 Ken Heyman
154 Tom Kelley/Alpha/FPG
155 Jeff Albertson/Stock, Boston
156, 158 Fredrik D. Bodin
160 UNICEF
161 Fredrik D. Bodin
162 (*top*) Robert Phillips/The Image Bank (*bottom*) Owen Franken/Stock, Boston
163 (*top*) Ken Heyman (*bottom*) Harald Sund/The Image Bank
165 (*top left*) David Hiser/The Image Bank (*top right*) W.H. Hodge/Peter Arnold (*bottom right*) Fredrik D. Bodin
166 Mayer Spivack
167 (*left*) Philip Bailey (*right*) Grant Heilman
168 Ellis Herwig/Stock, Boston
170, 171 Fredrik D. Bodin
172 USDA
173 Fredrik D. Bodin
176, 177 (*all*) Ken Ohara from *Book One*
178 (*left*) Blair Seitz/Editorial Photocolor Archives (*right*) Sybil Shackman/Monkmeyer Press Photos
180 Ellis Herwig/Stock, Boston
181 © Carroll H. Weiss, RBP, 1973
184 (*left*) Bruce Buchenholz (*right*) Raimondo Borea/Editorial Photocolor Archives
185 © Carroll H. Weiss, RBP, 1973
186 Ken Heyman

188, 189 (*all*) Ernst Haas
191 (*top left*) Culver Pictures (*top middle*) courtesy of Clairol Short and Sassy Conditioner and Shampoo (*top right*) Wide World (*bottom left*) Springer/Bettmann Film Archive (*bottom center & right*) Bettmann Archive
192 Erika Stone/Peter Arnold
193 Runk/Schoenberger/Grant Heilman
194 courtesy of Johnson Wax
197 San Diego Zoo
198 Fredrik D. Bodin
201 (*top*) Smithsonian Institution (*bottom*) The White House Collection
202 Fredrik D. Bodin
206, 207 (*all*) Martin Adler Levick/Black Star
208 Eric Simmons/Stock, Boston
209 Leo deWys, Inc.
210 Bohdan Hrynewych
212 Jon Chase
213 (*left*) Fredrik D. Bodin (*right*) Cary Wolinsky/Stock, Boston
214 Leonard Freed/Magnum
215 (*top*) Alon Reininger/Leo deWys, Inc. (*bottom*) Cary Wolinsky/Stock, Boston
216 Patricia Hollander Gross/Stock, Boston
217 (*top*) Bonnie D. Unsworth (*bottom*) Daniel S. Brody/Stock, Boston
219 Marvin Newman
220 Bill Owens/Magnum
221 Ray Ellis/Photo Researchers
223 Ralph Eugene Meatyard
224 (*top*) Charles Gatewood/Magnum (*bottom*) Leo deWys, Inc.
225 Cary Wolinsky/Stock, Boston
226 (*top left*) George Rodger/Magnum (*top right*) Roger Mallock/Magnum (*bottom*) Japan Air Lines
228 (*top left*) Suzanne Szasz (*top right*) Abigail Heyman/Magnum (*bottom*) Bohdan Hrynewych
229 Donald Dietz/Stock, Boston
230 Abigail Heyman/Magnum
234, 235 John Urban
236 Owen Franken/Stock, Boston
237 Bettmann Archive
239 Frank Siteman/Stock, Boston
240 (*left*) John Running/Stock, Boston (*right*) Owen Franken/Stock, Boston
242 Peter Vadnai/Editorial Photocolor Archives
243 Fredrik D. Bodin
245 Jean-Claude Lejeune/Stock, Boston
246 Fredrik D. Bodin
247 Owen Franken/Stock, Boston
248 Fredrik D. Bodin
249 Tyrone Hall/Stock, Boston
250 Ralph Eugene Meatyard

252 Abigail Heyman/Magnum
253 Sepp Seitz/Magnum
254 Owen Franken/Stock, Boston
258 (*top*) Joseph Koracs/Stock, Boston (*middle left*) Nicholas Sapieha/Stock, Boston (*middle right*) Charles Gatewood (*bottom*) Owen Franken/Stock, Boston
259 Ernest Baxter/Black Star
260 (*left*) Fredrik D. Bodin (*right*) Burt Glinn/Magnum
263 National Library of Medicine
266 Barbara L. Baumann
267 Mieke Maas/Stock, Boston
268 Fredrik D. Bodin
269 Charles Gatewood/Magnum
271 Hans Namuth/Photo Researchers
272 (*top*) Charles Gatewood (*bottom*) Rapho/Photo Researchers
274 Charles Harbutt/Magnum
275 Alex Webb/Magnum
276 Fredrik D. Bodin
278 Ellis Herwig/Stock, Boston
279 (*left*) Peter Menzel/Stock, Boston (*right*) Joe Covello/Black Star
282, 283 National Library of Medicine
285 Daniel Bernstein
286 Elizabeth Wilcox
287 (*left*) Lester V. Bergman (*middle*) Martin M. Rotker/Taurus Photos
288 (*left*) Photoreporters, Inc.
288 (*middle*) Lester V. Bergman (*right*) Martin M. Rotker/Taurus Photos
292 Elizabeth Wilcox
295 Daniel S. Brody/Stock, Boston
298 Jean-Claude Lejeune/Stock, Boston
299 Lawrence Frank/Rapho/Photo Researchers
303 Bruce Buchenholz/Photo Researchers
306 Alex Webb/Magnum
307 courtesy of Pfizer Inc.
310 Elizabeth Wilcox
311 Peter Menzel/Stock, Boston
313 Elizabeth Wilcox
314 courtesy of the McGovern Allergy Clinic, Houston, Texas
315 *University of Washington Medicine*
317 Mark Chester/Leo deWys, Inc.
318 American Diabetes Association, Inc./Fredrik D. Bodin
319 Wide World
320 (*top*) J.W. Berndt/Stock, Boston (*bottom*) Commonwealth Photographers
322 Grant Heilman
323 courtesy of Medtronic, Inc., Minneapolis, Minnesota
324 Wide World

326 Bohdan Hyrnewych
328 Perkins School for the Blind
330 Elizabeth Wilcox
332 Matthew Klein/Magnum
336, 337 Peter Menzel/Stock, Boston
339 Ellis Herwig/Stock, Boston
341 (*left*) Photography for Industry (*right*) Wide World
342 Hugh Rogers/Monkmeyer Press Photos
343 Sybil Shelton/Monkmeyer Press Photos
344 (*left*) John Urban (*right*) UPI
345 Zvi Lowenthal/Editorial Photocolor Archives
346 (*top*) Jeff Albertson/Stock, Boston (*bottom*) Jefferson/Monkmeyer Press Photos
347 (*top*) T.D. Lovering/Stock, Boston (*bottom*) Sam Falk/Monkmeyer Press Photos
348 Tom Rothschild/Stock, Boston
349 (*both*) American Cancer Society
351 Elizabeth Hamlin
352 (*both*) American Lung Association
353 American Cancer Society
355 American Cancer Society, Massachusetts Division
356 Elizabeth Hamlin
358 (*top*) UPI (*bottom*) Alcoa
362, 363 (*all*) General Motors Corporation
365 Wide World
366, 373 Fredrik D. Bodin
375 Goodyear Tire and Rubber Company
376 The 3M Company
379 Fredrik D. Bodin
382 (*both*) National Bureau of Standards
383 Urbanimage Corporation
384 Syd Greenberg/DPI
385 (*left*) H. Armstrong Roberts (*right*) The Toro Company
386 National Rifle Association
387 Ellis Herwig/Stock, Boston
388 Ted Carland/American Red Cross

392 American Red Cross
396 Elizabeth Hamlin/Stock, Boston
397 NBC
405 Boston Edison Company
408 (*top left*) Jean White/National Audubon Society Collection/PR (*top center*) Stephen Dalton/National Audubon Society Collection/PR (*top right*) David Greene (*bottom left*) Cesco Ciapanna/National Audubon Society Collection/PR (*bottom right*) Bucky Reeves/National Audubon Society Collection/PR
409 (*top left*) A.W. Ambler/National Audubon Society Collection/PR (*top right*) Karl H. Maslowski/National Audubon Society Collection/PR (*bottom left*) Jack Dermid/National Audubon Society Collection/PR (*bottom right*) John H. Gerard/National Audubon Society Collection/PR
411 (*top left*) A.W. Ambler/National Audubon Society Collection/PR (*top right*) Les Line/National Audubon Society Collection/PR (*bottom left*) C.G. Maxwell/National Audubon Society Collection/PR
413 Daniel Bernstein
414 Elizabeth Hamlin
422 Peter Southwick/Stock, Boston
423 Monkmeyer Press Photos
427 Elizabeth Hamlin
428 NBC
429 courtesy of the Visiting Nurse Association
431 Elizabeth Wilcox
432–437 (*all*) Fredrik D. Bodin
438 Massachusetts Eye and Ear Infirmary
443 (*top left*) Chris Maynard/Stock, Boston (*bottom left & top right*) Lester V. Bergman
445 Elizabeth Hamlin
452 Lester V. Bergman
453 Photoworld/FPG

Index

Numerals in italics (*443*) refer to pages with illustrations or tables.